Nanista

Photographs by

Eliot Porter
Andreas Feininger
Alfred Eisenstaedt
Fritz Goro
Emil Schulthess
Josef Muench
Rutherford Platt
James Simon
Ansel Adams
Steve McCutcheon
and others

The Continent

Ivan T. Sanderson

We Live On

A Chanticleer Press Edition

Random House, New York

Fifth Printing 1967

Planned and produced by Chanticleer Press, Inc., New York and

published by Random House, Inc.

Acknowledgment

The author wishes to inscribe this book to
Paul Steiner and Milton Rugoff
in recognition of their pioneering spirit in initiating this work
and of their patience and understanding throughout
the long process of its execution.

Distributed in Canada by
Random House of Canada Limited, Toronto.

Library of Congress Catalog Card Number: 61–8958

Contents

Foreword

THE idea for a book such as this originally came to me in Europe thirty years ago. I nursed it during travels in southeast Asia, as a field collector for the British Museum and Cambridge University in the Orient, Africa, and South America, and after World War II brought me permanently to the New World and to residence in the United States.

Then, in 1957, two things were brought to my attention. The first was a set of government statistics showing that the number of working farmers in the United States is only some 2 per cent of the population, indicating how urbanized this country has become. The other was a set of magnificent color photographs of North America's natural wonders. Since I had traveled widely during the previous ten years in the United States, Canada, and Mexico, these two items confirmed something that had been disturbing me increasingly. This was the fact that this continent is rapidly being covered by a man-made blight but that no one had as yet made a simple, non-technical record of its appearance as it was before the coming of the white man, or as it is today apart from his influence.

During the following year I made still another discovery which was, at least to me, astonishing; namely, that no one seems ever to have made an "expedition" specifically to inspect North America as a whole and in its purely natural and non-human aspects. I found vast libraries on special aspects or particular parts of this continent, but no over-all, non-technical description written from this point of view and covering the whole continent.

Because of my training, early work, and research, I regard almost everything in nature in terms of what is known as *ecology*. This term is derived from roots that mean "the study of nature's houses" and is succinctly defined by Professor Henry J. Oosting of Duke University as "the study of organisms, their environment, and all the inter-relationships between the two." I therefore proposed taking a long trip around the continent, the goal being a non-technical description, in pictures and text, that would present it as a whole, but on an ecological framework, with the "environment" playing as big a part as the "organisms" but excluding man and all his works.

To accomplish this obviously called for a very broad approach to the project. Although I had already visited and indeed driven through about thirty of the states, half of Mexico, and parts of Canada, I had no real concept of the whole continent. No amount of reading can substitute for firsthand investigation and sight, and, in any case, amazing as it may sound, there are not half a dozen states that have so much as a vegetation map of their territory—and vegetation (as opposed to mere distribution of plants or families of plants) is, as I shall try to make clear, the basis of everything in the world of wildlife. Therefore, it was agreed that I should spend a year traveling the continent.

This I did, starting in January of 1959 and ending in December of that year. The basic form of transport was a two-year-old station wagon with only a double roof for extra equipment and double rear main springs added to take the extra load. It had only six inches clearance under the chassis, but in 57,000 miles it was only once "mired"—and that in the middle of a desert where there was no road. We ran through eight sets of tires by the halfway mark but then bought eight-ply truck tires which lasted for six months after the trip. There were sixteen holes in our windshield and three other perforated windows by the time we had done with the Alaska Highway and the new road to Great Slave Lake. Side trips were made by plane, by boat, on horseback, and on foot. I had with me as companions at various times three friends: Roy Pinney, the photographer; Wendell Skousen, a young geologist from Arizona; and Robert Christie, a rancher and amateur ornithologist.

We started out from Washington, D.C., on the first leg to Florida and thence round the Gulf coast to Brownsville, Texas, with numerous side excursions. Then we proceeded down the east coast of Mexico to the twentieth parallel; up onto the central plateau; and back to Texas. (I had traveled the whole of the western Sierras and coast in previous years.) From there, we covered the south-central prairies, the Tularosa Basin, and the Southern Montane Block, ending in Arizona. We then toured the whole Southwest to Baja California. From there we drove back and forth through the western mountains and coastal regions to Seattle, ranging as far east as eastern Nevada and Idaho. We proceeded to British Columbia, which we crisscrossed by every road possible, and then went on to Alaska, where we made several side trips. Returning to Alberta, we drove up the new road to beyond the Great Slave Lake in the

Northwest Territories and then south again to Montana. Our route from there took us south as far as Nebraska and north to Winnipeg, from where we proceeded across Canada, north of the Great Lakes, to Quebec, with one flight north to Hudson Bay. (I had in previous years flown over Labrador, some of the islands, and the periphery of Greenland.)

Finally we made a great sweep, starting from Niagara, south through what I call the Heartland to the Ouachita Mountains and then east across the Mississippi bottomlands, and back north along the western piedmont of the Appalachians, to New England, and finally south to my home in New Jersey.

In this itinerary I covered this continent as nearly as is possible on a limited budget and within a year. I need hardly add that it was an eye-opening and unforgettable experience, but I am constrained to make certain other observations. It was our opinion by the end of the trip that the United States was indeed now essentially an urban and suburban nation. From Maine to the cays off Florida and thence around the Gulf coast to Port Arthur, with but one noticeable break on the Atlantic coast and one on the Gulf, there is virtually a continuous built-up strip. The coast of California from San Diego to San Francisco is much the same, and the Portland-Astoria and Tacoma-Seattle complexes in Oregon and Washington are almost as bad. Even Vancouver now sprawls like a giant octopus. As for inland sites, the Illinois-Ohio industrial area and the Allentown-Easton area in Pennsylvania are the worst, but the enormous spread of the cities of Texas is almost beyond belief.

However few actual farmers there may be, agriculture has engulfed much of the country, and a great part of it, classed as range, is today a sort of monstrous wire entanglement. Deserts there are and of vast extent; and mountain ranges that look untouched; but both, as often as not, prove to be dotted with oil wells, mines, and hamlets, while enormous stretches are cropped for timber. Roads also have now usurped an appreciable area of the land surface. But the worst feature of all—and it is an appalling blight in the United States compared to Europe, or even to Canada and Mexico—is the litter. Not only are there throughout the length and breadth of the country endless rubbish dumps, junk yards, abandoned industrial plants, and acres of littered lots and waste land, but there is also a veritable blanket of empty cans, bottles, cartons, and that almost indestructible material, paper tissue. We stumbled upon heaps of beer cans on the tops of mountains that look unexplored; tripped over old car bodies in the depths of swamps; and drove between almost continuous lines of empty bottles all across deserts; while the beaches of the entire coast are strewn with these same items and a lot else besides.

There is, in fact, but one haven of hope in this country, and that is the magnificent system of national parks and sanctuaries. By the grace of a few far-sighted persons, among whom Theodore Roosevelt was outstanding, many of the finest, most significant, and most typical areas of this country have been saved (though only just in time) by the creation of these parks. There are still many more areas that should be enclosed before it is too late. The management of national parks both in the United States and Canada cannot possibly be praised too highly; it is intelligent, practical, and scientific, and at the same time it provides the public with the finest opportunities to see the country as it really is. But, unless something drastic is done, and soon, the rest of this country will eventually become one great junk pile.

There are also noticeable absurdities. For instance, the best bottomlands in the drier areas have almost invariably been built over, so that agriculture and stock-raising have been forced outward onto marginal land; breeds of cattle have often been selected without regard to the environment to which they are best suited. As many writers have pointed out in recent years, water is being wasted by the oceanful everywhere, gushing down drains and polluted rivers to the sea. Forests are hacked and slashed until even the soil beneath is washed away. Incipient dust bowls are being created everywhere by indiscriminate stripping of the topsoil, yet deep plowing and contour planting are still the exception. What the white man has accomplished on this continent in three hundred years is staggering. But the result is appalling.

There are, nonetheless, still some utterly wild and even unexplored areas in the United States (17,000 square miles in northern California alone), and the major part of Canada is as yet untouched. In Mexico, too, man has not treated nature so harshly, and a great part of it also remains untouched. In the United States you have to search diligently for the true wilds and the original face of the land; in Mexico you live in the midst of it; in Canada you have to search for people in most areas.

What is needed is a complete and as far as possible detailed survey of the natural vegetation, so that other features may be integrated and planning undertaken on sound ecological principles. At the same time, all three countries might well adopt several laws passed by Arizona whereby traffic offenders, instead of paying fines or going to jail, scour the roads and countryside, picking up trash under supervision of the proper authorities.

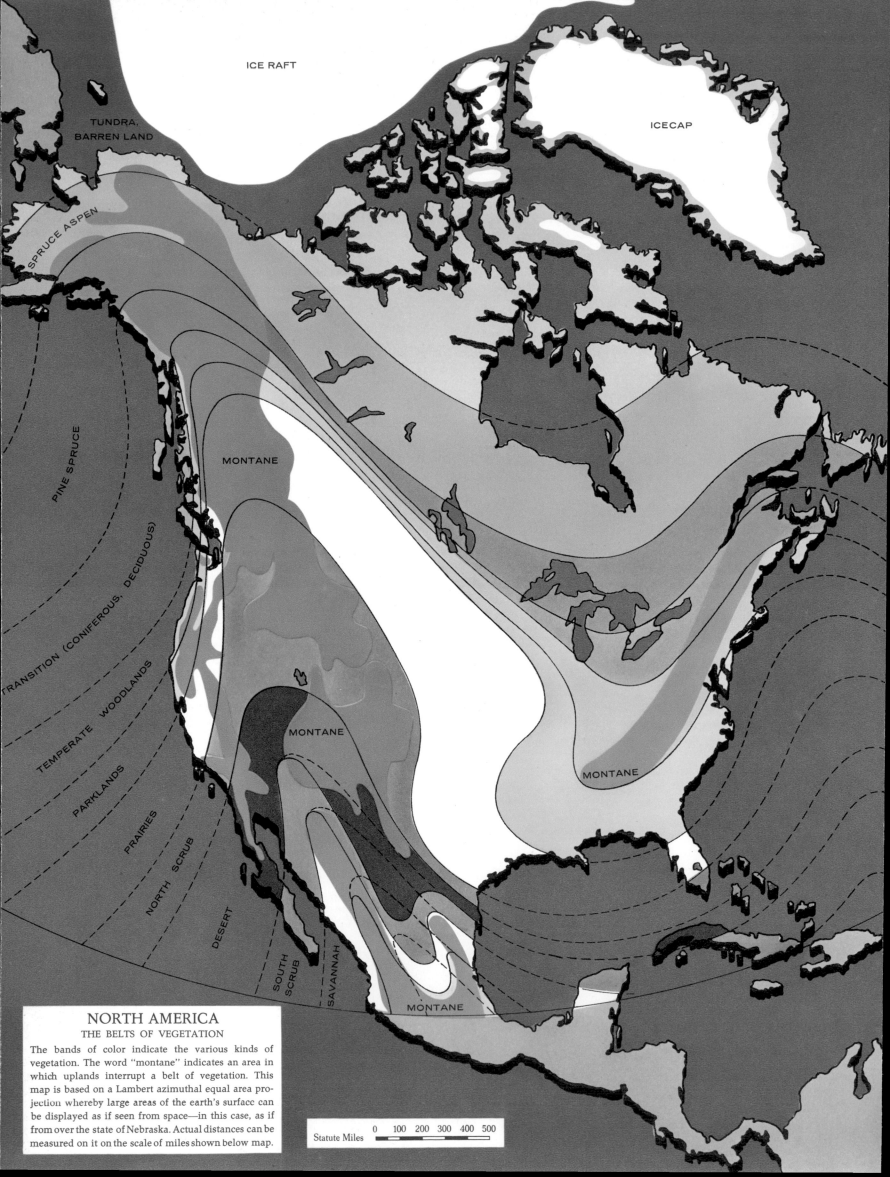

ICE RAFT

TUNDRA,
BARREN LAND

ICECAP

SPRUCE ASPEN

PINE SPRUCE

MONTANE

TRANSITION (CONIFEROUS, DECIDUOUS)

TEMPERATE WOODLANDS

PARKLANDS

PRAIRIES

MONTANE

NORTH SCRUB

MONTANE

DESERT

SOUTH SCRUB

SAVANNAH

MONTANE

NORTH AMERICA
THE BELTS OF VEGETATION

The bands of color indicate the various kinds of
vegetation. The word "montane" indicates an area in
which uplands interrupt a belt of vegetation. This
map is based on a Lambert azimuthal equal area projection whereby large areas of the earth's surface can
be displayed as if seen from space—in this case, as if
from over the state of Nebraska. Actual distances can be
measured on it on the scale of miles shown below map.

Statute Miles   0   100   200   300   400   500

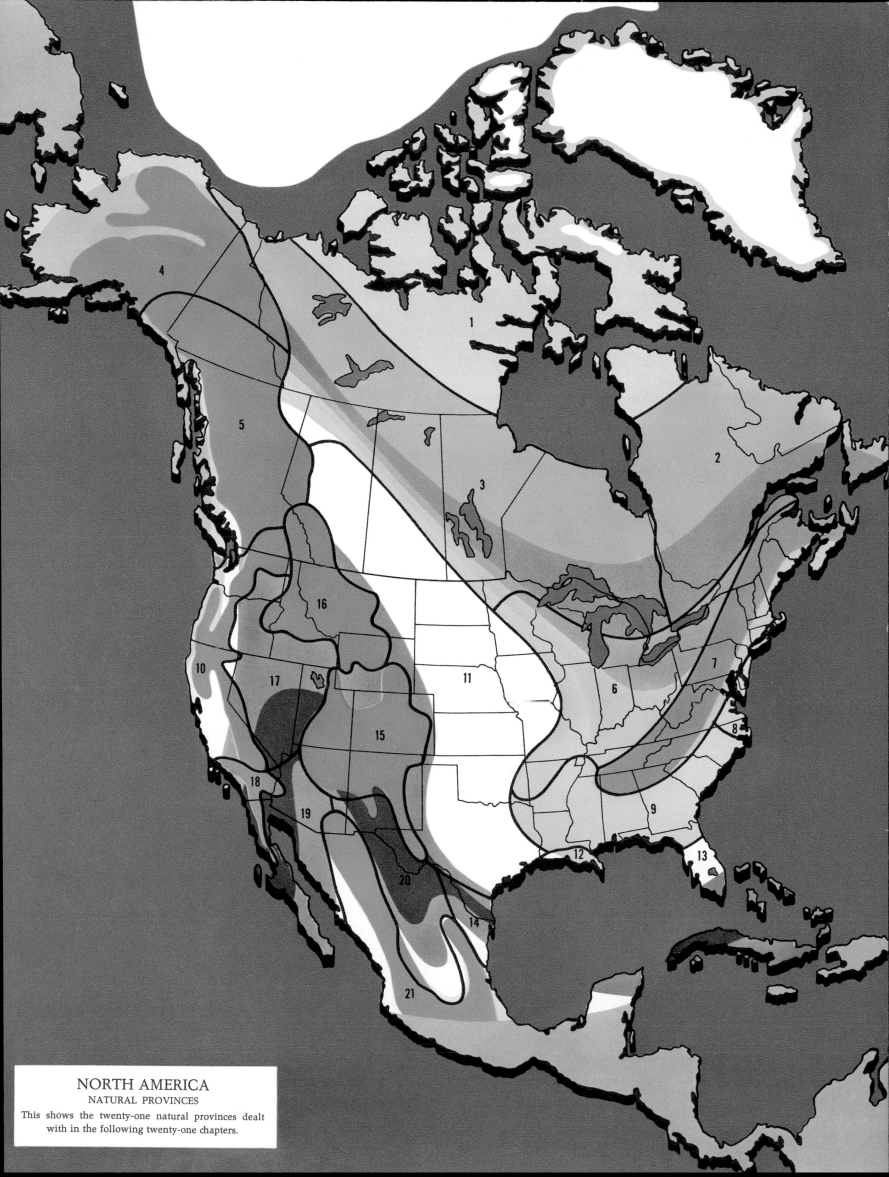

NORTH AMERICA
NATURAL PROVINCES
This shows the twenty-one natural provinces dealt with in the following twenty-one chapters.

Doorway to North America

The Arctic Ice Raft, Greenland,
the Islands, and the Barren Lands
of Keewatin and Ungava

1 Men have been coming to the continent of North America from other lands since sometime during the last so-called ice age. They came from two sides: the first, it would seem, from the west; the Europeans, from the east. Both parties consequently gained a somewhat lopsided impression of the land because both looked at it from only one angle, as it were. To the Eskimos and the Amerindians coming from Asia the horizon was to the east; to the Europeans and Africans it was to the west, though the Spaniards approached from the south and then veered west. The last remaining avenue of approach is from the north, and this is in any case the most desirable. It is not only modern and logical but it is also a convenient route, for we are primarily interested in those natural aspects of this continent that are not the outcome of human activity. These display an orderly procession and one arranged basically by latitude so that the easiest path along which to march across them is from north to south.

Maps are splendid devices but because we have to put them on flat, two-dimensional pieces of paper and have developed the habit of putting the north at the top, they give us, in most cases, a distorted idea of reality, and the more so the farther north or south we go. If, however, you look at a globe, both this and many other things will become immediately apparent. There is a huge circular area up north, well over 8,000,000 square miles in extent, of which more than 2,600,000 square miles are land or ice lying on land. From the center of this round area (namely, the North Pole) to its edge is almost 1600 miles. More than a quarter of the total land surface of our continent thus lies therein: namely, 2,506,000 out of a total of 9,355,000 square miles.

Within this arbitrary circle there is great variation in climate, land surface, and vegetation. The over-all concept that most of us hold of this great part of the surface of our earth is quite erroneous. For instance, there is no North Polar icecap; it is an ice raft, which is something quite different—though there is an icecap on Greenland. Icebergs and sea ice are not the same; the former is formed on land and is fresh, the latter is formed in the sea and is salt at first but goes fresh in two years. Although the soil of the Arctic is saturated and there is standing

Polar bears crossing Arctic ice pans. The lanes of water between the old hummocky pans have refrozen and the animals may have to trek to open water to hunt.

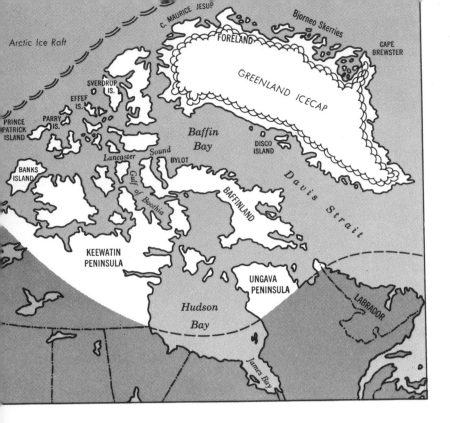

This is the largest natural province on this continent, covering over 2,500,000 square miles or almost one-third of its total land area. North America wraps almost halfway around the pole—i.e., through 160 degrees of longitude. What we here call the Arctic thus constitutes almost half of the earth's northern, dry, cold, desert belt.

For our purposes, the northern limit of this natural province is the northern shore of the Mackenzie District of the Canadian Northwest Territories, the Canadian Islands, such as Banks, Prince Patrick, Parry, Effef, Sverdrup, and Ellesmere; and the northern tip of Greenland. Its southern boundary is the northern limit of trees, which forms a line that makes a great sweep to the south as shown on the accompanying map.

There is also a narrow strip of truly Arctic vegetation that rims Alaska from the mouth of the Mackenzie River to Point Hope, and then south to Bristol Bay. It is, in some respects, a western outlier of this province, and it will be described with Alaska.

This Arctic province may be divided into four parts. First, to the west, a huge triangle extending along the northern coast of the Mackenzie District, then widening out to the east to include almost the whole Keewatin Peninsula; second, the western Islands, forming another triangle between the Arctic and Beaufort Seas on the west, Smith Sound, northern Baffin Bay, Lancaster Sound, and the Gulf of Boothia on the east, and the mainland on the south. Third, Baffinland and the northwestern tip of Labrador named the Ungava Peninsula; and, fourth, Greenland.

About one-third of this province is occupied by sea and almost half the remainder by an icecap. About a third is permanently covered with snow and nearly a quarter of that which is not is composed of fresh-water lakes. Sea ice covers almost the whole of the sea surfaces during the winter. The polar pack ice lies against its northern periphery, from Prince Patrick Island in the west to Foreland in Greenland in the northeast. The greater part of the land of this province, apart from Greenland, is at a low level (mostly below six hundred feet), but a chain of substantial mountain ranges extends from northern Ellesmereland to southern Baffinland.

Greenland is, in some respects, a world unto itself, 85 per cent of it being covered with a great dome of ice. There are three theories as to its true nature: one, that it is a huge mountainous island; a second, that it is two islands split almost up the middle by a deep channel; a third, that it is a large group of islands, many of them below sea level, with considerable distances between them. The icecap that now holds it all together is estimated to be almost two miles thick in some places near its center. It is the only substantial icecap in the Arctic, and it rises to almost ten thousand feet above sea level in the middle.

water everywhere, the area has a lower rainfall than the Sahara. A far greater menace than the winter snows are the summer dusts that sometimes transcend in choking oppressiveness anything produced in a hot desert. Mosquitoes and other blood-sucking flies may here surpass in number and virulence anything found in the tropics—the mangrove swamps of South America with their mosquitoes, ihenni, and sand flies not excluded. The coloring of even the Barren Lands may be brighter than almost any temperate land in the fall and the flowers are as gay, vividly colored, and numerous as in any other part of the world. Finally, the insects there form richer feed for birds than anywhere else on earth because of certain special circumstances.

Let us assume that we have been dropped on the north *axial* pole. This place is very odd in sundry respects. First, if you go from the equator to a pole, you will increase in weight at this point because there is no centrifugal force to partially counterbalance the pull of gravity. Second, you will partake of one less motion than everybody else in that you won't be going anywhere *around* the axis of our planet but, instead, will be stationary but revolving. This lack of one cosmic movement is not appreciable, but the increased weight must be taken into account in transporting freight. Much else is also at first very strange. For two parts of the year, days alternate with nights in a fairly

normal manner, but for a time in the summer the sun stays above the horizon all day and all night, whereas in winter it goes away below the horizon for several weeks. In spring and autumn there are periods when it is perpetual sunrise or sunset.

The show that the polar ice can put on during fine weather in spring and autumn is almost unbelievable. One cannot, of course, see the fullest display everywhere in the north, and least often at the pole itself, which is in the middle of a huge, inverted saucer of sea ice with little surface topography. There is little but a white glare there, though the sky can sometimes be of an intense turquoise or sapphire blue, with clouds that form a sort of tent over one's head because of the uninterrupted horizon. Rather, it is in those places within the Arctic Circle where coastal ice of one kind or another is present that purely fantastic effects are encountered. This is particularly true where the tongues of glaciers, sea ice, and other residuals of snowfall are framed by dark rock or decorated with bright-colored lichens.

Ice, according to its origin, age, and location, varies in color all the way from white to black and crosswise through every shade of the spectrum, but intrinsically and for the most part its shades are in the blues and greens. When the rays of a perpetually rising or setting sun glance across the gently curving surface of the earth and strike upon mountains of faceted and

This polar bear with twin cubs on a rotting ice floe may have drifted for several miles and will swim back to shore or to the ice front.

tumbled ice, the whole world seems to be floodlighted with ten million colored arcs for twenty-four hours a day, never quite the same but never going away, and all often cast upon a backdrop of dark rocks and sculptured ice.

THE POLAR ICE RAFT

Even the Arctic ice raft itself is not, despite its somewhat deplorable appearance at first, a complete waste. It is a great cap of sea ice, very slightly curved to fit the earth, varying in thickness from a few feet to—as the submarines which have now traveled under it have shown—some four hundred feet, and compounded of frozen sea surface and snow that has fallen upon the surface of the ice and compacted. It is a thousand miles wide measured from the top of the Atlantic via the Pole to the Pacific, but only six hundred miles wide measured at right angles to that line. The extra mass lies on the Pacific side, north of Siberia and Alaska. It is not homogeneous, for there is ice of various origins and ages in its composition, and it contains some vast rafts of what are called palaeocrystic ice. These behave like huge floating islands and are very ancient; they may even be relics of an

ice raft formed before this great sea unfroze the last time—this it may have done, according to some climatologists, in immediately prehistoric times. Some of these ice islands are today used as permanent bases and landing fields for aircraft. Held in the thinner, newer ice, they drift slowly round the pole. The polar ice raft as a whole is not, however, permanent. It is continuously being added to on top and melting away below; and it is augmented all around its edge by sea-formed pack ice. It has holes in it that open and close hither and yon, and its various parts move reciprocally about among themselves so that ships caught in it may wander in all directions, their courses leaving extraordinary patterns on a chart. As a whole, it revolves slowly relative to the adjoining land, due to being unable to quite keep up with the spin of the earth, so that its edge moves from east to west as looked at from the south.

The polar pack ice lies right against the upper edge of this continent. One would have thought, therefore, that these shores would also be profoundly icebound and snow-covered. Very surprisingly, this is not the case; the Cape Maurice Jesup area at the northern tip of Greenland is not glaciated at all. Even in winter comparatively little snow falls there and this usually melts off quite fast. In summer it is an almost lush land with a

13

Jaeger in flight. These relatives of the petrels are robbers, predators, carrion feeders, and powerful fliers.

Facing page: Numerous glaciers depend from the Greenland icecap. If they reach the sea, their tongues fan out and float, and great chunks break off, or are "calved," to form icebergs.

The Arctic Tern, greatest traveler of all birds, flies the Atlantic route 11,000 miles to the Antarctic in our autumn and back again in our spring to nest in the American Arctic.

considerable growth of lowly plants and many flowers above which butterflies flutter and bumblebees buzz. There is even an indigenous species of weasel that does not have an especially thick coat or underfur. In summer it can be very hot there. The reasons for this apparent reversal of what might be expected are several. Lack of precipitation is one factor, the proximity of open ocean is another, and the fact that what are called adiabatic winds—consisting of great blankets of supercooled air that roll outward off icecaps—are stopped by the elevation of the land from reaching the coast in this area is a third. On the other hand, there is a small icecap on Ellesmere Island; and the other northern islands are bleak and dreary places, their northern fringes covered for the most part all year round with incipient icefields, ancient snow beds, or fresh snow. Otherwise the land surface is truly barren ground, being mostly bare rock and lacking even lichens. Yet there is life here, just as on the very polar ice raft itself.

WHITE ANIMALS OF THE FAR NORTH

Under the ice raft there are various whales and seals, which appear to be able to travel very considerable distances from peripheral leads in its edge to holes and open spaces well within its main body. Upon the ice there are polar bears, arctic foxes, and gulls. The polar bears are the hunters and killers, the foxes and gulls the scavengers, for there are no other animals available as live food. Bears, foxes, and gulls all come ashore and travel considerable distances inland. When on land in the summer the bears feed on lemmings and any other small animals that they can catch or dig up, and they eat great quantities of berries and even some seaweed.

The Polar Bear is one of the few really dangerous animals on this planet. While you can walk through a pride of wild lions by day without their doing more than turning their heads to look at you, and while almost all other large animals will leave you severely alone, polar bears may hunt you deliberately by either day or night, on land, on the ice, or in the water. But polar bears, besides being potentially dangerous, are devilishly clever and seem actually to use their brains, arriving at short-cuts to many enterprises, having good memories, and, like cats, apparently being able to correlate more than one set of facts and come up with a third quite original plan. They scout around human places of permanent occupation and not infrequently take deliberate pains to cover their tracks. A polar bear can travel at an astonishing speed even on glaze ice which is as polished as a mirror and more slippery, and with their sharp claws they can climb the steepest ice pinnacle much faster than a man can. However, there are cases on record of Eskimos having killed polar bears singlehandedly with hand blades.

There is continuing debate as to whether there are two distinct kinds or even species of polar bears—a small yellow one, and a large pure white one. Some contend that these differences, which may be very marked even in one locality, are merely racial; others, that they are age groups; others, again, that they are seasonal; and still others, that they develop in each individual due to the type of "country"—if we may call it that—which it inhabits. Thus the big whites are said to inhabit the open ocean, the floating pack ice, and the ice raft, whereas the small yellow ones live along the coastal ice and travel inland in summer. Whatever be the answer, both kinds may sometimes be met with far out on the open ocean; and an altogether bizarre sight it is to be steaming along over a sparkling blue sea under a cloudless sky with no sign of any ice anywhere and suddenly see

a family party of these great white mammals lounging about on the surface, on their backs, with their heads sticking up inquiringly and their huge forepaws languidly crossed on their chests.

The Arctic Fox or Snow Dog is a strange little creature. It is not a true fox *(Vulpes)* but quite a different animal, *Alopex,* with small, squarish ears, short, sharp muzzle, and narrow little body. In winter these animals are pure white and clothed in a long and beautiful fluffy fur; in summer they are scraggly-looking creatures with short maroon-brown coats and apparently out-

This curious crystalline substance is known as "weather ice" and forms from repeated partial melting and refreezing of snow. It breaks into candle-shaped sticks.

sized feet. However, some of them, at one time of the year or another, develop long, fluffy coats like the winter pelage but colored like the summer one. This we know as a blue fox. The Arctic Fox has a habit of collecting small mammals and birds in late summer and fall, and stashing them away in caches between rocks or in cracks between land ice, as food for the long period of total winter darkness. These animals appear, in fact, to enjoy quite a good living, for not only do they have these caches to supply them in emergencies, but they also find certain lemmings that are active under the snow during that season. They seem also to wander about all over the icecap and even the ice raft itself, and feed on scraps left by the polar bears.

The number of these animals in this province can hardly be conceived, for they are found everywhere south to the tree line, and they have been trapped by the thousands for two centuries and form the basis of the northern fur trade. However, their numbers wax and wane regularly over the years. This is dependent upon the cyclical increase and decrease in the numbers of the lemmings—small tailless rodents that we shall meet more intimately in the next province.

Other animals of the far north, too, vary in numbers accordingly, notably the great Snowy Owls. As the lemmings diminish in numbers, the carnivores do likewise, partly through starvation, partly through decreased breeding, and partly through diseases that then invariably strike them very hard. Only the owls partially overcome their plight by flying south, sometimes in vast numbers and reaching as far as the northern United States. However, it is a mysterious fact that all of these, too, die off very rapidly, and never breed or become established in the south. Even in captivity, snowy owls caught in the far north in peak lemming years and brought south die in a few weeks, whereas identical birds caught in lean years in the north may survive for years in cages and be very hardy.

The other birds of these northern lands and of the ice raft are the huge, almost pure white Glaucous Gull, which has a pale gray mantle but white wing tips, and the little pigeon-shaped Ivory Gull, which is pristine white all over but has jet-black legs. There is also the Icelandic Gull—killer, carrion feeder, and robber of nests. Another common bird of the coasts is the Arctic Tern, which spends *our* winter in the Antarctic, flying 11,000 miles across the Atlantic every year and thence down the European and African coasts and off into the latitudes known as the "roaring forties" south of the Cape of Good Hope. Then there are the jaegers that rob the gulls and terns—dark brown birds with two long central tail feathers.

THE GREENLAND ICECAP

Almost half the land of this province is composed of what we call Greenland. This is not altogether improperly named. While 85 per cent of it is covered by an icecap, the remaining 15 per cent, which almost completely rims it, is composed of coastal plains and bare rock cliffs. Considerable portions of the former are a truly green and verdant land for a part of the year.

Greenland has been found and then lost again more than once. It was first reported by Eric the Red in 1000 A.D. as being a *green land;* but mostly—as the ancient Icelandic writings imply—for the purpose of recruiting settlers. But then it proved to be just that. It seems, however, that great cold descended upon it about 1400 A.D. and it then became considerably less green. Next, for two centuries, it was lost altogether. The whalers of the early seventeenth century "refound" it and said that it was glaring white. Then it was again more or less forgotten, until finally the modern world came to know—what the Danes alone had known for three hundred years—that it is once more habitable and in some respects nearly a salubrious land.

Greenland seems always to have had a central icecap since before the arrival of the first Eskimos, a Mongolian people who came from east Siberia. An icecap is not just an accumulation of compacted snow, nor just a place where snow never melts. It has a definite structure and a life cycle. It is made, fundamentally, of snow which falls on a land mass in sufficient quantities and in a place where less of it melts than falls. As a result the snow piles up and the upper layers compact those below, until the whole is converted in a semicrystalline substance called *firn.*

This in turn, by further compacting or pressure from above, changes to ice by partial melting and immediate *regelation,* or refreezing. This new ice is white and usually opaque, due to its myriad included crystalline faces and many minute air pockets. Later still, as the snows pile up above, this ice goes through another change and is converted into pure crystalline ice. The air is absorbed, the crystal faces are obliterated, and the whole becomes one vast homogeneous and amorphous mass of clear material, usually of a pale blue color and quite translucent. This

When an icecap forms over a land surface—and one cannot form over water for various mechanical and chemical reasons—it continues to grow as long as the mean average annual temperature remains below a certain point and there is sufficient precipitation. The latter is by far the more important. Even the center of the Greenland icecap is by no means the coldest place in the world, especially as compared to the Antarctic and to some places in Siberia. The all-time record low temperature was recorded on Graham Land in the Antarctic during a blizzard and

About nine-tenths of an iceberg are below the surface of the water. Such bergs often contain caves and wave-cut platforms.

substance is hard, breaks like a shard, and has some rather strange properties.

In fact, water is altogether an extraordinary substance. Both as a gas (steam) and as a liquid and as a solid (i.e. ice, which is really a rock) it comes in many forms. Then there are all manner of intermediate conditions of a meteorological nature, such as water vapor, fog, mist, snow, hail, and so forth, as well as many most bizarre forms of ice; for instance, there is columnar ice that looks like cigars packed together. In Siberia there are large areas where, under the Arctic soil, lie as much as two thousand feet of palaeocrystic or "fossil" ice; some of this is jet-black, but when a quantity of it is melted in a glass container, the resultant water is as colorless as clear spring water.

was —132 degrees F. The coldest known in the northern hemisphere was —97 degrees F. in Siberia, which was actually south of the Arctic Circle.

Once an icecap is born it grows just like some vast amoeba, and then it begins to move. As a rule it moves outward in all directions because, however rigid and crystalline it may appear to be, ice is still plastic and it becomes positively fluid under extreme pressure. It then either flows outward, sliding over itself in layers under the influence of gravity, or it is literally

Overleaf: Icebergs are constantly calved by Greenland's glaciers and then drift away; many end in the North Atlantic.

A herd of musk ox in full flight. These "sheep-oxen" are true relics of the Ice Age and, though they look lumpish, can outpace most other animals.

squeezed out underneath as taffy would be in a shallow bowl if a large solid weight were placed upon it.

Thus an icecap grows in both depth and area and pushes out in all directions. If it comes against a substantial mountain range, it pushes up and over the lower passes or flows around the obstacle, scouring its sides with millions of tons of pressure and billion-foot-pound scooping actions. It finally covers the whole land and leaves only the peaks of the tallest mountains sticking out. These are called *nunataks*. Such are strewn all around the edge of Greenland. But finally its edge reaches some seacoast. If the coast is a rocky barrier with cliffs, the ice, in the form of glaciers or rivers of ice, cascades down these through whatever gaps there are and, on reaching the sea below, becomes water-borne— ice being lighter than water. As a result, the front ends or "tongues" of these break off in great bits by being bent upward, often with thunderous noises like gunfire, and then go drifting away as icebergs. This is called *calving*.

If, on the other hand, the coast is low but wide, the ice front may push slowly out onto it, building up a mountainous and bulbous front, actually thicker at that front than just behind it, so that the whole curls over like a vast wave and huge masses of ice crash to the bare ground ahead of it. Then the ice slowly creeps over these chunks and reabsorbs them. In still other circumstances, where the coastal plain is narrow and only just above sea level and extends out under the water to form a very shallow sea, the vast ice mass may move slowly out from the land—sometimes for hundreds of miles as in the Antarctic— before its buoyancy counteracts its weight and vast slices of it snap off and become water-borne. This is known as shelf ice; and it is prevalent around enormous stretches of the Antarctic coast but it is not found in the Arctic. When this shelf ice— sometimes hundreds of feet thick—breaks away, it forms flat-topped icebergs that have been recorded up to two hundred miles long and a hundred miles wide.

Sooner or later, however, the climate changes once more and the icecap begins to suffer starvation. Perhaps nothing more than a diminution in annual precipitation takes place, so that no new snow piles up on the center or it does so in such small quantities that it cannot keep up with the summer thaw. Then the movement of the ice ceases; its peripheral glaciers melt backward up their gorges; on low land, its bulbous front flattens out into a thin, tapering sheet and develops melt caves beneath it; and the great ice shelves begin to slant downward to the sea and then slowly retreat back onto the land. Such is Greenland today— though perhaps only temporarily—a really vast and fairly ancient icecap just a little past its prime, shrinking visibly almost all around and with considerably reduced edges on land but still calving icebergs along both its northwestern and eastern coasts. An icy blanket of air still pours off its edges in most places forcefully enough to be termed idiabatic winds, but it is not nearly so formidable or aggressive as it was even a century ago.

Things have been warming up generally in those parts for some time now, so that all manner of animals once found only in temperate seas now occur there. Codfish, which only fifty years ago were never caught north of 64 degrees north, now form commercial catches north of 73 degrees north. This is a tremendous movement for fish, which are ultrasensitive to water temperatures, being nearly six hundred miles of latitude. All kinds of other changes have been taking place, too. The sea ice has become thinner and narrower, and it melts sooner and stays away for longer periods than it did previously. This has upset the inshore habits of such marine mammals as whales and seals. The graves of the Norse settlers of pre-Columbian times have thawed out of the permafrost; quite a number of new plants have appeared on the coastal fringe in summer; and birds not seen before are now common in many areas. These are not unalloyed blessings: rather the contrary, for they have removed far to the north many of the natural products, such as whales and seals, on which the Greenlanders relied for food and clothing. Much the same is happening on the Canadian islands, but the change there is not so apparent and is possibly not so profound. In Greenland it seems to be caused primarily by changes in the warmer ocean currents and the wilting of the icecap, and it is believed that it is not an increase of warm water but of cold that is causing the latter, for as the warm water goes farther away it carries the moisture-laden air that brings precipitation.

GARDENS BY THE ICE

The coastal strips of Greenland are very unlike what most of us suppose. Even in midwinter the climate is not really any colder than that of the northern United States, and in summer it can be very (though never disagreeably) hot, so that people go swimming in lakes and wander about in shorts even as far north as upper Baffin Bay. There are places within the Arctic Circle that

have recorded temperatures of over one hundred degrees F. While the steeper mountains either are, or may appear to be, bare and rather grim, most of them are covered with lichens and mosses, and the lowlands are carpeted with flowers. Vegetation is really rather profuse. Several hundred plants have been recorded from Greenland, and in the south there are birch trees over thirty feet tall though their trunks are paltry. There are lush growths of sedges all along the fresh waterways, huge moorlands of very fine grass on level places, and all manner of seagrass marshes. In the more sheltered valleys many things will grow, including all kinds of vegetables. In fact, they grow so fast that they often have to be covered with mats on frames for a few hours each day to prevent them from getting too much sunlight. The greater part of the unglaciated land is covered with a mat of tundra, and this contains tiny dwarf willows only two inches tall, probably the smallest woody plant or true tree in the world.

The most interesting part of Greenland is undoubtedly its eastern face running from Cape Brewster, north of Iceland and west of Jan Mayen Land, north to the northeast of Foreland. This is a rugged and indented coast with numerous glaciers and huge fjords cut into towering, absolutely vegetationless mountains, and leading to great valleys filled with nothing but naked rock and stones. Here geology is laid completely bare, and the results of glaciation, reglaciation, and glacial retreat may be seen and understood by anybody. Moraines lie prostrate in all manner of ways: valleys are carved into perfect U-shaped sections by goug-

ing ice, and there are huge cirques high above, either still ice-filled with bits spilling over their edges in slow-motion cascades like corn out of a bowl, or dead and dry like old frying pans. Despite the use made of this coast during World War II by both sides in the contest, there is still much of it to be explored.

On the west coast there are many interesting things to see, but perhaps the most odd is Disco Island, which lies at 70 degrees north about halfway up that coast. This is pitted with hot springs and other signs of a dying volcanic activity, and the whole island is composed of basaltic rocks. The springs are not hot by our standards, ranging from only 36 to 65 degrees, but they remain constant throughout the year, and, although they are covered by snow in winter, they are sufficiently warm to melt out caves in which thousands of flies stay active. Eventually blowholes break through the roofs of these caves and the warmer air then puffs out like steam. They produce enough heat to keep the sea ice from joining the shore in many of the bays, so that the coast remains ice-free. Around these springs in summer all manner of unexpected plants grow, including several species of orchids. Orchids are not really uncommon in Greenland, but of course their presence comes as a considerable surprise.

THE ENDLESS ISLANDS

The western coast of Greenland is mountainous and rugged. That of the opposite side of Baffin Bay and the Davis Strait that

21

Top to bottom:

Arctic Cotton, a kind of sedge that bears puffball-like white flower clusters, is a surprising sight on the Barren Grounds.

The flowers, fruits, berries, and seeds of many Arctic plants are often astonishingly colorful and exotic: for example, this specimen of a Silene from Bylot Island.

The fruit of the Black Crawberry, an Arctic plant of dwarf stature, is eaten by animals but is highly caustic to humans.

An exotic lichen. Such plants, forming a great part of the Arctic flora, really consist of certain funguses and algae growing together as one.

The taiga (a Siberian term for spruce forests) extends onto the tundra in long tongues and little isolated patches of stunted trees bordering watercourses.

A red lichen, one of many striking and colorful forms among the thousands of known lichens. Although each is a composite plant, it reproduces its own kind.

Musk ox are regular swimmers and can travel fast enough to set up bow waves like tugboats.

separates it from the Islands is also rugged but not nearly so much so. On frozen Ellesmereland, Devon Island, and Bylot, the sea is faced by cliffs, but the real mountains lie somewhat inland; along the east coast of Baffinland the true uplands are even farther away from the sea. These coasts are also heavily indented with inlets and fjords—the results of both gouging by the ice glaciers, which can dig below sea level, and the sinking of the land, plus the rising of the waters. These islands are more barren than the coastal strip of West Greenland, but they too support a remarkably varied vegetation. The tiny dwarf willows, Arctic heathers, and cinquefoils cluster each in their own preferred microcosm, some facing the wind, some hiding from it, some blooming where the snow melts first, others where it melts last—a wonderful tapestry of growing things as perfectly integrated with the environment as it could possibly be.

The other Islands (of the Canadian Arctic), as they are now simply and conveniently called, form a most peculiar territory. For most purposes the salt-water lanes between them may be ignored and all of them treated as a whole, though the mountainous strip from Ellesmereland to southern Baffinland is somewhat distinct. Taken together, they form a great triangle, the northern two-thirds of which is snow-covered or utterly barren. The southern portion is snow- and ice-free in summer, from about late July till mid-October, and is for the most part covered with true tundra interspersed with barren lands—which is to say, naked rock. South of the Islands there are two huge triangles on the mainland—the Keewatin and Ungava peninsulas—which are

nonetheless Arctic lands and are covered with the same tundra. On tundra lands there is a thin, acid, airless, and sodden topsoil that melts in the summer and, under this, a greater or lesser depth of frozen soil or permafrost, which we will consider later. There are, however, also large areas of sandy and absolutely moistureless soil. From the air, especially at certain times when the snow is melting off or the lowly vegetation is beginning to leaf, it may be seen that this whole land is covered with one or another kind of an almost geometrically perfect giant grid. This is often so precise that it is hard to believe that it is not man-made but is the result of the purely natural physical forces of frost and melt. In this land you will also find other geometric-looking arrangements, such as "ditches" running for miles in perfect alignment, and whole islands completely covered by a checkerboard of hexagonal, rhomboidal, or other conformations of either enormous or foot-sized dimensions. These sharp rock ridges or earth bowls—some round with small blisters in the middle—cover the whole earth often for miles, just like the patterns formed by a shattered automobile windshield. As a result of the slight differences in elevation between these ridges and depressions, and the resultant variations in soil moisture content, exposure to sunlight, and other factors, different plants grow on each level and so accentuate the differences among these bizarre patterns by color, tone, and shade. Here the rock surface of the land is as brittle as ice and often behaves not unlike that substance: and when the rocks do crack, they may make noises like gunfire.

The Arctic areas of the mainland as seen from ground level appear endless and repellent—in summer, just bare rocks and dun-colored tundra, alternating with icy cold meandering waters as far as the eye can see; in winter, they are nothing but a blank whiteness. But even this monstrous nothingness blooms in spring and bursts into glorious color in the fall, with every plant turning another vivid hue and the stubborn lichens "burning" away in their violent colors.

From the air this land appears chaotic. Land, semi-land, and water are intimately intertwined in endless spits, sloughs, ponds, lakes, ridges, and domes so that the eye becomes utterly confused and maps are worthless. The vastness of these lands is quite beyond our conception. The Ungava portion of Labrador is a triangle 250 miles on a side; the Keewatin 400 miles, apart from the panhandle that stretches west to the mouth of the Mackenzie, which is another 300 miles long. There are distinct geological and vegetational differences between the Ungava and the Keewatin parts, and between both these and the Islands. Ungava is more closely associated with the Baffinland-to-Ellesmereland string, and the Keewatin portion with the rest of the Islands.

ICE-AGE ANIMALS

Greenland and the Islands are inhabited by a species of reindeer known as the Arctic Caribou, which stays in the northern latitudes and grubs for a winter living under the snows. It is the smallest of the American reindeer or caribou and most closely related to the true reindeer of the Old World. Another outstanding animal of this province is that strange beast known as the Musk Ox. This has been given the delightful scientific name of *Ovibos* or the "sheep-ox," but it is not even quite that, for its only relatives are some strange animals known as takin that live in the mountains of southern China and northern Thailand and Burma. Today musk oxen are comparatively rare, but they still maintain themselves on the Islands, in northern Greenland, and on the Keewatin triangle. They are large, very shaggy beasts with downcurving horns and big feet. Somehow they manage to grub a living from the tundra mosses and lichens by browsing and grazing in summer and by digging under the snow with their forefeet in winter.

Musk oxen seem to be able to survive the most intolerable cold and blizzards. They protect themselves from the local predators, notably wolves, by a means that sounds fanciful but seems actually to be true. When threatened, they at first mill around in a state of complete disorder until somehow the horned males arrange themselves in a rough circle all facing outward and with the breeding females and young inside. They then lower their heads, breathe hot air in streams like old-time dragons, rumble menacingly, and present a united front in all directions. And to get into the circle is, for wolves or even for men armed with high-powered repeating rifles (or, I am told, with a helicopter) impossible, because the great bumbling beasts are not nearly so stupid as they look and have a habit of shifting the whole formation at a rapid pace and in fine order from side to side or back and forth. A bull (or should it be ram?) musk ox will not charge, but, acting in unison, a group will not give way either. Their upturning horns are exceedingly sharp, and they can jerk them up with lightning speed.

They are, in fact, most efficient beasts, and they know their terrain, their enemies, and a lot else about Arctic living, including how to swim most agilely. This does not, somehow, seem quite proper, for these animals look more like vast animated toys constructed to plod about, apparently stiff-legged and somewhat unsurely. Yet, when alarmed, they take off at a speed which makes any mere ox look like a slowpoke, and often, in their headlong flight, they hurl themselves into icy waters and go churning off like traditional lake monsters.

Lemmings, Meteorites, and Belugas

The Labradorian Peninsula.
Tundra, Spruce Forests, and the
St. Lawrence Valley and Gulf

2   When Leif Ericson missed his way home to Greenland from Europe in the year 995 A.D., he came upon a long, grim shore that he called Helluland, or the Land of Flat Stones. This is the earliest date recorded for the European discovery of the North American mainland. According to his later accounts, it appears that he had run into the coast of what we now call Labrador, which is indeed for mile after mile a land of flat stones—and very little else, as seen from the sea. Leif did not land, and he seems to have taken a dim view of the place. Later Norse expeditions went a-viking to and down this coast and penetrated some of its deep fjords, where they found to their utmost delight great forests of straight trees that they needed so much for ship-building and other purposes in treeless Greenland.

Today, if you fly over Labrador, you will probably sympathize with Leif, for it at first appears to be utterly barren. What is more, behind the rugged, rocky, and everywhere deeply indented coast stretch two forms of desolation that are quite overwhelming in their seemingly lifeless infinity. One is the mighty *taiga* or spruce forest, a four-hundred-mile-wide belt that goes on and on for three thousand miles, making a great sweep to the south and then to the north, and reaching the mountain barrier of the Rockies just beyond the Mackenzie River. As this country is not particularly mountainous, it is covered to the horizon with an uninterrupted blanket of somber green so dark as to appear almost black under a cloudy sky. The other is a belt of treeless, true tundra lying just behind the coast. This is of even more depressing appearance when seen from the air, for the whole world appears to be covered with a vast, irregular maze of waterways interspersed with meandering curlicues of lowland. This tundraland stretches right around the northern periphery of the province, across the northwestern peninsula from Ungava Bay to the Hudson Bay coast, where it merges with the vast marshes that ring the southern shore of that inland sea.

Great colonies of gannets—here shown on St. Bonaventure Island—as well as gulls and other sea birds nest all along the Atlantic coast of this province and especially around the Gulf of St. Lawrence, where fish is plentiful inshore.

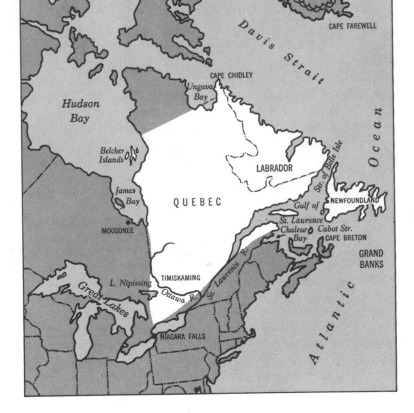

There is a massive block of our American northlands that constitutes a good fifth of the whole. It has no specific name but is slowly coming to be referred to as the Labradorian Peninsula. It forms a huge inverted triangle extending from the northeastern corner of this continent, and, since each of its three sides is more than 1200 miles long, it is approximately 720,000 square miles in area. This is equivalent to the block of United States territory contained between New York, Miami, and Omaha.

It runs from the southern extension of James Bay up the east coast of Hudson Bay, around the south coast of Hudson Strait to Ungava Bay, and thence along the Labradorian coast to the Strait of Belle Isle. Off this lies Newfoundland, and the whole of this island is included in the province. Its periphery, in fact, crosses the Cabot Strait from Cape Race to Cape Breton and swings up the Gulf of St. Lawrence to Chaleur Bay south of the Gaspé Peninsula, then crosses that peninsula to Quebec. From there it follows the junction of the pine-spruce forest and the mixed or transition zone composed of conifers (principally pines) and hardwoods (notably maples) west to Lake Nipissing. From that point north to James Bay once more, its boundary is almost entirely empirical, since there is no real difference in the vegetation as one travels west across this line. However, there is a natural gutter cutting the great, lowland, clay-covered plain, from south of Moosonee on James Bay to the upper Ottawa River about Tamiskaming, and continuing thence south to the barrier at Niagara Falls. This was the junction line of the east and west icecaps of old, and there are subtle differences still remaining between the lands on either side.

This is a forest province, apart from the triangle of tundra and barren lands lying to the northwest of an irregular transition belt stretching from southern Ungava Bay to the region of the Belcher Islands in Hudson Bay, which is part of the Arctic province. South and east of this tundraland lies a huge stretch of spruce forest, four hundred miles wide, with some aspen and birch and endless muskegs. This is but the eastern extension of the great boreal spruce belt that stretches all the way from the Mackenzie River via the Canadian lakes district. To the south and east however this belt gradually merges with a belt of pines and spruces and then with a strip roughly two hundred miles wide composed of Transition forest. This sweeps across the continent just north of the Great Lakes, strikes the St. Lawrence valley between Quebec and the Strait of Belle Isle on the one side and, crossing it, encompasses the Gaspé Peninsula and Newfoundland along with the rest of both shores of the Gulf of St. Lawrence.

Forests are, of course, areas covered with trees, but the definition of a forest is not nearly so simple as we might suppose. For our purposes we will use the term to denote areas on which trees grow sufficiently close together for some part of their foliage to touch that of all surrounding trees, thus forming what is called a *closed canopy*. Tundra is, of course, not a forest though it could be argued that its vegetation forms a closed canopy, albeit a very low one, and also contains "trees," at least by one definition—namely, the tiny, two-inch, dwarf, woody-stemmed willows already mentioned. However, tundra is more typically a treeless type of country clothed in a dense mat of lichens, mosses, stunted herbs, and dwarfed creeping bushes, with some grasses and sedges.

The cause of these conditions is, of course, the permafrost (see Chapter 4) which stops rain, melted snow, and other aerially derived moisture from sinking into the ground, while the flatness of the whole country prevents the formation of drainage systems. It is a curious fact that the precipitation over this area is lower than that of the central Sahara, but the evaporation is very slight. If there were a high winter snowfall or a summer rainfall, proper drainage systems would develop simply through the pressure of the water trying to flow off the land. If, on the other hand, the snowfall were great enough, an icecap would build up.

Despite its barren appearance this country is not a wilderness.

It is seething with life, and not only during the summer. The variety of the flora, though all of modest individual proportions, is very great, with one group of flowering herbaceous plants coming out the moment the meager snow has melted, and continuing until it again blankets the land in the late fall. Predominant is the tiny tree known as the Arctic Willow, and there are several mosses that form endless sodden cushions into which one can sink to the waist or even on occasion right through. Where there is bare rock, the lichens are particularly profuse and brightly colored. There are no true bogs (in the sense described in Chapter 9) because the permafrost and the nature of the terrain inhibit their growth.

The geological structure of this province is most interesting. It is for the most part composed of the main block of what is called the Laurentian Shield. This is a vast dome of extremely ancient, if not absolutely primary, surface rocks that seem to have been formed by the deposits laid down when the hydrosphere or water layer first formed on this planet. These rocks are anchored in the next layer below the surface, forming what is called by geologists a *horst*. This is a sort of island with roots, of such solidity and for so long in "balance" with surrounding areas that it cannot any more be compressed or pushed down into the crust. It is, in fact, said to be in *isostatic balance*, a term which implies that it long ago adjusted itself like a block of wood put in a bathtub that has finally done with absorbing water and

The weasels of the north (which turn white in winter and are then called ermines) are agile little predators that keep down the hordes of lemmings and other rodents.

expanding, and has reached equilibrium. There are only a few such horsts on the surface of the earth—others are in Scandinavia, eastern Siberia, and, it now seems, Antarctica. They are all very rich in mineral veins.

THE REMARKABLE LICHENS

Lichens are in many respects the most remarkable of all plants. They are among the first living things to appear after any part of the surface of the earth has been scoured by anything from an icecap to a landslide, and they are the last to go when conditions deteriorate to the point of death for all others. It is true that the first living things to reach an utterly denuded and devastated area are not always lichens but most usually spiders; thus, for example, after the island of Krakatoa blew up, spiders turned up on lava beds before they were cool, prior to any reported plants. Very few air-breathing animals of a purely terrestrial nature have been found in the Antarctic, but lichens grow on almost all exposed rocks there, and lichens occur right up to the tops of the highest mountains. The other astonishing thing about lichens is that there is actually no such plant as a lichen; all of them are combinations of two plants—an *alga* (the seaweed group) and a *fungus*—growing in most intimate association and according to their kinds, each combination in its own form; yet both fungus and alga can often get along alone and each looks entirely different from the other. Strangest of all is that some of these combinations grow into very complex

structures, sometimes surpassing any alga or fungus in this respect. The underlying process is more like that of the "growth" of human artifacts than the true growth of a plant—more like cooking, by which a cake may be produced out of the more or less haphazard mixing of various unlike ingredients and subjecting the result to some heat. Lichens are the basis of the entire Arctic economy of both man and beast, for there are actually two lines of life that start with them and are dependent upon them, one great, the other small.

The first starts with the Barren Ground Caribou or American Reindeer, which subsist to a very large extent on lichens, especially during the winter on the Ungava tundras. The only large predator is the Wolf, though the Polar Bear is found all around the coast and sometimes wanders quite far inland. The Black Bear does not even venture out onto the tundra, and the dish-faced or "brown" bears are of course a purely western form. The only other animal that may take the young of the caribou is the Wolverine, which is here quite common. The other food cycle starts with those curious little rodents called the lemmings, on which all the small predators appear to rely almost wholly.

THE LEMMINGS

There are two distinct species of lemmings on the tundra and two more in the taiga. The Common or Brown Lemming *(Lemmus trimurcronatus)* is a small brown rodent about five inches long with only an apology for a tail. Its head is slightly grayish, and the position of the ears can barely be determined under the thick fur and hairy overcoat. The other species is named the Collared Lemming *(Dicrostonyx hudsonius)* and is quite remarkable in several respects. First, it turns pure white in winter. Second, its ears are reduced to small ridges completely buried under its fur, and they may be closed by little brushes of stiff backward-pointing bristles that can be raised or depressed by special muscles under the skin just in front of the ear passage. Third and oddest of all is that in the fall it grows a huge additional claw under the normal claws of the third and fourth fingers of the forefeet, and then sheds them again each spring. Both these little animals are very active throughout the summer among the tundra mosses and low, tangled growth; in the winter they make endless tunnels under the snow, but the Common Lemming spends much time in semihibernation. The Collared may, however, be met with in early spring, as soon as the sunlight returns, on top of the snow.

Everybody has heard the story of the lemmings of Norway, which are supposed to come down out of the mountains in countless droves every ten years or so, in what is called a "migration," and then plunge into the Atlantic Ocean and drown. Practically everything about this story is misleading if not simply untrue. First, these periodic appearances of large numbers of lemmings are not migrations (which are periodic movements to another place followed by a return to the original point) but *emigrations,* which are initiated, maintained, and guided by quite different biophysical factors. Secondly, the animals do not come down out of the mountains every ten years or, in Norway, at any exactly regular intervals. Their occurrence may vary by as many as ten years. Thirdly, they do not all head straight for the Atlantic; to the contrary, they move outward in all directions—as often and in as great numbers directly away from any seashore as toward it. Nor do they all come bowling down the hillsides at once; the swarm moves slowly outward, sometimes taking years to reach its farthest point—seashore or other—and the animals keep breeding and dying along the way. Since our lemmings of the Ungava and other Arctic regions behave in a like manner, it may be worth inquiring what does happen.

The whole phenomenon is cyclical and in some places has a very regular rhythm. Through studies of the records kept by the Hudson's Bay and other fur companies of the pelts of those predators that live largely on the lemmings, scientists have now been able to construct a graph of these fluctuations going back a century. Due to the great fecundity of the animals, each pair could theoretically leave over seven hundred descendants at the end of each brief summer breeding season. The normal cycle rises to a peak of numbers every four years. During this time an increasing number of them are, however, taken by predatory birds like falcons, the great snowy owls, skuas, gulls, and also by ermines, red foxes, Arctic foxes, and wolverines—all of which, enjoying increasing food supply, also multiply rapidly in numbers. At the same time, the lemmings begin to get crowded and start impinging upon each others' feeding grounds until they may even become improperly nourished, whereupon disease breaks out and rips through the whole population like a prairie fire; and in a surprisingly short time all the vast hordes have completely vanished and one would not believe that any had ever existed. However, some do survive and start the cycle all over again. Meantime the predators, finding no food, also die off in droves, though the birds try to emigrate, the skuas and gulls going to the seashores, the falcons and owls going south. Strangely, neither of the latter seems to survive or ever to return even if they find fat pickings in the forested regions. But this natural rhythm does not produce the great emigrations. These result from a sort of superbreeding

craze that breaks out just as a normal peak is reached. In this case the individual animals seem to grow bigger, are much stronger, and become very aggressive. They also give birth to larger litters at ever shorter intervals, and the young breed at an earlier age. Then, slowly, the whole horde starts to move outward from its most crowded focal points, increasing in numbers and vigor as it spreads and comes upon more ample food supplies. It is believed that the initial trigger is the acquisition by the animals of unexpected amounts of vitamins A and E from lichens upon which they feed during the winter under the snow. These lichens are known to be very rich in these vitamins but to produce them in varying amounts due to climatic factors.

Once the lemmings start emigrating they keep going, those at the outer edge of the mass being pushed forward by those coming behind, who take their food away from them. If the mass reaches a water barrier, they, being used to modest sloughs in tundras, may attempt to swim it; but if it is too wide or happens to be the open sea, they finally become exhausted like any other land animal and drown. As time goes on, the food in the center becomes scarce and all but a very few either feeble or very stalwart animals have left on the irrevocable exodus. The horde moves ever outward, breeding, dying in multitudes, fighting, and often rife with disease; but eventually they all perish even if, as was actually observed in Norway many years ago, they reach what appears to be an ideal locality for their kind, devoid of rivals and free from predators. If disease does not kill them off, they seem simply to breed themselves to death, and it has been suggested that this decline is due to the dissemination and loss of the vitamin build-up.

The animal life of the Pine-Spruce subbelt (see general map) is considerably more varied than that of the Spruce-Aspen-Birch, and a certain number of southern forms like Chipmunks and Skunks are to be found therein. To list just a few of the mammals; there are both the Hairy-tailed Mole and the Star-nosed Mole; the Water Shrew; and several bats other than the Little Brown Bat, which ranges in summer right up to the Arctic province. The Groundhog and the White-tailed Deer also make their appearance. Mink, Otter, Muskrat, Porcupine, and Black Bear are found throughout both belts.

The highest point of land in this province is probably Mount Gaspé, which is measured at a modest 4350 feet, but there could still be peaks of slightly greater height within the fastnesses of the great northern peninsula about the borders of Labrador and Quebec, though the average height of these uplands does not top 3000 feet. Apart from the Ungava area (which lies within the Arctic province), this whole country forms the transition between the Arctic and the truly temperate zones. Its vegetation and wildlife are more exclusively of the latter, but, since it lies at such high latitudes, even a rise in land surface of 3000 feet can have very marked effects. Nobody really knows much about the greater part of this province. It is possible that many wonderful and perhaps unique things will be brought to light as detailed exploration proceeds, as may be indicated by the discovery of at least one striking phenomenon therein—the Chubb Crater.

THE GREAT METEOR CRATERS

Since the middle of this century a whole new concept of our planet has been slowly emerging from several different branches

A collared lemming. In winter this rodent becomes white and remains active under the snow.

Ringed Seal. Enormous numbers of this and other species congregate each spring on the ice off these coasts to give birth and then breed again.

A famous pinnacle, known as Mother Burke's Rock, near La Scie, White Bay, on the rugged coast of Newfoundland.

of research, and the discovery of the vast Chubb Crater has played a not inconsiderable part in the formulation of this over-all picture. After much debate, and in the face of several dia-metrically opposed theories, it now seems to have been at least temporarily decided that the so-called craters that all of us can see on our satellite, the Moon, were made by meteors. This was thought to be rather odd in that the whole surface of that as-tronomical object was pock-marked with such, while our much bigger planet was not. We are now slowly changing our opinion about this.

On June 20, 1943, an immense circular hole filled with water was spotted from the air by a U. S. Air Force plane at the south-eastern edge of the Ungava district. This had the usual impact ridge of shattered surface rocks piled up all around it, and it lay in an area where there was no sign of volcanic activity such as might possibly have promoted a vast crater. On being reported, its existence was doubted, but the Royal Canadian Air Force mapped it from the air in 1948, and their findings were pub-lished in 1950. An experienced prospector—Frederick W. Chubb—brought these to the attention of Dr. V. Ben Meen, director of the Royal Ontario Museum of Geology and Mineralogy, and these two then first flew over and later went overland (1951) to inves-tigate the discovery. It proved to be the largest meteor crater so far discovered on earth. The Canadian authorities then initiated a detailed reappraisal and examination of the aerial surveys of their country and came up with the astonishing fact that many other objects that could be meteor craters were scattered all across the continent within their boundaries. These varied greatly

in apparent age, in that some were just as bold and fresh-look-ing as this Chubb Crater, while others looked what might be called "fossilized." These latter no longer appeared as raised rings on the surface of the land and were noticeable only by their circularity as disclosed in photographs because of different forms of vegetation that grew where their ridges had once been. Some contained circular lakes or parts of such lakes. Detailed studies by drilling, and the use of modern electronic equipment, further proved that these were indeed meteor craters, showing all the typical features of smashed and pulverized surface rocks down to considerable depths under the crater itself, warped and broken rock around its rim, and even the presence of meteoric iron scattered within and all around. How many more craters remain to be revealed, not only in Canada but throughout the world in areas clothed in blankets of forest, has yet to be ascer-tained.

It is becoming increasingly obvious that the earth was pep-pered by a much greater number of meteors big enough to break through our atmosphere without burning up than had previously been supposed. Meteorites, in fact, form a prominent feature of what we call generally "natural history." Instead of being mere oddities, they take their place as something that even the amateur may "collect." Let me therefore offer a few of the more remarkable facts that have been discovered about these cosmic visitors.

The meteorite that caused this Chubb Crater must have been of truly monumental proportions, considering that the hole it left is some 320 times the size of that left by the famous Arizona

example, the weight of which has been estimated at four million tons. The diameter of the Arizona crater is about 4000 feet; that of the Chubb is over three times greater. When the Chubb meteorite walloped into the bare rock of the Ungava plateau it must have set up a very considerable seismic disturbance. So also must several of the others that landed in Canada. Now meteorites are thought to be bits of some much greater body, possibly a planet, that broke up or exploded somewhere within our solar system, for they come in three major types—iron, iron-rock, and rock. The actual chemical composition of these is odd, in that among the iron and iron-rock types there are found some minerals that do not exist on this earth.

The falls of meteorites have been observed through the ages and recorded since history was first written. Also, considerable numbers of meteorites of all three classes, plus another type known as glass meteorites or *tectites*, have also been found scattered all over the surface of the earth, in most recent deposits. Meteorites have also been among the most holy and therefore priceless collections of men since the Stone Age. Further, large numbers of iron meteorites were "used up" by primitive man before he learned to extract that metal from ores, as has been shown by a chemical analysis of many of the earliest iron artifacts so far discovered. Meteoritic iron seems to have been man's first source of that metal. However—and this is the really extraordinary fact—although iron and iron-stone meteorites seem, on a purely statistical basis, to have been falling all over the earth at a regular though now diminishing rate throughout historic and prehistoric times, not one single one or

even tiniest part of one has ever been found in any of the billions of tons of building stone, coal, salt, or any other rocks or deposits that have now been mined by man for thousands of years. The earliest known whole meteorites come from comparatively recent surface deposits laid down not earlier than half a million years ago; so it would seem that, prior to that time, no meteorites fell on this earth.

At the same time, working from quite another angle, there are those investigators who have brought forward evidence to show that, whatever large planetary body broke up to give rise to the iron, iron-stone, and possibly stone meteorites, it did so at least 500,000,000 years ago. Some of these investigators, along with other scientists, have suggested that a planet between Mars and Saturn then blew up, giving rise both to meteorites and to the Asteroid Belt. Some of the resulting "junk" then for a period crossed the path of our planet, which gathered it up slowly by running into it and so clearing a path through it. The Moon, because of its lack of atmosphere, acts like a vast broom as it sweeps around the earth, covering a much wider front than we do. Most of this debris was received by the Moon and because of its lack of atmosphere was not burned up. Also, if its surface is covered with deep ultrafine dust, even a small meteor might make a tremendous impression on its surface.

The pursuit of meteoritic craters can be fascinating, and their discovery can yield some really unique insights into the vegetation, and thus into animal life; for they constitute the one truly erratic and unpredictable physical force coming from outside that may upset the even tenor of events on this earth. If they—

apart from the glassy tectites, which may be the end product of an earlier cosmic body of vitreous composition, which also broke up—started peppering this planet only about the time man was preparing to become organized, and then did so with great emphasis, they may have had the profoundest effect on his history and that of other forms of life.

OFFSHORE HOSTS

One day we may be able to drive to the Chubb Crater and look into these matters for ourselves. Today, however, most of this province is still more or less unapproachable. Its known centers of interest are to be found around its periphery, and 75 per cent of this is represented by coast line. Hudson Bay is a very odd sea which, although not without its quota of submarine life and its shore and oceanic birds, always appears to be somewhat dead. In winter it freezes splendidly and remains a great flat sheet of white nothingness for months. However, as soon as we enter the Hudson Strait, between Baffinland and Ungava, we encounter quite other conditions. This is a channel leading from the true oceans, and into it all manner of deep-water denizens penetrate; while, as we round Cape Chidley at the east end of Ungava Bay, we find ourselves in that arm of the Atlantic which leads to Davis Strait. From this flows the mighty Polar Current of cold water, which brings abundant food for a multitude of animals such as fish, seals, and whales. This current flows south along the Labradorian coast, and to it come endless hosts of sea life both below and above water. Here coastal sea birds such as Puffins, Guillemots (or Murres), Razorbills, Gannets, gulls, and others crowd in great swarms, nesting on the rugged rocky coasts and roaring out to sea to fish by day. In the waters are fish, stratified layer upon layer to great depths.

Jutting out into the ocean from the eastern tip of Newfoundland are the famous Grand Banks, to which Europeans have apparently sailed since the beginning of the Christian era, if not before, to fish for cod; and to this also come the ocean predators to feed on the fish. Also, wallowing along behind, come the whales of all sizes, from the little porpoises and the ocean speedsters, the dolphins, to the great, bumbling Rorquals and the even more ponderous Black and Greenland Right Whales to feed upon the multitudinous little crustaceans and other plankton. Then there are also the terrible Killer Whales, the greatest flesh-eaters presently on this planet, of which the larger bulls can measure up to thirty feet in length, weigh forty tons, and have mouths armed with big enough teeth to take a bite four feet wide out of the underbelly of a mighty Blue Whale, or actually dive into the mouth of a Right Whale and tear out its one-ton, bulbous, fleshy tongue.

All around this coast and into the Gulf of St. Lawrence, the sea swarms with life. The world of the oceans is not a part of our story, but nonetheless that of its coasts has played such a notable part in both the natural and human economy of such a large peripheral belt of this continent that it must be taken into account in any description of the natural history of the whole. Sea products have always been not only a major constituent of the coastal life of all land masses, they also have a profound effect extending very deeply into the largest continents. Further, they provide an abundance of salts and other minerals that are not readily available to animal life in the middle of large land areas, but that almost all animals crave. This seems to bring both short-term and long-term immigrations of all manner of living things to the ocean fringes, while sea products are somehow carried or otherwise filter inland to great distances;

and this by other agencies, as well as human ones. The Gulf of St. Lawrence is a major source of "sea food" on this continent.

WHALES AND SEALS

Whaling has always been pursued from the ice front at the north head of Baffin Bay all the way down the coasts of Greenland, Labrador, and on to New England, both by the early colonists, the earlier Norse, and the Eskimos and Amerindians before them. The Norse relied to a considerable extent on this enterprise in Greenland, pursuing the White-sided and other species of dolphins, the large Greenland Right Whale when possible, and particularly specializing in the capture of the fabulous Narwhal, a small species of whale of a special family which otherwise contains only the equally strange Beluga or White Whale. The Narwhal grows to sixteen feet, but the adult males carry on the front of the head a tremendous, spirally-twisted, spiked tooth which may measure as much as twelve feet. In olden times these twisted ivories used to be imported to Europe and used for the legs of episcopal thrones, and, cut into sections, as sword hilts. Today this industry has become redundant, but the capture of the Beluga is still of importance in the area, notably in the Gulf of St. Lawrence. There a regular fishery from small boats using rifles to shoot the animals and then harpoons to land them has continued through the years.

The Beluga is born a nondescript dirty brown-colored creature, but as it grows it gets whiter and whiter till the adult bulls are of a pristine, opaque whiteness that surpasses the whiteness even of newly fallen snow. These animals have very thick but supple skins overlying a four-to-eight-inch layer of blubber which forms a delicious article of Eskimo diet called *mukluk*. The larger whales actually have skins hardly thicker than a sheet of carbon paper. Some dolphins, and the porpoises (which are really quite different creatures), have thick enough skins to provide leather of high grade, but that of the Beluga surpasses them all in this respect, and has always been the main reason for their pursuit by man.

Of the larger whales and whaling we will not speak; for, although several of their kinds enter the fjords of this province regularly to feed during their annual migrations, they are not animals of the land. Some other marine mammals, however, must be mentioned. These are certain seals, three species of which occur off these coasts in untold numbers and which still visit them annually in sufficient quantities to form the basis of a considerable industry. These are known as the Greenland Seal (Phoca groenlandica), the Hooded Seal (Cystophora cristata), and the Bearded Seal (Erignathus barbatus). The last is today comparatively rare. Off the Labrador coast and in the Gulf of St. Lawrence the young of the Greenland seals are born on the sea ice in late March, and it is then that the sealing ships descend upon them, massacring the helpless little white, fluffy babies which cannot even swim. The method used to collect their pelts was once the most revolting activity ever devised by man, entailing clubbing them on the head and immediately stripping off their pelts. However, the clubbing was often neglected, and the helpless little creatures were skinned alive and left to flounder on the ice. It is to be hoped that these practices have now (as the industry officially declares) been discontinued.

Kittiwakes, a small species of gull, common on both sides of the Atlantic. Their eggs were at one time eagerly sought after by mariners.

Ptarmigan are game birds of Northern and Upper Montane moorlands. Most species change color with the seasons. The White-tailed Ptarmigan above are in winter plumage. The Willow Ptarmigan on the facing page is in summer dress.

The Crested or Hooded Seal belongs to a separate family, which contains in addition only the Sea Elephants. It grows to about eight feet in length and is rather an aggressive beast. Through the years, there develops on its nose a remarkable kind of bladder, which can be inflated from within and through which the males when fighting at the mating season make ghastly gurgling noises—like prolonged snorts—that can be heard for miles over the ice. The Bearded Seal is misnamed in that it really carries a super "Old Bill" moustache of extraordinary, flattened, horny, recurved bristles that are believed to act as a guard against the spines borne by many of the sea creatures on which it feeds, such as certain fish and sea urchins. Like the Greenland Seal, it belongs to the family of ordinary seals containing the little Harbor Seal of our coasts, the Ringed Seal, and the large Gray Seal, none of which assembles in great enough numbers at any one place to form the basis of commercial sealing operations. The Bearded, Hooded, and Greenland Seals spread out over the ocean and along all its coasts after giving birth and breeding. Then they all turn up—on schedule—at these breeding areas the next year. They perform true migrations.

FLIGHT OF THE GREATER SNOW GOOSE

There are other aspects of migration to be seen in this province at almost any time of the year, but there is one that is really very arresting. This is the passing, or rather visiting, of the Greater Snow Goose, a magnificent pure white bird with a few black-tipped wing feathers that make it look, when at rest, as if it had a black tail. These birds nest, raise their young, and spend the summer away up in Ellesmereland in the northern part of the Arctic Province but migrate south to the coasts of Maryland, Virginia, and North Carolina to spend the winter. There used to be millions of them, but they were slaughtered so unmercifully that by 1908 there were only about 3000 left. Strict conservation efforts came just in time, and there are today more than 100,000, all living in one great flock, moving north and south together, nesting together, and spending the winter together. The odd thing about their annual migration now is that all of them put down twice a year at a place called Cap Tourmente, which is some twenty-five miles downstream from Quebec on the St. Lawrence. In the spring they arrive there in March from the south and stay until May; in the fall they arrive about late September and again stay about three months. Their massed flight looks disorganized at first appearance, but photos taken from the air far above them and from certain angles disclose that the masses are divided into squadrons of fairly equal num-

bers, each of which makes use of a staggered regimentation, *en echelon,* to gain the advantage of each other's slip streams, and that the squadrons themselves are also arranged for the same purpose. The lead birds in such regimented flights are relieved by others from time to time, as they have to "split open the air" (as may be said) and so get weary sooner than those behind. They then fall to the rear of the line where, provided they keep in formation, they have to expend hardly any effort at all, being swept along within the turbulence created by those ahead. These birds arrange for the squadrons to aid each other in the same

way, so that pairs of them form compressed rhombs and keep equidistant from each other and from surrounding pairs but at a greater distance from them. Thus the air is cleft on the bias, as it were, and the whole mass slips through with much less expenditure of effort by the majority than would have been necessary in a purely haphazard flight.

Although we have spoiled the face of a large part of this continent, there are endless happenings all about us every day that can only be called miracles. Each natural country or province has its own particular wonders to offer.

Moose, Spruce, and Muskeg

The Canadian Northwest Territories or Lake District

3

As may be seen from our map of America's natural provinces, there are three such provinces adjacent to the Arctic. Thus, in leaving the great peninsular province of Quebec and Labrador with its attendant islands, we enter next that vast, more or less flat territory which lies athwart central Canada. We are calling this the Canadian Lakes District.

The size of this province is almost impossible to grasp even by those who visit it. Probably only those who have traveled therein extensively, like the Royal Canadian Mounted Police who now patrol it by air, really have any true concept of its extent. To gain a proper impression of this land, it is preferable to approach it from the Barren Lands across the tundra from the north; the impact is far more spectacular than penetrating it from the south—which one can do only by canoe, by one railroad, or by one road. This is a forest province and it forms the second-largest continuous forest on the surface of the earth, being surpassed only by the great taiga of Siberia. Let us retrace our steps for a moment and imagine that we are on a walk directly from the North Pole to the Equator down, say, the 100th meridian. This would, of course, entail an enormously long trek over the polar ice raft, the great Canadian Islands and the channels dividing them, and finally across the huge Keewatin Peninsula. So far, even if one could make the trek in the brief northern summer, we would have seen nothing but ice, snow, bare rock, and tundra. What is more, we would have had to walk almost two thousand miles down this particular meridian before we reached the northern fringe of the great forest province that we are now discussing. This is no less than one-third of our journey to the Equator, for it is 6215 miles from the North Pole to the Equator going straight down any meridian or line of longitude. Should one make this trek at even a rate of twenty miles a day, it would be fourteen weeks before one saw a tree—which is to say, reached the northern limit of this Lakes Province of Canada. Then, if there was an unencumbered path leading directly south through this, it would take another five weeks to reach its southern boundary, which is, incidentally, the United States border near Winnipeg. But perhaps even more astonishing is the consideration that, should one continue south at the same rate, it would take us only twelve weeks to cross the whole United States—and at its deepest from north to south at that. This province is on an average just one-half the depth of the whole United States, and measured from northeast to southwest. over three-quarters its width.

This province appears on most maps as little more than an enormous stretch of featureless territory. But if you come to analyze it, some hint of why it is as it is will eventually become apparent. In this case a really good physiographic map such as the one prepared by Dr. Edwin Raiz of Boston (which is printed in black and white but with surface waters shown in blue) brings to light something that is not otherwise apparent.

One sees immediately that this whole area of the map is littered with blue dots, spots, and patches, representing lakes of all sizes. Their number is literally legion. But most notable is the fact that these are greatest in number around the edge of Hudson Bay to the east but are there smallest in size, whereas they become less numerous to the west but larger. At first this seems odd, but once it has been suggested that Hudson Bay may have been caused in the first place by a gargantuan mass of ice pressing down the earth's crust at that point, it all begins to seem much more comprehensible. If we assume that this happened, a very wide area all around that depression must also have been to varying extents depressed. It apparently was, but the tough Laurentian Shield would not so "go down." The land to the west, however, apparently did so. Then, after the ice had melted away, it started to spring back; but in the meantime it was flooded.

Now we have noted that the surface of the land had become deep-frozen under the icecap. Therefore it could not absorb surface water. Moreover, apart from the melting ice, there was very little water available in the form of precipitation, so that no surface drainage system formed. The water just lay there in various depressions. Then plants came in, and forests grew on the slightly higher surfaces, while endless lakes and ponds formed in the lower ones; then these began to fill in with humus and other debris and formed what are called muskegs. The lands farthest from the Hudson depression rose first and highest so that more of their surfaces have drained off, only the larger depressions remaining as the great Canadian lakes of the Northwest Territories.

TAIGA AND MUSKEG

And what is this land like? This is a fairly simple question to answer though, paradoxically, it cannot yet be answered either wholly or categorically. As far as we know from aerial reconnaissance and surveys, the accounts of trappers, traders, missionaries, and others who have traveled therein, plus the accounts of the Amerindians, it appears to be a fairly uniform land of continuous forest and what is called muskeg, endlessly intersected by ponds, lakes, rivers, and sloughs. Its southern border merges with a type of forest called the Transition Belt, wherein pines and hardwoods grow, as opposed to the pure stands of small spruce (with some aspen) or spruce, firs, and pines, which is not only characteristic but actually definitive of this northwest territory. Its northern edge is the northern limit of trees; and most peculiar that is.

Tropical forests or jungles often, if not usually, end abruptly. Even temperate woodlands may do likewise, as in North Dakota,

The great taiga (or spruce) forest thins out in the far north, the individual trees becoming scraggly, stunted, and isolated, and finally dying away altogether in an expanse of tundra and bare rocks. Tongues of forest may reach for miles onto the tundra along watercourses.

This, the second of the three natural provinces which abut onto the tundras and barren lands of the Arctic, is of enormous extent but is one of the most homogeneous on this continent. Approached from the north, it is a vast plateau that rises steadily southward to about an average of 2500 feet from the Arctic shore line and the west and southern shores of Hudson Bay. Physiographic maps show it dotted with numerous highlands that are called "mountains," but one can fly, drive, or walk over these without ever knowing that they are areas of comparatively greater altitude than the surrounding flat country. They are, in fact, simply groups of huge low domes; so big that even from their "summits" (as determined by survey) no views are obtained unless many acres of the massed spruce

trees that cover the land have been cleared away. Then the world seems simply to drop away slightly to the horizon all around.

This province is very clearly defined on all but its narrow eastern side. Its northern boundary is the tree line that runs from the mouth of the great Mackenzie River in the northwest almost due southeast to Button Bay on the west coast of Hudson Bay just about the port of Churchill. After that it follows the south coast of Hudson Bay to Moosonee at the bottom of James Bay. Its western border is even more clearly defined, being no less than the great barrierlike eastern face of the Rockies. This barrier follows the western bank of the Mackenzie River from the Arctic Ocean (here the Barents Sea) south to its confluence with the Liard River, and then runs almost due south to the headwaters of the Peace River in central British Columbia.

The southern boundary of the province is plainly marked on almost any map, however crude, that purports to show the distribution of vegetation. Yet it is not easy to define, since there are very few place names along its length. It is equally difficult to outline precisely in the field because, although it is a radical change-over line, half a dozen subbelts are here compressed into a very limited strip of territory. This boundary marks the transition from the northern boreal forests to the great prairies, but the latter extend much farther north than is generally realized. This dividing line runs almost exactly southeast from Fort Nelson to Winnipeg, thence due east to Port Arthur on Lake Superior.

The narrow eastern boundary of the province is arbitrary but runs from Heron Bay northeast to Moosonee. The "break" here is actually, as shown on the accompanying map, that between the great clay belt which surrounds James Bay, and the ancient rocks of the Laurentian Shield. On the latter, maples become prominent, whereas they are absent or insignificant in the province under discussion.

---

where they abut onto the prairie. In the far north, on the other hand, the forest sort of "peters out"—the trees becoming ever more scraggly and standing wider apart, and finally becoming very tattered in appearance and growing isolated in a sea of tundra. Only along the shallow valleys do they finger out onto the barren lands in mass, and even then they are usually stunted and look very forlorn. Yet, as seen by one tramping down from the north, they signify something that is very dear to the hearts of all of us, except perhaps the Eskimos.

It is not until one visits these lands that one comes to realize just how much trees mean to us. In both the tropics and the so-called temperate zones there are great deserts, but, even to people raised in those, the vision and significance of trees is inborn. The impact of a solid mass of trees such as we find in the Northwest Territories thus, at first sight, comes as somewhat of a shock, for their pure "massiveness" is really awe-inspiring. For hundreds of miles they stand, their branches inextricably interwined like—and indeed forming—a great barrier. However, almost a third of this province is covered with water. This consists of lakes varying in size from some of almost sealike dimensions—the Great Bear and Great Slave, for instance—to lesser ones of all sizes down to ponds only a few feet in diameter. And then there is the *muskeg.*

By most people other than Canadians, this term is often con-

fused with *tundra.* Tundra is open land without trees, the vegetative covering of which is composed of mosses, lichens, and tiny stunted plants of other sorts growing to only a few inches in height—though moss domes may be several feet deep. Muskeg, on the other hand, while having a ground cover similar to but much deeper than the tundra, is also clogged with rushes, sedges, grasses, and either continuous stands or clumps of thin-branched bushes, such as willows, varying in height from a man's knee to about the top of his head. Muskegs are swamps and in most cases probably filled-in ponds and lakes, and they meander through the taiga or spruce forest in every conceivable shape, and form sort of vegetational lakes in its midst.

The whole of the northern belt of this province lies upon frozen soil, though the depth of this and its nearness to the surface varies greatly. In winter the soil is of course frozen right up to the surface and the whole is covered with snow. However, the spruce forests are often so dense that the snow forms a great blanket-like roof over the top and the ground surface may remain quite bare and, because of the blanket of snow above, may not, in exceptional cases I am told, even freeze. In the muskegs, however, everything congeals and the snow lies directly on the ground. In summer, conditions are almost exactly reversed in that the soil surface under the trees, being sheltered from the sun's rays, remains cold, while the open muskegs thaw down to a considerable depth. These curious conditions serve to keep the two types of growth quite distinct, for the vegetation of both is highly adapted to these particular seasonal alternations of comparative heat and cold, and more especially to concurrent changes in moisture and aridity, so that trees cannot get a hold in the muskeg, while the muskeg bushes cannot grow in the deep shade under the trees. Thus, the whole of this land becomes a vast jigsaw puzzle, as is plain when it is seen from the air and is only too patent when you try to cross it on the ground.

As we mentioned in the previous chapter, there is comparatively (to the mean world average) low precipitation in these northlands. That there is an excess of standing water on the surface is due to the fact that the ground is permanently frozen, which prevents water from sinking into the earth. These conditions pertain throughout this province and almost to its southern periphery. However, the frozen soil is not the result of the high latitude or even of the long, very cold winters. It actually results from what we may call "fossilized frozenness," something left over from the last southward advance of the north polar ice—or "Ice Age" as it is popularly but misleadingly called.

THE LAST FREEZE-UP

The whole northern part of the North American continent, from the great barrier of the Rockies to Newfoundland, was recently, by geological reckoning, covered by an enormous icecap, estimated to have been about two miles thick at its maximum, and extending south to Montana in the west, St. Louis in the center, and Long Island, New York, in the east. This icecap seems to have spread out from a point approximately in the middle of Hudson Bay.

While there were countless vast glaciers on the Rockies, and Quebec and Labrador were covered at the same time, neither area went down beneath the load of ice. Parenthetically, it should be explained that, while glaciers may in exceptional circumstances coalesce to form "icefields," they do not form an "icecap." Glaciers are moving rivers of ice that flow downward from icefields; an icecap is something quite different and of quite uncomparable dimensions; it is, in fact, a vast dome of ice formed from compressed and recongealed snow that covers the whole land, including mountain ranges and their icefields and glaciers. Today there are but two in existence, on Greenland and the Antarctic continent. Around the edge of icecaps there may, of course, be glaciers. For this reason, while there are manifold signs of recently past glaciation in the Rockies and in Labrador, these are confined to the scouring of valleys and the creation of certain peculiar phenomena in them.

This mass of ice, piled up upon the whole northeastern part of what is now the United States and Canada, weighed a tremendous amount. At the same time, the surface rocks of the earth, although appearing absolutely solid, are actually quite plastic but they are only to a limited extent compressible, while the next layer of material beneath them is not entirely rigid. If, therefore, you pile enough extra weight on the surface it will sag and, where the surface rocks are what is called "sedimentary"—i.e. those formed under seas and lakes—they may also be

A young bull moose browsing on pond plants in a mixed coniferous-deciduous forest. Largest of the deer, moose, like all other species, shed their antlers annually.

fairly compressible, so that if miles of ice are piled on them a great basin may gradually be formed on the surface of the earth.

When, however, this load of ice is removed, the "basin" thus formed first fills with water—salt, if a channel to an ocean is available, or otherwise with fresh. But then, the land as a whole begins slowly to rise again, and the water begins to flow out of the basin (as it is doing to the sea from Hudson Bay today). However, if there is no ready outlet it just floods over the surrounding land and forms numerous lakes until they find new overflow points as have the Great Lakes. Only ancient blocks of non-sedimentary rocks that have their roots deep in the subsurface layer of the earth—like the northern Rockies and the Laurentian Shield in Quebec—do not sag appreciably under a temporary load of ice.

All across the great plateau and lowlands of the north central part of this continent there are the most profound evidences of glaciation. These include *drumlins,* rounded, elongated, oval hills of ice-borne debris up to about a mile wide, and from 100 to 200 feet high; *eskers,* or narrow, dykelike sand or gravel ridges, from about 25 to 100 feet high, which may be as much as fifty miles long, and sometimes appear to be perfectly straight; and *fossil beaches,* low ridges of sand which often run parallel to coasts and to each other and sometimes mount to some hundred feet in height. Hudson Bay is completely ringed by all these and by numerous other evidences of the presence of an icecap and of the movements of vast depths of ice outward from a common center.

What has been happening in this area is that, since the ice last melted away or "retreated" northward, the land has been springing back; Hudson Bay has been draining off into the Davis Strait, and the Great Lakes have been struggling to get out through the St. Lawrence valley, and thus cutting back the Niagara Falls at a startling rate. However, a great deal of surface water has become temporarily caught in the countless millions of little lakes and ponds all around the Hudson Bay basin itself and all the way to the Mackenzie. This has resulted in a country unlike anything seen anywhere else in the world. It is clothed in solid stands of somber spruce trees interspersed with muskeg all across its northern belt. South of this the spruce is increasingly interlarded with, first, isolated aspen and then groups of them; then white birch and other hardwoods come in, and this eventually merges with the deciduous forest belt, which stretches right across the continent from sea level in British Columbia to and around the Great Lakes and thence to the St. Lawrence valley and New England.

Here, one stage removed from the Arctic, the seasons are considerably different. The black night of winter is not quite so long; the day-round painted dawns of spring and the sunsets of winter go on longer; the spring is a little earlier and more colorful; the summer is longer and more riotous; the fall is much longer and absolutely breath-taking in its magnificence. In winter this whole province is covered with deep snow from which the spiky spruce heads emerge like discarded Christmas trees. The snows begin in October; the break-up of the ice on the Mackenzie River does not come till mid-May, so that for a full seven months the greater part of this province is, as it were, submerged. Once the snow melts, the land burgeons miraculously; mammals, birds, and insects appear in their multitudes, flowers bloom, and the trees put out shoots with a rush. Although there is actually a long spring from a climatic point of view, there is virtually none from the visual. One day the winter is still rotting; the next, and especially if the sun shines, it is early summer, with the aspens a delicate bluish green and a sort of chartreuse fuzz all over the spruce.

As in all the sub-Arctic provinces, the summers are very hot and dry. The ground is covered with a thick carpet of sphagnum and other mosses with lichens and fungi and small lush herbs both on the muskeg and under the trees, and this always retains water like a sponge. In the north it rests upon permafrost which does not thaw during the summer. Farther south it acts somewhat unexpectedly, in an exactly contrary manner, insulating the subsoil from the winter cold by freezing solid and preventing deep penetration of frost. The results are surprising. If the land is cleared—as in modern road construction—and the few feet of black soil under the muskeg and the forest is scraped off, the land dries out completely in summer, resulting in choking dusts that range from fairly coarse-grained sand to stuff so fine that it penetrates anything not hermetically sealed. The dust of the sub-Arctic is worse than anything blown up by any hot desert, and in those areas where the subsurface of the whole land is formed of clay, as around the southern end of Hudson Bay, it has the cloying quality, the consistency and permeability, of a rubber-based paint.

GOLDEN WATERS

Although this province is said to lie on the western curve of the great Canadian Shield from a geological point of view, it has little if any similarity to the eastern curve of the Laurentians and Labrador. Apart from the great clay belt south of Hudson Bay, the whole land surface is covered with a few feet of black, peaty soil, lying on comparatively recent—geologically speaking—glacial deposits composed of gravels, sands, and clays. These in turn are spread over sedimentary rather than the ancient plutonic rocks so typical of the Laurentians and the east. The great rivers that flow northward across this territory drop down from the central continental plateau in steps, meandering along for some hundred miles, then suddenly discharging into gorges cut deep into the apparently level surface, and wandering along again until the whole land has fallen the equivalent of another step. Then the rivers drop into another canyon, the walls of which gradually diminish. The most beautiful and interesting of these gorges may be seen about thirty miles south of Great Slave Lake, and is now named the Alexandra Falls. There, the Hay River drops over a 110-foot fall into a gorge cut back into the vast plateau that slopes down to the sealike lake.

The water of this river is clear but is the color of dark sherry, and when it pours over a hundred-foot cliff in the vivid northern sunlight it becomes a vast half-dome of glutinous amber. The rocks of the gorges lie exactly horizontal and are formed of countless thin beds of hard-compacted, flintlike limestone, each bed being about two to three inches thick. They have been eroded off above the falls in such a way that the river passes between huge platforms composed of sheets of rock that look for all the world like the leaves of an opened book. These rock faces are full of fossils.

Even in winter this country has a smooth, austere beauty, and in summer it is exquisitely mellow. For two or three weeks at the end of September it blazes with colors that are unbelievably vivid and outrageously contrasted. The river valleys that cut into the apparently level plateau also present unforgettable spectacles in fall. Their bottoms and the lower ends of the side creeks that

The so-called Arctic Fox, a small foxlike dog of the tundra, preys mostly on lemmings and may store them in caches for the following winter.

Left: The Golden Eagle is still found all over the continent but only sparsely in the United States. Throughout the whole northwest they are large and abundant. Below: The Raven, probably the commonest bird of the Northwest Territories of Canada.

merge with them are choked with solid stands of aspens; the somber dark green spruce stand upon the slopes; while here and there some of the more exposed hillsides are devoid of trees but are instead clothed in mosses and lichens of a most strange soft olive-green-gray color. Upon these soft faces there are also often great swaths of those stunted bushes common to the upland muskegs which are of an intense rust-red color. As yet, there is but one road that penetrates this land, and it might appear to anyone tearing along its gravel surface, enveloped in a cloud of dust, that these forests are indeed lifeless and almost of a oneness throughout. But if you walk into them you will find they are quite otherwise. Before the coming of the airplane most

The American Marten or Sable, famous for its valuable fur, is a large relative of the weasels and of the Mink, Fisher, and Pine Marten of Europe.

travel was, of course, by water, but how anybody could find his way through that maze of wandering channels and connecting lakes is almost incomprehensible. The Hudson's Bay Company and Catholic missionaries, however, did so over a century ago, and there are considerable outposts all along the bigger rivers and around the great lakes. Four of these lakes—the Great Bear, Great Slave, Athabasca, and Winnipeg—are miniature inland seas with long stretches of narrow sandy beach on which the little cold waves break in miniature foamless surf. These look singularly "dead" though they teem with fish. Most of the wild-life gathers in the mouths of the rivers that pour into or flow out of them, and a number of these are often black with ducks of all kinds.

HUNTERS IN THE SKY

The second most noticeable group of birds in this province are sea gulls. It is, of course, absurd to be startled at the sight of these birds far from oceanic coasts and in the middle of a large continent, but I must admit to experiencing a considerable shock when I come across them standing on rocks in deserts, pecking about on prairies, perching on fir trees in mountain gorges, or especially tearing up a dead hare on a muskeg slough in a spruce forest five hundred miles from the nearest seacoast. Pattering about the roofs of log cabins and paddling about the smaller tree-girt ponds in the depth of the taiga spruce they seem altogether out of place. It makes one wonder whether gulls have always been as prevalent inland as they are today or as widespread. It is certain that they have within the memory of man considerably extended their ranges inland in many areas, but if they have done so in the sub-Arctic, man has had nothing to do with the matter. The commonest gull in this territory is the Herring Gull, but there do occur a few Black-backed, and occasionally some lone individuals of the great white Glaucous Gull of the Arctic.

The gulls seem to maintain a somewhat precarious existence in this area, having two armies of rival killers and scavengers to contend with. On the one hand are really extraordinary numbers of eagles and hawks (in the wider sense of that word) several of which get their living principally along the rivers and the shores of the lakes; on the other are even vaster battalions of ravens of really startling size. We look upon the Raven as a comparatively rare bird throughout large parts of the United States, and it is almost everywhere regarded as a lone fellow and as keeping to the more rugged and out-of-the-way places. In the sub-Arctic they are perhaps the commonest birds, at least among those that are readily seen, and in the Northwest Territories their numbers are fantastic and, very unexpectedly, they operate in large flocks like crows. They are enormous creatures with huge gorgets that splay out from their chests way beyond their folded wings when at rest. How so many manage to maintain a living not even the local Amerindians can explain satisfactorily. While it is true that all manner of carrion-eaters tend to gather along roads on which many animals are customarily killed by human traffic, I have passed along a two-hundred-mile stretch and never been out of sight of a flock, one batch after another rising before me at intervals of a few hundred feet. When, however, we traveled even far away from any road by water or on foot, we encountered the same multitudes in every open place. Ravens will kill anything they can catch and overcome, but for the most part they have to rely on the carrion left by predators, and although they are omnivorous, they thrive most on flesh. Just who kills enough of what animals in that country to maintain these hungry hosts is more than I would attempt to explain.

Golden Eagles are common all over, as far as I have been able to ascertain from bush pilots, the police, and others who spend their lives traversing this country; but there are places, especially among rocky outcrops or gorges, where they positively swarm. The bird called the "Osprey" in North America (namely, *Pandion haliaetus*) is also found in this region but rather in the eastern areas around the Hudson Bay. The variety and aggregate numbers of other birds of prey is equally astonishing. Possibly due to being unused to man as a whole or, contrarily, having over millennia come to a sort of understanding with the local Amerindians, these birds usually behave in a most surprising manner. They will sit on the ground, on a rock, or a bough at low level and just blink at you until you almost touch them, and those perched on the tops of trees often have to be literally shaken off before they consent to glide to the nearest available vantage point. This gives one a splendid opportunity to observe them at the closest ranges but leads to many frustrating experiences because of the long list of species all resident together, all of which seem to vary widely in both general tone and arrange-

The Sharp-shinned Hawk, a terror to small ground-living animals, is one of more than two dozen species of birds of prey found in the Northwest Territories.

ment of plumage even when adult. Also, in the area to the west of Hudson Bay there is a mingling of the Rocky Mountain and even the west coast species with the eastern forms, with some typically Arctic forms (such as the beautiful Gyrfalcons, the Marsh Harrier, and others), and with Redwings and Broadwings from the south. Goshawks are common along with Harlan's and Sharp-shinned Hawks and Rough-legs. Peregrines (Duck Hawks) are very common and Merlins (Pigeon Hawks) are numerous in many areas. Then, there is another predatory bird that holds a special position in our esteem and which is common in this country. This is the Bald-headed Eagle, which has long been the national symbol of the United States.

This fine bird has now become quite widely rumored to be a "second-hand" fisherman, relying on others to catch its prey, and it has even been dubbed a coward and a scavenger. I have talked to a considerable number of field naturalists who have observed these birds over long periods and at points all the way from Florida to the Arctic, and I must say that, while the Bald Eagle may justifiably be accused of indulging in such habits from time to time, there is no justification for assigning to it a sort of second-class status among birds of prey. It certainly hunts over land and fishes over water for itself in the north, and with

extraordinary adroitness at the latter, as I can confirm from watching one in a gorge in this territory. The bird was a large adult in full plumage and worked up and down the river systematically without ever flapping a wing. I was perched on the edge of the cliff above it, and it presented a magnificent spectacle as it came riffling by, sometimes not more than a few feet from my place of concealment. Twice during the hour while I watched, though both times unfortunately when it was farthest from me downstream on its circuit, it tilted and swooped down on the racing surface of the river and appeared to belly-flop on the water with outstretched wings, making a great splash. Then, hefting a very large fish, it heaved itself into the air with one wing beat, flapped violently once or twice, cunningly caught an updraft, and just sailed upward in a tight spiral, gaining the rim of the canyon in an amazingly short space of time. In each instance, it took the fish somewhere and must have dropped or stashed it away, for almost immediately it came sailing back again into the gorge, just topping the trees on its rim. I would sorely like to have seen just what it did with those fish so quickly, more especially because when I asked an Amerindian professional hunter, I got a story that I had never heard before. This was to the effect that these birds deliberately drop large

45

fish into small ponds, where they die and float to the surface and are then retaken and eaten.

GREAT BEASTS

These forests teem with life, but as in equatorial jungles the great part of it remains carefully concealed. The spruce stands are more or less impenetrable to man, the trees standing so close together in many places that, even if they were devoid of their endless intertwined tangle of stiff dead branches at lower levels, a man of normal girth would be hard put to it to squeeze between their trunks. The wildlife here has a habit of playing possum, but at the same time, some of the larger animals may be approached closely; or they will approach you closely and seemingly through lack of experience combined with extreme inquisitiveness. In fact, they may approach far too close and be far too inquisitive. Such encounters usually occur in the open muskegs, though the new roads are veritable show strips.

The commonest large animal of the country is the Moose. They are numbered in the hundreds of thousands in Canada as a whole, and over three thousand were counted from the air in one area of British Columbia alone in a few days during a game survey. The Moose is a very large animal, not just the largest of the deer, and the largest of all are in the Northwest Territories. A big bull encountered at close quarters is as impressive as anything short of a lone elephant and appears to tower above you. If he has a full rack of horn, his head seems to fill your whole vision, and in this country of comparatively small trees the effect is little short of overwhelming. Bull moose are also rather aggressive and it is advisable to retreat promptly and at fair speed if you meet one on land unexpectedly, for they do not like being stared at and they seem to be able—unlike many animals, and notably the big cats—to detect man just as well when he is standing still as when he is moving. They may take off after a prolonged look, but they are just as apt to charge, and they can cover the tangled ground cover in gargantuan strides, or jump over it with an agility that is most unexpected. They are one of the very few animals that will do this when completely unprovoked; and, if you are hunting, you will need a powerful weapon to protect yourself because, as any north woodsman will tell you, small-caliber bullets have no effect upon them whatsoever. They will even charge automobiles and trucks, with devastating effect on the former and usually appreciable on the latter. I once met a huge bull in a little glade among tall fir and spruce standing belly deep in moss and stunted bushes. It was near evening and I had thought it was a large tree stump till it moved its head and its vast spread of amber-colored antlers became disassociated from the dead branches. I made the reflex actions of precipitate retreat, but about five pounds of clay had adhered to each of my feet, so I had to stand there more or less immobile, longingly eyeing the nearest climbable tree. Fortunately, the huge brute turned with a snort and went off up a steep incline at a pace that would have done credit to the best horse. What amazed me was its stride, which was a sort of monstrous prance with a jog-trot gait so that its enormous hoofs came up level with its belly, alternately front right and back left and front left and back right, and so were clear of the thick underbrush.

This strange prancing gait is typical also of the other deer of this country—the White-tailed (which, contrary to popular belief, is not uncommon right up to the Great Slave Lake) and the Woodland Caribou. These latter are wondrous beasts. There are very great numbers of them throughout the province. In summer they wander about in family parties, but in winter they join up in considerable herds and push in under the trees and the snow blanket to grub for mosses and other winter food. Yet, I have met people born and raised in these areas who have never seen one. I was more fortunate, having walked right into a large family party on one occasion. Caribou, as mentioned, are reindeer. There are three distinct kinds, indigenous to this continent—the little Arctic or Island species already described; a very large mountain form in Alaska and the Yukon; and these Woodland animals. The last are intermediate in size but can stand a good four feet at the shoulder and have the most palmated and comparatively the largest horns of all. Their appearance in life is quite different from any stuffed specimen or picture of them I have ever seen. They are shaped like large rectangular boxes with a bull neck, small head, and the huge antlers stuck on in front. When they run they look quite mechanical, their prancing legs forming right angles and the whole creature bouncing along so that you automatically say "chup-chup-chup-chup" as they go. They are of a very dark brown almost to black in summer, and they have very long tails which they carry stiffly erect as they run and which stand up almost as high as the tops of the antlers of the largest adults. These tails bear an enormous sort of fan of stiff white bristly hair which far surpasses both in actual size and in proportion to its bearer anything displayed by a White-tailed Deer.

THE WOODLAND BISON

It is in this country also that the last remnants of our largest land animal still survive. These are the great Woodland Bison, which are now preserved in a huge area west of the Peace River just south of Great Slave Lake. Unfortunately, a number of the "ordinary" Plains Bison were shipped up into this region some years ago and interbred with the Woodland species so that the latter are no longer all entirely of pure blood. However, the plains animals do not stand the cold and appear to have died off, while there are still pureblooded Woodlanders. In 1960 a whole herd of pure-breeds was found some distance to the west of the refuge, the most exciting big-game discovery since that of the mighty Couprey, also a kind of ox, in Indochina in 1938. These are magnificent beasts, more like the European Bison, without a hump, with very close and tightly curled wool all over the head and shoulders, horns that are much stouter at the base, and with two other conspicuous characteristics. As Dr. George G. Goodwin of the American Museum of Natural History, who made a study of them during both summer and winter, once described them to me: "Their heads are not sort of stuck on like the Plains animals but are carried higher like normal cattle, and they have rather big eyes that never show any of the white." These great beasts scratch down through the snow with their hoofs in winter and then browse on the mosses. However, there are sort of "lakes" of prairie with good lush grasses scattered through the forest right up to the latitude where they live, and the animals graze on these in summer. There are also many salt licks, and it is around these that they prefer to stay.

One of the many species of weasels found all over this continent. They are rarely seen elsewhere but in this province are very numerous and hunt by day as well as by night. Though primarily terrestrial, they can climb well and rob the nests of birds in trees.

It is in fact very surprising to see just how far north the prairies do extend in their great swing up the western half of our continent, and how the animal life of much more southern latitudes inhabits this during the summer, though most of it migrates southward each fall. It is on and about the outliers of prairie, deep into the taiga forests, that an abundance of rabbits, as opposed to the typically northern hares, are to be found. Their great numbers, which do not seem to fluctuate from year to year like those of the hares, attract an assemblage of the smaller predators. Whereas wolves are common throughout the rest of the country, they are replaced by coyotes on the prairies. This is also just about the only place on the continent where one is almost sure to see more than one weasel a day. Red Fox and Bobcat also abound, while the Lynx stays in the forests. Residents assert that there are even Gray Fox on these prairies.

Once more I would like to note the profusion and abundance of animal life in this area. It is to some extent true that the forests as a whole may be regarded as monotonous, but not in any degree is this so when compared to those of the next province we shall visit; namely, Alaska. A few moments of silence and the proper use of one's eyes will disclose, as if by magic, hosts of living things great and small everywhere. And, despite the occasional rambunctiousness of a bull moose or perhaps an irritable mother bear, it is a friendly land. The most alarming things—to me at least—are the grouse. They are so well camouflaged, so unafraid to begin with, and such adept vanishing artists, that one is invariably stepping on them, whereupon they let out piteous cries and roar into the air scattering gray feathers beneath them and making more noise for their size than a four-engined plane.

Scattered throughout the taiga forests are endless swampy areas, known as muskegs, *which support a profuse flora of thin-stemmed shrubs, various mosses, and such sedges as this Cottongrass. These freeze deeply in winter but become quagmires in summer while the surrounding ground remains frozen almost to the surface.*

Mammoths, Volcanos, and Mountains

The Aleutian Islands, Alaska, and the Yukon

4

To the west of the great Canadian Lakes District there is a huge peninsular province known as Alaska. As we are defining such units, this comprises considerably more than the political state known by that name, for it begins at the great mountain barrier which slices down our continent just to the west of the Mackenzie River, while its eastern periphery envelopes two-thirds of the Canadian Yukon.

Apart from the fact that this is a mountainous as opposed to a more or less level plateau province, it differs very markedly from the Northwest Territories and the central northern lowlands of Canada. It has, around its northern and western periphery, a belt of truly Arctic tundra, appearing at first very like that of the Keewatin Peninsula and even of the Islands, which for most of the year is just flat, featureless, and usually colorless. It also slopes very gently to the shores of the Arctic Ocean and the Bering Sea. This is a grim land, even when the sun shines and its multitudinous dwarf plants are in flower. It seems never to assume the vividness of color of the other central and eastern tundras, and that coast which faces eastern Asia over the narrow Bering Strait generally has a most dismal aspect.

It may surprise the uninitiated to find that this tundra belt turns abruptly south and even southeast through Kodiak Island, so that it comes to lie far south of even some part of the luxuriant rain forests of the coast of the Gulf of Alaska. This would appear to be "all wrong" had we not an over-all map showing the continent-wide distribution of all the vegetational belts. The reasons for these apparently somewhat erratic performances are of course climatic; and these, in turn, are based primarily on the major ocean currents.

One of the most remarkable facts about the past history of Alaska is that it does not seem to have been covered by an icecap in recent geological times. When some two miles of ice lay over the Canadian Lakes District and Hudson Bay, and even when that icecap extended south to Missouri and Long Island, this area (which is today a far northland) apparently remained at least as free of snow as it is at present. There is even evidence

Snow-covered Mounts Trident and Mageik of the Katmai volcanic complex after a mild eruption.

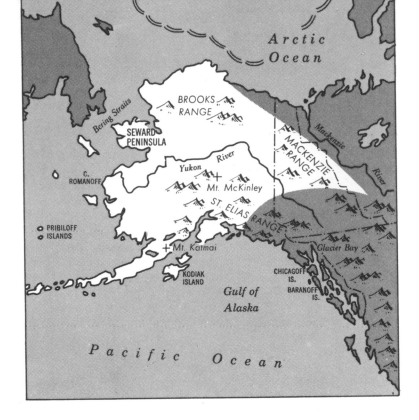

Arctic
Ocean

BROOKS
RANGE

SEWARD
PENINSULA

Bering Straits

MACKENZIE
RANGE

Mackenzie

River

C.
ROMANOFF

Yukon   River

Mt. McKinley

ST. ELIAS
RANGE

PRIBILOFF
ISLANDS

Mt. Katmai

Glacier Bay

CHICAGOFF
IS.
BARANOFF
IS.

KODIAK
ISLAND

Gulf of
Alaska

Pacific   Ocean

Because of their north polar orientation, most maps and atlases, especially those of North America, show Alaska extending up to the far left-hand corner (like a pterodactyl's wing with its elongated little finger) and with its long axis running almost north to south. If, however, you make your map on Kodiak Island and orient it to the Pole from there, you will find that the country runs from east to west and that the Pacific coast is on the south side, the Arctic to the north, the Bering Sea to the west, and Canada to the east. The Mackenzie River will thus form part of your northern boundary.

Alaska is clearly divided into three parts, partly but by no means entirely due to topography. It is fringed on the north, west, and southwest by true Arctic tundras, and this type of

vegetation extends along the Aleutian Islands far to the south. But, surprisingly, the south coast from Kodiak Island eastward is clothed in moss-laden spruce, firs, and hemlocks and dense alder thickets, a type of growth which is referred to as "rain forest" and which extends south along the Pacific coast to Vancouver Island. The central, inland, and main body of the province, which includes two-thirds of the Yukon and a strip of the Canadian Northwest Territories, is mountainous and is really an extension of the great Spruce-Aspen or Hudsonian Forest Belt.

The eastern edge of the province locks around the pine-spruce transition belt which, as we shall see in the next chapter, pushes westward to the headwaters of the Yukon. However, it must be emphasized that the provinces as here defined, while primarily dependent upon the distribution of the major vegetational belts that girdle the earth latitudinally, actually contain but sections of those belts, like the variously colored bands of a coral snake. Further, two or more major belts may be compressed into a single province; in fact, we have in this province Tundra, the Boreal, Hudsonian, or Spruce-Aspen Coniferous Belt, and some of the Pine-Spruce Subbelt. The dense forests of the southern coast are not really contained within the Deciduous Forest Belt, but are rather an extension of it, due to certain exigencies of climate produced by ocean currents.

Alaska and its Aleutian Islands form a very distinct natural country with many features that are unique—notably in its geological history and present-day make-up, which is quite unlike any other part of the world. Its fauna, and to some extent its flora, include some forms not found elsewhere, but both are on the whole typical of the three belts represented. Also, it is of enormous size, spreading over 2800 miles from west to east and being over 800 miles on the average from north to south. The southwestern peninsula and the Aleutian Islands account for half its width. At one point—Diomede Island—it is only four miles from Asia.

that it was much freer of snow; that, although there may have been permafrost at depth (left over from some previous refrigeration), its surface was not frozen down to a considerable depth; and that it supported, even on the lowlands, a much lusher and taller growth of vegetation than it does today. The reason for so supposing is the extraordinary volume of animal remains, including not only fresh bones but also flesh, that has been found in it. This state of affairs resembles that found all across northern Siberia on the other side of the Bering Strait, and is quite contrary to that on the central and eastern tundras of Canada.

Permafrost means simply permanently frozen ground, notably soils and subsoil. Such soil, like the surface of your garden at more southern latitudes in midwinter, is really a sort of rock, just as solid and just as impermeable to water. In Arctic lands this permafrost may extend downward for hundreds or even thousands of feet and may contain within it at various levels (as has been discovered by borings in Siberia) great strata of ancient ice. From this it is manifest that the whole mass has not melted at any one time since it was laid down, and that seems to have been very long ago. Certain frozen soils have been estimated to be as much as 100,000 years old. The really puzzling thing is that this permafrost in Alaska and Siberia contains enormous

quantities of animal bones and flesh, half-decayed vegetation, wood, and other remains of living things that, in some areas, together constitute a sizable percentage of the whole.

THE FROZEN HORDES

Few, if any, of these forms of life are found today in these countries or anywhere near them. Further, a high percentage of all these remains are of large animals like Woolly Rhinoceroses, giant Lions, giant Beaver, extinct species of huge Bison, Musk Ox, and Hairy Elephants or Mammoths; while there are also abundant remains of large trees, even fruit-bearing, broad-leafed trees. It is manifest, therefore, that the country prior to being refrigerated—and right up to the time that it was—must not only have had a very much milder climate but also must have been outside the Arctic, since within the Arctic Circle there is simply not enough sunlight distributed throughout the year in a suitable manner for such plants to grow, let alone in sufficient quantity to maintain these great numbers of large animals.

Just to take one example, great numbers of huge mammoths have been found preserved in this frozen soil, or "muck" as it is called, all of them in good health and most of them with full bellies at the time of their death—this in what is now a more or less foodless wilderness. You just cannot support such herds of huge animals, needing literally tons of fresh food and roughage daily simply to maintain themselves, on the present meager tundra vegetation—which, incidentally, is available for only a few weeks every year. When you add all the other creatures mentioned above (and the volume of their remains shows that they existed by the tens of thousands), the whole matter verges on the incomprehensible. Thus, it seems that, while the center and northeast of our continent were lying under the grip of an icecap, this today slightly more northern land was somewhere farther south, down in the sun, bathed in a much longer day than now, and so able to grow abundant food for vast herds of large animals and to support deciduous trees bearing soft fruits. This seems to be a logical conclusion.

How, why, and when did all these animals that we now find in the muck get killed; and so suddenly that their bodies did not have time to rot or even start to decay in some instances: indeed so abruptly in one case that flowering buttercups they were feeding on when death struck, were found still lodged unswallowed between their teeth? This is truly a conundrum, but there is another one even more inexplicable. How did they get instantly deep-frozen, a state which, according to frozen-food specialists, requires an enormous and almost instantaneous drop in temperature? And how, beyond this, did so many of them get torn limb from limb? What natural force is strong enough to tear the whole head off an elephant in a fresh condition and hurl it into a mass of smashed tree trunks, bits of other animals, boulders, and sludge, and then freeze the whole mass so suddenly and deeply that it has remained unspoiled for thousands or tens of thousands of years? But not all these heaps of animal flesh and particulated vegetation are fresh. Some are either partly or most pronouncedly decomposed, and on occasion the stench from this (on opening up the permafrost, which is now done with cold-water jets for gold-mining in this area) is so nauseating that the hardiest operators quit.

Permafrost is altogether remarkable. It prevents atmospheric moisture from sinking into the soil and so literally floods the land, helping in the creation of bog and swamp conditions, stunting vegetal growth by drowning roots, and bringing on all manner of other unpleasantnesses. Yet under proper circumstances the most luxuriant vegetables can be grown on the shallow surface layer that does thaw out in the short and violent Arctic summer. So rapid is this growth in some cases—the area around Dawson City is notable for this—that plants have to be shaded from the sun to prevent their running to seed. It is weird to think that one-seventh of the land surface of our earth is covered with permafrost and that about half of this (mostly in Siberia) is riddled with plant and animal remains aggregating untold millions of tons.

FIN-FOOTED NOMADS

Although the Bering Sea and the North Pacific are heavily populated with a wide variety of mammalian, bird, fish, and invertebrate life, there are two animals that command our special attention in this area. These are the Sea Bear or Fur Seal, and the Sea Otter. The story of both is a sad one but with a

Overleaf: Sundry forms of the Dish-faced or Brown Bears are found in Alaska and on its offshore islands, the largest on Kodiak Island and the adjacent mainland.

fairly happy ending. The Sea Bear is a relative of the Sea Lions and is thus an eared seal, as distinct from the ordinary or earless seals. One species is native to this part of the North Pacific, and it once existed there in millions. However, the white man, soon after his arrival both from the east and the west, discovered that these animals assembled once a year, all together, and in only a few places, notably on islands and in particular on the little Pribiloff Islands, to give birth to their young and then to breed. With their customary avarice, these new human arrivals went to work slaughtering these animals without any regard to conserving a breeding stock.

As a result of this atrocious activity, the numbers of these magnificent beasts, yielding such beautiful soft fur, were by 1910 reduced to an estimated 150,000. Then, fortunately, modern ideas of conservation gained the ascendancy; open-ocean sealing was banned and annual quotas were established. Today there are estimated to be once again over 3,000,000 of these animals. Sea Bears are fairly large animals, the bulls reaching six feet, the cows some four feet; but the former may weigh over five hundred pounds. They have a dense yellow underfur, but the coarse overfur of the males is almost black and that of the females gray; both are reddish below. They give birth to only one young once a year, but the older males assemble large harems and guard these with tremendous vigor during the breeding period on the islands. During the rest of the year they cruise the ocean, extending their range as far south as California. There are smaller southern species, one of which may still not be extinct and used to concentrate around the islands of Baja California.

Another remarkable marine animal of this area that is still

Below: A young Canadian lynx. This cat is predominantly a bird-eater but does not disdain lemmings and mice.

fairly common and may be encountered in considerable congregations is the mighty Walrus. This, although classed with the seals generally (as the Pinnipedia, or "fin-footed ones"), is really a distinct and altogether extraordinary beast. It has the rather delightful scientific name of *Odobaenus rosmarus*, the first word of which means "those that walk with their teeth." This is to our eyes a quite grotesque creature, especially if it be a male and of respectable age. As almost everybody knows, these animals develop the two upper canine teeth into enormous ivory tusks that protrude downward over the lower lip and may be more than two feet in length. Moreover, it is true that the animals employ these tusks to hook their vast bulk onto ice floes or even up seaweed-covered rocks. However, the sheer bulk of these animals is even more impressive, for large males may be more than twelve feet long and weigh over a ton and three-quarters. They are covered with a warty skin and have bulbous upper lips and grotesque "Old Bill" moustaches. They feed for the most part on shellfish, sea urchins, and other hard-shelled denizens of the sea bottoms for which they dive, and they do not concern themselves much with fish or other more agile food. They are rather rambunctious and aggressive beasts, and they can be extremely dangerous both on land and in the water. The pups, of which there are usually twins each year, are extremely amiable little hundred-pounders that seem to have much intelligence, are unabashed, and become very friendly. But they must be fed clams or they pine away.

The Sea Otter has a recent history somewhat similar to that

A rare photograph of a rare event—over 3000 walruses assembled on the Walrus Islands in the Bering Sea.
Facing page: Male walruses may weigh over a ton and have tusks almost two feet long, which they may use for hooking themselves onto the ice. They dive to the bottom of the sea to get their shellfish food.

Overleaf: Barren Ground Caribou, a form of reindeer, migrating. These vast herds move annually north to south and back again between the taiga forest edge and the tundralands.

of the Fur Seal in that, having a most beautiful and valuable pelt, it was mercilessly persecuted by white men from the moment they discovered its existence among the vast kelp beds of the North Pacific coasts. Being a lone or a family animal and spending most of its time on the high seas, floating apparently uninterestedly on its back, munching on sea urchins and so forth, which it holds with its forepaws on its chest like an overindulgent Roman senator at a banquet, it was rapidly reduced to near extinction. However, once again good conservation practices came to the rescue just in time, and it is now so busily on the increase that in recent years it has again been reported as far south as California.

The Sea Otter is a member of the weasel family and thus is related to the ordinary otters that inhabit lakes and rivers and is a sort of end product of the weasels, in many respects halfway to a seal, with much reduced tail and stubby little limbs more or less inside its loose, flabby jacket. It uses its hind pair of legs to form a sort of horizontal whale-like rudder, as the seals do. All its fingers and toes are completely webbed, and its head is flattened almost like that of a shark. It is reputed to be able to dive to a depth of over three hundred feet to obtain food. To watch one eating off its chest as it lies on its back on the surface, oblivious of surf and spray, is one of the most amusing experiences provided by nature that I know of. Sea otters have a habit of dropping choice bits "overboard" and, just as you think they have irretrievably lost them, they roll over quite casually, duck under, and retrieve them. They may play with a sea urchin or a fish like this for hours.

SNOW-CLAD FIRES

On the Alaska Peninsula (see map) there is a string of fabulous volcanic peaks. These range today from non-functioning or allegedly "dead" cones, a few of monumental proportions, to some extremely active volcanos which have the fascinating habit of "puffing" like a chain of old-time coal-burning steam engines. No two seem ever to puff in unison. The real glory of these volcanos is that most of them are either usually or perpetually snow-covered. There is a certain ephemeral beauty about snow-covered volcanic peaks, while they seem in some manner a contradiction in terms. Perhaps the most extraordinary is the only known active volcano in Antarctica, Mt. Erebus, which smokes away all alone in its illimitable barren glaciated surroundings.

There is a volcano on the Alaska Peninsula named Mt. Katmai that made the biggest noise ever recorded by man. Before June 2, 1912, this peak was the third-highest in Alaska. It was just another great snow-capped and seemingly peaceful mountain. There were numerous crevices in the earth all the way from the middle Aleutians to central Alaska from which steam, gases, or fine ash were extruded on a fairly continuous basis, but for the most part the country surrounding Mt. Katmai was clothed in lush summer vegetation and considerable stands of trees. Then suddenly at the end of May of that year the earth began to quake. This continued for four days, during which all the local inhabitants—mostly Eskimos—very sensibly packed up and left. And just in time, because the peaceful valley alongside this mountain suddenly was convulsed and enormous cracks opened

up all over it. From these, furiously hissing and incandescent gases and glowing hot sand boiled up and covered everything to a depth of more than a hundred feet, and spread for over fifteen miles like the foam on a bowl of detergent. It has been estimated that more than a cubic mile of this glowing sand appeared all of a sudden.

But no sooner had this phenomenon died down than Mt. Katmai itself literally blew up in a series of world-shaking explosions, causing some two cubic miles of molten rock and lava to be projected into the upper atmosphere, where it broke up into tiny particles, cooled, and then wandered all around the

White or Dall's wild sheep. A flock of ewes and young, as shown here, may leave the rams on other grazing grounds for some weeks.

earth, causing incredible sunsets for four years and appreciably lowering the over-all world temperature. Hot ashes and pumice stone fell all over an area of several hundred square miles, completely blocking harbors and rivers as far away as Kodiak Island, where fine ash piled up to almost a foot.

The valley over which the masses of glowing sand were extruded was later named the Valley of Ten Thousand Smokes because of the endless fumaroles that were left smoking about its surface. These have now died down so that only a hundred

or so are still reliably active, but among these are half a dozen properly impressive ones that send up plumes about five hundred feet tall. Although all wildlife was destroyed by these volcanic excesses only half a century ago, it is now creeping inexorably back and reclaiming the land. Lichens are now well within the sand area, and the waters are again filled with Rainbow and Lake Trout, Dolly Varden, Grayling, Whitefish, Northern Pike, and even Salmon. The convulsions have not recurred but this does not mean that they may not blast out again at any time, for this area lies on the very brink of the great circum-Pacific crack in the earth's crust.

If more than half a dozen volcanos of the size of Mt. Katmai ever went off at once, we might well enter a new ice age, and literally overnight, for their combined effect in cutting out the sun's radiation by dust clouds in the upper atmosphere could well drop the over-all surface temperature of the earth for one or two seasons to a point where winter snows would not melt. Was this what happened to the poor shredded and frozen mammoths?

NAKED MOUNTAINS

The main body of this province is, in its way, as fabulous as the area of volcanic mountains. Nobody who has not visited this country and few of those who have, even by air, can gain any real conception of its sheer size. Instead of having a "spine" this land has a sort of central gutter or gut. This is an enormous valley containing the Yukon River, which rises away to the east in the Stikine Mountains. It is thus divided into two major blocks, each of which is subdivided into a number of perfectly distinct mountain ranges.

North and east of the Yukon there are two enormous mountain complexes, called the Brooks and the Mackenzie Ranges. These are not as yet fully explored, and their size is little appreciated. The former is for the most part a barren wilderness of ranges and peaks, though its valleys are choked with the ubiquitous spruce balsam and aspen of the north timberland. The Mackenzie Range really towers into the skies but is cleft by endless deep forested valleys. It is really remarkable how little is known about this land.

That part of central or inland Alaska that lies south of the Yukon is somewhat better known. It is composed, basically, of two great parts. The first is the stem of the volcanic string that leads from the Aleutians via the Alaska Peninsula to culminate in Mt. McKinley, a peak that tops 20,000 feet. The second comprises the whole of the territory south of the Yukon and east of Cook Inlet. This contains many subcomplexes of mountains, each of stunning proportions, all of which pile up to the St. Elias Range, the peak of which is over 18,000 feet in height. At 60 degrees north such altitudes result in most of the upper slopes of these ranges being glaciated. We have met glaciers before in Greenland, but there they are the sprouts of a true icecap. Here, in Alaska, they are of another gender. They are montane glaciers, and from them we can learn a great deal about the past history of our earth.

RIVERS OF ICE

If you want to see and study glaciers, there is no better place to go to than Glacier Bay National Park. This encompasses almost 230,000 acres of magnificent territory about Glacier Bay, which lies at the extreme southeastern corner of the Alaskan province.

Glacier Bay itself is a sixty-mile-deep fjord that leads in from the channel that separates Chichagof Island from the mainland. This narrow channel is walled by towering mountains, for the most part of a rather modest aspect but here and there, notably in the Fairweather Range, of extremely alpine and aggressive mien. Among these, snow gathers and is converted into what is called firn, and then into montane ice to form icefields on the higher cols. From these are born many glaciers (or ice rivers) that do all the things described by the specialists and do them in a sort of textbook orderliness that anybody can understand. In fact, they are classic glaciers.

Having gathered a sufficient overload of ice high up, the mountains disgorge the surplus in the form of perfectly clean-

resultant ice at the bottom, the glacier grows ever onward. If the snowfall drops, or if the air temperature in the valley at the foot of the glacier rises and stays above a certain point, the front of the glacier will diminish in thickness and eventually start melting backward. At such time it simply dumps all the broken rock that it is bearing (either under it, in it, or on top of it) on the valley floor. If it then begins to grow again, its front pushes all this material ahead of it like a great bulldozer to form what is called a terminal moraine. The glory of some of these Alaskan glaciers is that they reach the sea at the head of their fjords. Then they "calve" their beautiful peacock-blue-green ice directly into the water in the form of icebergs. However not all of them now do so, for, at the moment, we appear to be in a warm phase

White sheep rams resting. Despite their glaring whiteness, these animals have an uncanny way of becoming invisible, through shadow breakup, against the face of a bare dark gray mountain side.

cut rivers of ice. These come down the valleys in a slightly cur-vaceous manner that belies their inherent power and destruc-tiveness. They burr off all the corners of the valleys through which they pass, and they carry everything loose or movable down with them. Most of them move only an inch or so a day, but there are some, such as the famous Muir Glacier, that may move downhill as much as thirty feet a day. This is a veritable torrent. As long as the snowfall above is greater than the melting of the

so that most glaciers, especially those in Alaska, are retreating. Some are, strangely, advancing.

Advances and retreats of glaciers are cyclical, or at least

Overleaf: The Brown Bears are agile and can become ag-gressive. They can cover ground at unexpected speed but are most dangerous in shallow water.

periodic, which does not mean quite the same thing. In Glacier Bay this phenomenon has now been watched for over 250 years. In 1700 the whole of the bay was clogged with solid ice about three thousand feet thick extending almost to its mouth in Icy Strait. Thereafter the ice apparently began to melt faster than it formed, and this process continued till the end of the nineteenth century. Then, in 1899, a violent earthquake seems to have shaken the whole area, and this is said to have speeded the break-up and retreat of the ice. These effects were short-lived, but the steady retreat went on, so that by 1913 the Muir Glacier had retreated eight miles from the coast and by 1946 another five miles.

The speed of this change, whether it be permanent or only temporary, should give us pause. The fact that fifty miles of solid ice three thousand feet deep can completely vanish in a little over a hundred years, and then vast glaciers that once formed parts of them retreat another ten miles or more overland in a further century, should make us reappraise our ideas about icecaps and so-called ice ages. This is probably the single most important aspect of nature as regards not only the past and the present but also the future, for everything that we see on this continent—and, for that matter, throughout the world—is ultimately controlled by changes in the volume and distribution of polar ice.

That almost all parts of the land surface of the earth have at one time or another been covered with icecaps is now well established. Even areas such as the Congo and the Indian or Deccan Peninsula, which now lie in the tropics, have been so covered. Northwestern Europe and northeastern North America were covered, as it now appears, until only ten thousand years ago. However, since it is undeniable that plants and animals that cannot live or breed in polar conditions of temperature and more especially of light are found fossilized not only all around but well within both polar regions, as they are today, the land or sea where those animals once lived must at one time have been somewhere else on the earth's surface where it was warmer and where sunlight was more evenly distributed throughout the year. Thus, the land must have moved in and out under the polar ice, rather than the polar icecaps over the land.

The last movement that presumably brought on the current series of so-called ice ages was, until recently, supposed to have taken place about a million years ago, initiating what is called the Pleistocene Period of geological history. Since then, there have been four marked climatic swings in both northern Europe and North America, and these have been marked by the formation of large icecaps on these continents. The centers of these icecaps do not seem to have been in the same place, but as we have seen, the last one on this continent appears to have been in Hudson Bay. In addition to these major climatic and temperature swings, which may have been brought about by such processes as the blocking of warm water from the Arctic Ocean and so forth, there have also been numerous minor swings in temperature, as evinced by the behavior of these Alaskan glaciers during the past 250 years. There is no evidence that these are caused by movements of the crust, but they do bring us to another aspect of the problem—namely, the time factor. If fifty miles of ice three thousand feet thick can vanish in a couple of centuries (and at high latitudes at that), how quickly, we would like to know, can large icecaps "retreat" or the land shift?

The last icecap we had on this continent changed just about everything from climate to soils, plant and animal distribution, rivers, lakes, and deserts. Perhaps forty days and forty nights of snow or rainfall could bring on an "ice age" or a flood. We do not know, but in Glacier Bay National Park you may look around and ponder these matters with gigantic visual aids all about you. Two hundred and fifty years is nothing, cosmically speaking, yet a fifty-mile icefield vanished from here in that time. What is more, vegetation has appeared again and forests are growing where a mile of ice was before. And that there were great forests there *before* the ice came is also proved by the endless tree stumps that are bulldozed out of the moraines left by ancient glaciers.

THE COMPLEXITY OF BEARS

The forests on the southern coast of this province are, as we mentioned above, moss-festooned "jungles" of spruce and hemlock with a vast tangle of alders and ferns below. This supports a marvelously rich fauna. There is even a salamander found here (by the name of *Batracochoseps*), a weird, immensely elongated thing like a worm with tiny limbs. There are two species of frogs and a plethora of insects. Birds are everywhere—ducks, geese, loons, cormorants, eider ducks, gulls, murrelets, puffins, and guillemots about the waters, and falcons, eagles, ravens, and ptarmigan on shore. There are even hummingbirds from spring to late fall—something that is more than merely surprising. The mammalian fauna is almost as varied. On the mountains are the famous white or Dall's sheep, which unfortunately also come in three other color phases—brown, gray, and black—mountain goat, black-tailed deer, wolverine, red fox, marten, mink, porcupine, and both bobcat and lynx. But above all there are the bears.

There are three kinds of bears on this continent—the Polar Bear *(Thalarctos)*; the "Black" or American Bear *(Euarctos)*; and the Dish-faced or "Brown" Bears *(Ursus)*. There is one or just possibly two species of the first, as discussed above; one of the second, with several color phases and two or three apparently stable varieties; and today, two major groups of the last. If you want to understand the bears, or know just what you are looking at if you are wandering about in Alaska, the first thing you have to do is forget all references to color in bears. This means that "black," "brown," "blue," "cinnamon," "grizzly," and "white" are not only redundant terms but misleading. Although there are plenty of bears alive today that may be described as of these colors, there are no such things specifically as Black, Brown, Blue, Cinnamon, Grizzly, or White bears. These are merely color phases, any and sometimes all of which may turn up among either American Black or Dish-faced Bears, very often in twins in the same litter.

There were once races of pure-breeding dish-faced bears of huge size, with grizzled pelts; these dwelt on the central prairies and fed on the bison herds. They are now extinct. However, there remain in some parts of the western montane regions and in British Columbia, the Yukon, Alaska, and the Great Bear Lake district of the Canadian Northwest Territories, sundry races of grizzled bears belonging to the Dish-faced or "Brown" bear group. When grizzled, these may be referred to legitimately as Grizzly Bears, but it must be stressed that these do not necessarily breed true to color nor even stay the same shade individually from year to year.

The big Dish-faced or true "Brown" Bears—related to those of Asia and Europe—form a rather well-knit group that are

The Valdez Glacier flowing into Prince William Sound from the Chugach Mountains. This is a classic "ice river," flowing strongly but generally receding, and carrying much debris.

more easily distinguished. They live today only along a narrow strip of territory from the tip of the Alaska Peninsula to Glacier Bay and they stay strictly within the coastal rain-forest belt. These animals vary considerably in size, and there are eight distinct races described. These are *Ursus sitkensis* from the Baranof and Chichagof Islands; *U. shirisi* from Admiralty Island only; *U. sheldoni* from Montague Island; *U. dalli, gyas,* and *kenaiensis* from the mainland; and finally the famous *Ursus middendorffi* from Kodiak Island and the adjacent mainland. The last is customarily stated to be the largest flesh-eater on earth. This is inaccurate, since the Killer Whale exceeds it in bulk by about one hundred times. A large male Kodiak Bear standing on its hind legs can top twelve feet, and is indeed the largest *land* animal that (sometimes) eats flesh.

These so-called Brown Bears are not by any means all brown. Some of the island races are black, at least in certain phases or at certain times of the year, or even from year to year. They are, however, quite distinct, as may be seen by the shape of their muzzles seen in profile, which are concave in front of the eyes, instead of convex like those of the Polar and Black Bears. The largest of these bears are very splendid and may weigh up to fifteen hundred pounds. They are primarily fish-eaters but take a great deal of vegetable food as well, and they eat insects, shellfish, mice, and more or less anything else they can get. They will readily smack down any larger animal they happen to stumble upon, but they are not hunters. As a general rule they do not take umbrage at the approach of humans, but they have a habit of gathering in considerable numbers; and if they are encountered thus gathered in areas where they do not know humans, they may become exceedingly aggressive and are then frightfully dangerous due to their enormous strength and great speed. They can outgallop a horse, track through water faster than any other animal, and outswim almost any other land animal. A large brown bear has been seen pulling the head off an adult moose!

The Black Bear *(Euarctos),* which we will meet more inti-

mately later, is also found in this province and, most confusingly, all over it, including the territory of both the grizzled and the ordinary Brown Bears. Even more confusing for the naturalist, it also varies greatly in size and comes in a variety of colors from almost pure white on Gribble Island in British Columbia, through pale grayish blue (the "Glacier" Bear) mostly from around Yakutat Bay, coffee colored, cinnamon, reddish brown, and black with brown face, to pure black. Even so, this species should never be mistaken, for the shape of its head is distinctive and it does not have the hump over the shoulders that is so characteristic of the dish-faced bears.

Alaska is a country in every sense of the word—politically, naturally, and actually. We have really only started to learn what is in it. It has already produced many surprises; it will assuredly produce more, and if you can believe the hints the old-timers give you, the best place to look for these is probably in the great Mackenzie Range, tucked away in the back of nowhere.

Trees, Fjords, and Salmon

British Columbia and the Yukon

5 The outstanding feature of this province is its trees. We remarked earlier the impression that the first paltry and isolated specimens that we encountered on coming down from the Arctic made upon us, and in the Canadian Lakes province we have already seen trees in as great a mass as anywhere on earth. But these were really very modest plants, having trunks of only a foot or so in diameter at the base; and few, even in the deeper and more sheltered valleys, topped more than fifty feet in height. As soon as we enter this province, however, we see many changes, most notably in the variety, size, and height of the trees.

In order to understand this province properly one should probably attempt to see it both by sailing down the coast and by traveling overland. On land the ideal would be to start from a point east of Lake Mayo and travel straight south over the great Pelly Range to the region of Lake Teslin, cross the Alaska Highway there, and then proceed somewhat east of south over the Cassiar, Stikine, and Skeena mountains to Hazelton on the west-to-east road from Prince Rupert to Prince George (the only one that crosses the province apart from the Alaska Highway). From there it would be best to turn slightly to the east again along the Bulkley Mountains to Tweedsmuir National Park, and then go straight ahead via Lake Chilko to Vancouver. But you cannot do this today unless you organize a fairly large and expensive expedition because there are no roads, or even paths or hunting trails, anywhere along this line, while the country goes up and down like a mammoth roller coaster and is mostly unmapped and unexplored. Further, though the climate except in deep winter is comparatively mild, the country is exceedingly rugged in other respects, especially in the deep valleys, which are choked with vegetation great and small, and littered with rotting logs, boulders, and botanical debris. There is game here ample to support active humans, but it is very hard to see and for travelers bent on making a lengthy passage it takes too long to hunt.

There is, however, an alternative journey which can be undertaken in perfect comfort by automobile but on which one sees little of the country, and not only on account of the trees that

The coast of Alaska from Kodiak Island to the panhandle and south to Vancouver Island and the Olympic Range is clothed in "rain forest" resulting from warm ocean currents.

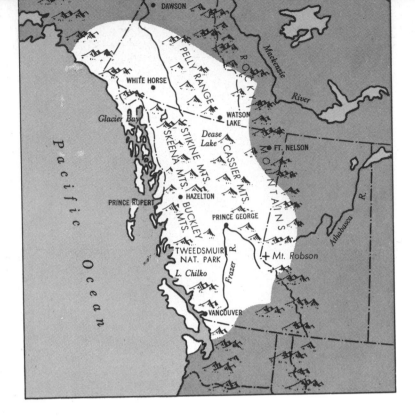

Looked at globally, the major vegetational belts run from west to east. However, as we have seen, they make considerable swings to north or south due to certain major climatic influences. Neither the position nor the extent of these swings is influenced by altitude; mountain ranges are, rather, superimposed upon them. Since the mountain ranges on our continent run more or less from north to south—especially the whole complex on the western side of this land mass—they cut across the different belts of vegetation. This is most notable in this province, which we call British Columbia. However, here we have two further complications.

First, the belts themselves are grossly distorted (see map) and secondly, the influence of the adjacent ocean is so strong that a unique situation has arisen all along the coast and on the innumerable offshore islands, where there is a most luxuriant growth. This is a southward extension of the forests of the south

coast of Alaska; it reaches to the lower Fraser River and across the Strait of San Juan de Fuca to the Olympic Mountains. In fact, this unique plant assemblage then moves somewhat inland to the region of Kamloops and then continues south in a slightly different form, covering the whole of the mighty Cascades.

Two of the four boundaries of this province are therefore in a way arbitrary. One boundary, the northeastern, is the edge of the great mountain barrier that fronts on the central plains and lowlands. The north and northwestern boundary—with the Alaskan province—is determined by the dividing line between the Pine-Spruce and Transition (coniferous-deciduous) subbelts, which forms a great bow, turning south about Glacier Bay and skirting the coast to Hecate Strait. (It is interesting to note that the apparently illogical United States Alaskan Panhandle, over which there is now discussion of an interchange of territory with Canada, follows exactly this line of demarcation.) What we may call the southern coast, from Hecate Strait to Vancouver, with Vancouver Island and the Olympic Peninsula below, is heavily indented, densely forested, and edged by steep mountains.

It is the eastern border of this province that is most arbitrary, not so much so from the Olympics to the Fraser River but north of that. Both the vegetational type and the botanical composition of the Northern Montane Block actually continue from the region of the upper Athabasca River and Mt. Robson all the way to the Alaskan Province border, and clothe the mountains of the major part of the British Columbian Province. However, there is a difference between the vegetation in the valleys in these two blocks.

This province is 1100 miles in length and on an average some 450 miles wide. It is wholly mountainous and forested except for the upper parts of the higher ranges, which are clothed in alpine tundra or are bald, or even snow-covered throughout the year. However, in the deeper valleys one encounters more southerly types of growth, including Parklands, Prairies, and even small areas covered with sagebrush so typical of the Scrub Belts.

---

line the road for mile after mile. This is the famous "Dawson (City) to Dawson (Creek)" run. Today one can drive southeast from Fairbanks to the Alaska-Yukon boundary and thence on to Dawson City. From there a road runs south to Whitehorse, where you pick up the Alaska (Alcan) Highway, which then cuts east via Watson Lake to Fort Nelson and thence southeast to the Alberta border. If you are of a more rugged disposition you may turn right at Watson Lake, drive to Dease Lake, and then pack or ride some two-hundred-odd miles down to a place named Stewart at the head of the fjord known as the Portland Canal. From there the journey must be completed by coastal boat to Vancouver.

Only by cutting across country can you gain any proper concept of the size of this province, its tremendously mountainous nature, and its unexplored condition. Along the six-hundred-odd miles from Lake Mayo to Lake Teslin there is but one recognized trail; along the seven hundred miles from there to Hazelton you would cross only one road or trail; and on the eight-hundred-mile hike from that place, across the Tweedsmuir Park and on to Vancouver, there would be only two secondary roads to cross. The triangle between the coast, the most southerly of these roads, and the Fraser River is the ruggedest of all. But

you still will not have seen the best of the trees, for they grow in the great valleys that lead down to the coast west of your route. Only in the last lap of your journey from Lake Chilko to Vancouver would you come to realize their significance and their awe-inspiring dimensions.

OCEANS OF TREES

The valleys and lower slopes of the mountains of the inland areas, forming the great bulk of the country, are clothed in forests that differ little, if at all, from those that cover—predominantly with pines—the Northern Montane Block of the Rockies. Above this growth is a zone, variable in width, of alpine tundra that thins out upward to barren grounds; above this lie year-round snowfields, icefields, and glaciers.

The coastal strip, on the other hand, is not just often but nowadays very often called a "jungle." A precise definition of this term is difficult, since it is derived from a Persian word, *djaenghal*, which actually means leafless scrub on a hot desert. Somehow the word was transferred to India from Persia by the

The ubiquitous Canada Geese migrate north in spring and south in fall but now live all year in almost every province.

British in the last century and was applied by them first to the desert scrub there, then to dry woodlands, then to wet woodlands, and finally to the Tropical Tall Deciduous Forest. It seems first to have been Rudyard Kipling and then such writers as Edgar Rice Burroughs who popularized the word in English, and in doing so transferred it to the Equatorial Rain Forests. Nowadays people call any tall, dense, and tangled mass of vegetation a jungle. It would seem better to confine the word to tropical growth, and to apply the term "rain forest"—in the absence of any valid local name—to these magnificent forests that rim the northwest coast of North America. And they need a name, for they are quite different from any other forests found elsewhere. Also, it is indeed the warm rain and mist that drift in from the Pacific that have created them.

It may seem odd that the coast of this far northern province, from 60 degrees to 48 degrees north, should be blanketed with a sort of treble-layered forest, denser and more lush and dripping than almost anything found in the equatorial zones; but this is the fact because tropical forests are "hollow" and clear below. One cannot describe adequately this forest, especially when the skies are clear and brilliant sunlight filters down to its lower levels. As in tropical jungles, the light is actually bright green,

as photographers learn either immediately or to their cost later. The floor of this forest is often hard to find, being many feet below the apparent surface, and in virgin areas you have to be extremely careful or you may break through the mat of mosses, ferns, dead branches, and general tangle and drop down into a tridimensional latticework of fallen and rotting tree trunks below. A companion of mine once so vanished instantly, right before my eyes, and I had to fetch a rope to get him out, for he was wedged between two great logs about ten feet down in a sort of cave with overhanging sides formed by a crisscross of age-old rotting logs. This rain forest that clothes the coastal strip is built in three tiers, the uppermost being composed of the head foliage of giant conifers, the middle of smaller conifers and some broad-leafed trees, and the bottom one of bushes and ferns. The middle and bottom strata are bound together and festooned with mosses and lichens.

THE LARGEST LIVING THING

The principal coniferous trees are the Douglas Fir, the Sitka Spruce, the Western Red Cedar, and the Western Hemlock.

Among these are both the tallest and the largest trees in the world. There are many claims made for these records, the most popular being the Giant Redwoods of the Sierra Nevada in California as the biggest (in volume) and the Redwood *(Sequoia sempervirens)* as the tallest. These trees we will consider later (see Chapter 10), so suffice it to remark here that the specimen of the latter claimed, after measurement, to be the world's tallest stood 340 feet. This is, however, almost paltry compared to some of the Douglas Firs recorded from British Columbia, as, for instance, the one measured, after it was felled, by Dr. R. Leckie-Ewing in the Lyn Valley in 1940. It was 417 feet tall, and the first limbs did not sprout from the trunk until 300 feet above the ground. It was 25 feet in diameter at three feet above the ground, had bark 16 inches thick and a circumference of 77 feet, and was 9 feet in diameter at a height of 200 feet. Dr. Leckie-Ewing stated in a letter to the highly respected British magazine *The Field* that there had been even larger specimens felled and that experienced local timbermen believed there were more of even greater proportions still standing. This tree would have topped a forty-story building.

To lie under one of these great trees and look upward with a pair of powerful binoculars is an unforgettable experience. Even 250-footers seem to reach literally into the sky, so that one comes to understand certain Amerindian legends to the effect that in times of stress in bygone ages whole tribes assembled at the tallest tree in the world and then ascended it into heaven. At the same time, if you are of scientific turn of mind, you may find yourself doubting the current explanation of the method by which water in the form of sap is lifted from the ground to the head foliage of such monsters, defying not only gravity but, it would seem, several basic principles of hydrodynamics. But there are the little needles waving in the wind almost at the limit of vision, fresh and green and obviously breathing out moisture.

WHAT IS A TREE?

There are some forty-five species of trees listed from the coastal belt of this province, half of which are conifers. In actual numbers of trees the latter predominate, as they also do in size. In addition to the four dominant conifers there are four species of pines, the Alpine Larch and the Tamarack in the far north, two other species of spruce, the Mountain Hemlock, three true firs, the Yellow Cypress, the Rocky Mountain Red Cypress (or so-called Cedar with the tongue-twisting Latin name of *Chamoecyparis nootkatensis),* the common Dwarf Juniper, and the Western Yew. Among the deciduous trees are half a dozen species of willows that grow as trees rather than mere bushes, the well-known Aspen, two birches, and two alders. In the extreme south of the province there are patches of Garry Oak at low altitudes in the strip shown as "Deciduous Forest" on the general map. There are three maples—the Broadleaf, Vine, and Dwarf—two cherries, a Serviceberry, the Black Haw, an Elderberry and a Dogwood, a Madroña *(Arbutus),* and the beautiful Oregon Crab Apple *(Malus rivularis),* which extends very far north. The bushes are of even wider variety, and the herbaceous plants multitudinous.

As we are now in the land of trees and shall remain therein till the end of our journey, despite seemingly endless prairies and some treeless near-deserts, it behooves us to define a tree. This is not quite so obvious as might at first appear, so that one sometimes sees even in print phrases such as "trees, plants, and flowers." All trees are plants, and almost all of them "flower,"

as do shrubs and herbs. A sounder generality is "trees, shrubs, herbs, grasses, and mosses and other lower plants." A tree must have a woody and a single stem, with a more or less definitely formed crown of branches and leaves above. This includes palms, yuccas, cycads, and some cactuses, though the stems of the last are only partially woody and that wood is internal. Botanists prefer also to confine the term *tree* to plants of at least eight feet in height with stems not less than two inches in diameter. However, there is no sharp line between treelike shrubs and shrublike trees, and quite a number of woody plants may grow in one form in one area or at one altitude, and in another in another place or at a different height.

THE CONE-BEARERS

There are six families of coniferous trees, examples of four of which are found on this continent. (The other two are confined to the southern hemisphere.) The largest family is that of the pines and includes also the larches, the spruces, the so-called Douglas Fir, the hemlocks, and the true firs. The second-largest family is that of the cedars, which includes also the junipers. The third family contains the cypresses and the redwoods; the fourth, the yews, of which there are three odd species in North America, and two very strange trees known as the California Nutmeg *(Torreya californica)* and the Stinking Cedar *(T. taxifolia),* which is found only in one small area along the Apalachicola River in northern Florida. Conifers may be said to be more ancient and in some respects more primitive than the broad-leafed trees, and there are fewer forms of them than of other trees. However, conifers cover many hundreds of times more of the area of the earth's land surface than do all other woody growth put together. On the whole, they do better than other trees in cooler climates, at altitude, and in sandy or waterlogged soils. The two largest forests in the world, lying all across northern Asia and North America, are predominantly and in some places exclusively coniferous. It is surprising to find that almost the whole of this continent that is forested is clothed in coniferous trees, predominantly pines or spruces. Pure stands of deciduous or other broad-leafed, non-coniferous trees are actually confined to very limited areas, mostly around the lower slopes of mountain ranges at middle latitudes and in narrow, winding belts fringing the prairies and parklands.

There are some thirty-five species of pines found on this continent, and although pine-cone collecting may sound like a rather unexciting hobby, it has its more fascinating aspects. Identification of the trees is a highly specialized pursuit, as they have a habit of varying in needle form and arrangement that can drive even a professional botanist to distraction. If you branch out into collecting the cones of other conifers you have manifestly become an addict. In fact, anybody traveling widely on this continent, however uninterested in vegetation to start with, will probably find that, sooner or later, he is irked into attempts to identify firs, cedars, pines, and so forth. Unfortunately, there does not appear to be any one available book that shows all of them with pictures of both the cones *and* the foliage. There are also other pitfalls, notably in the popular names, which not only differ from region to region, but many of which may be applied to different species in the same region. Perhaps the most muddling example is the so-called Douglas "Fir" *(Pseudotsuga taxifolia* or *menziesii),* which is not a fir but a member of a genus that contains otherwise only the so-called Bigcone "Spruce" *(P. macrocarpa),* which is of course not a spruce! The final conundrum for the layman is that the timber of the

The Wolverine, sometimes known as the Glutton, the largest of the weasel family on this continent. Once reputed to be violently aggressive and untamable, it has now been proved to be an amenable pet and highly intelligent. A predator and very strong for its size, it can pull down deer and even young moose. It is a bold and courageous animal that needs a rather large individual hunting territory, which it defends vigorously against encroachment.

Douglas Fir, which is the finest wood for making masts of ships, is renowned throughout the world as "Oregon Pine"!

The vast area of mountains back from the coast and coastal range in this province is clothed up to about five thousand feet in a mixed growth of coniferous trees with a noticeable number of the Western White Pine *(Pinus monticola)*; the presence of this tree has been used by plant geographers to identify the limits of the province. This species grows to about 63 degrees north latitude in these mountains, thus reaching to the confluence of the Pelly and Lewes rivers—which are the headwaters of the mighty Yukon—just south of Dawson. However, if you go up the Fraser River north of its junction with the Thompson, you will enter a most unexpected strip of territory extending all the way to Prince George and thence west up the valley of the Hako River to the Babine Mountains, which mark the eastern fringe of the rain forest. This open grassland country, on which cattle graze today, consists of even, low, hummocky hills covered in typical scrubland sagebrush that in some places approaches the paucity of the true desert belt. This is really an outlier of the Prairie Belt that, as is shown on the map, swings north to the sixtieth parallel of latitude at Fort Nelson. It is a dry strip and has a typical prairie fauna, with larks and other such birds that come as a surprise to the visitor who sees them for the first time.

WILDLIFE

The "pine" forests that surround this strip and fill the valleys of the other inland part of this province do not support a large fauna, and what there is of it is typical of the Northern Montane Province, which we will meet later. The fauna of the Alpine or montane tundra is an intermingling of that of southern Alaska and the Northern Montane. The inner belt of this province is really an extended transition zone from the sub-Arctic, bridging several major belts and carrying a northern flora and fauna high up into the Rockies. The fauna of the coastal rain forest, on the other hand, is quite distinct from this. In some respects it is merely a northern extension of that of the Pacific Coast Ranges of Washington and Oregon with its woodpeckers and its more than two hundred other distinctive species of birds, which spread all the way up to the south coast of Alaska and even in some cases over onto Kodiak Island. We have already described the more notable examples of the sub-Arctic fauna, and we shall meet the coastal one later. The fauna of this province is, in fact, an amalgam and, apart from small mammals and some lesser forms (and few enough of these), it does not have a distinctive wildlife. Yet there are some wonderful animals to be seen here.

LIVING SUN SYMBOLS

One aspect of the fauna in particular strikes the visitor to British Columbia; this is its aquatic life, both marine and fresh water. Nor does one have to be a fisherman—amateur, professional, or sportsman—to be so struck. The really surprising thing is that the "fish" that are the most stunning and extraordinary, and both typical of and unique to this province, are not normally seen and are not fish per se. To find and marvel at

A Sea Bat, one of many indigenous starfish that are a notable feature of the coastal life of this province.

these, you have to go boating and do some dredging; or, if you are of less robust inclination, you may go to the delightful little aquarium in the city of Vancouver. I am speaking of sea creatures commonly called starfishes.

These belong to a group of animals arranged on a radial basis of, fundamentally, five points. They are called collectively Echinodermata or the "Spiny-skinned Ones" and include five great groups of creatures: the sea lilies, which mostly grow on stalks like plants, in deep water; the sea cucumbers, rather obnoxious looking, sausage-shaped, leathery bags; the sea urchins, which are ovoid or circular and often covered with spines; the brittle or sand stars, shaped like coins but with five long, slender, vermiform limbs; and the starfish proper. These last are extremely numerous and varied in form, there being no less than twenty-three families of them, some containing dozens of genera, many with dozens of species. Starfishes are hardy creatures and are found throughout the seas and oceans of the world from the polar regions to the equator, even in many land-locked brackish waters. They constitute food for quite a number of other forms of life but are themselves terrible predators, specializing in the opening of the two-valved shellfish such as clams, oysters, and the like. In fact, they are a great menace to commercial oyster beds and have been responsible for the bankruptcy of many such enterprises, including those devoted to the culture of pearls, for they may suddenly appear in great numbers and totally destroy the molluskan crop.

One may say with some assurance that more starfish are to be found on sandy bottoms of shallow seas; but there are certain parts of the world, notably along deeply indented coasts such as that of the province under discussion, that seem to promote starfishes in a big way. I do not know of any part of the world that rivals this coast in this respect. The profusion of these animals found here and their variety of size, form, and above all color, is almost beyond belief. Probably the most outstanding are the enormous "sun stars" *(Heliaster)* that look like super-soup-plate-sized artificial suns designed by some primitive people. They grow to three feet in diameter and have as many as forty-four "arms" or "rays." These may be of the most gorgeous colors, ranging all the way from yellow through the oranges to flame, reds, red-browns, brown, and even a deep purple. These creatures do not look real, and it is hard to believe that they are alive when seen on the deck of a boat.

There are now over 1750 described kinds of true starfishes divided among some 300 genera. On the coast of British Columbia there are hundreds of species of all shapes and sizes, from tiny five-radial forms that bury themselves in the sand to the above-mentioned enormous sunbursts; to normal-sized five-fingered stars; and to more or less pentagonal creatures that seem to be halfway to sea urchins, as flat as pancakes, of all manner of colors, and decorated with all kinds of little spines, knobs, buttons, and pimples. Their beauty of color and form is seemingly endless.

Starfish are covered with leathery skin in which are embedded regularly arranged plates of calcium carbonate. These may carry spikes, bosses, or other exotic structures, often so closely adjacent that they form a sort of complete jointed exoskeleton. Among the spines are scattered tiny pairs of snapping jaws on pedestals called pedicellariae which work on the principle of scissors or that of the jaws of a crocodile. These serve to keep the upper surface of the animal clear of parasites and sundry free loaders that would otherwise settle down and grow on them as they do on the shells of many other slow-moving marine animals. On the underside of the arms are rows of multitudinous mobile structures called tube-feet, which can

The Mountain Goat, a typical animal of the British Columbian mountains, is a relative of the Swiss Chamois. It prefers the uppermost slopes and is a great jumper.

grasp objects by suction at will and by which the animal crawls about. It is with these that starfishes open shellfish. They first envelop them, attaching as many tube-feet as possible, and then exert a steady pull. Bivalve shells can withstand a sudden jerk, but they finally give up against persistent pulling; the starfish then extrudes its stomach into the shell and ingests the flesh. Some starfish can swim, but most of them crawl about slowly on the bottom, speedier examples making about one yard an hour. The number of arms may be four, five, six, eight, eleven, fifteen, nineteen to twenty-five, or even forty-four.

SOCKEYES AND CHUMS

This coast is one of the richest in fish life to be found anywhere in the world, and the variety is enormous. The most outstanding are the salmon. There are five distinct species of salmon (genus *Oncorhynchus*) in this area, all with most peculiar names both "English" and scientific, to wit: the Sockeye *(O. nerka)*, the Pink *(O. gorbuscha)*, the Coho *(O. kisutch)*, the Chum *(O. keta)*, and the Spring or Chinook *(O. tschawytscha)*. The reason for these very

un-Latin-sounding "Latin" names is that these fish were first studied and described by Russian scientists on the Asiatic coast of the North Pacific. From a commercial point of view the Sockeye is the most valuable in this province, whereas farther south, about the Columbia River, the Chinook is the most important. The species vary in size and habits, and although all make seasonal migrations to fresh water to breed, they do so at different times. These fish change colors throughout the year, the outstanding example being the Sockeye, which, just before spawning time, turns bright red except for its silvery head. As the shape of all them is somewhat similar, it takes first-hand experience to identify any one fish at any one time.

The life story of a salmon, although so often told, still remains somewhat of a miracle to us. Let us start at the beginning with one round egg in a mass of red caviar, lying on the gravel at the bottom of a shallow rill of crystal-clear water somewhere far up in the inland mountains. This is one of some five thousand eggs laid by one mother and happens to be one of only fifty or so that are destined to hatch and not be eaten by ducks or trout or some lesser creature. The tiny fish that emerges feeds on insect larvae and begins to drift slowly downstream into the big river and then onto the ocean, taking several months to reach the mouth of the river in most cases. There the little fish, called a fingerling or parr, comes to a temporary halt while it adjusts its metabolism to salt as opposed to fresh water. In some cases this may take quite a long time, especially if the individual started life not too far from the sea.

The young salmon must also get used to entirely new food, substituting crustaceans for insects. This food consists of small true shrimps—as opposed to prawns, which the inhabitants of the east coast erroneously call shrimps—the larvae of crabs, and other small animals, most especially krill or "whale food," which are otherwise known as euphausiids. These come in great swarms so tightly packed that they may turn the whole sea pink for miles. Before the fingerlings can get to this richest of all planktonic or surface marine food, however, they wean themselves on other crustaceans that live on the bottoms of the river estuaries, such as sandhoppers or amphipods, salt-water sourbugs or isopods, mysid shrimps, and so forth. Then finally they head out to sea, seeking out the krill and drifting with it. Since the major inshore ocean current along this coast travels northward, most of the little fish go that way. Most salmon are gone for about four years, during which time they slowly reach maturity and graduate from crustacean food to a diet of other fish, mostly anchovies, pilchard, and herrings—if they are lucky, that is, for they in turn are preyed upon unmercifully by great hosts of other fish, birds, and beasts that rush up at them from below and dive down upon them from above.

Ducks, loons, grebes, and other diving birds wait for their coming in huge flocks; seals and sea lions gobble them up by the barrel-load; sharks, dogfish, ling, bass, and other fish chase and eat them; and even sea otters get into the act. But perhaps most frightening of all are the insidious lampreys, that lowly relative of the fish, with an eel-shaped body and a circular mouth full of rasping teeth that attaches itself to the body of the salmon and then bores into its vitals. But somehow, despite the toll taken on the eggs, on the fingerlings in the rivers, by waiting hordes at the river's mouth, and by all these predators in the open ocean, great numbers of salmon somehow survive and grow into large, robust, and extremely agile fish that may weigh up to a hundred pounds and be as much as five feet long. And very soon they are giving as good as they take, preying on other fish and even on some of their enemies. Salmon are known as fighting fish, and not only on a fishing line. They have strong jaws and fine teeth, and they can become quite aggressive in their own environment.

In due course when the fish are fat and filled with oil, they turn homeward, and when once the urge to spawn comes upon them they cease to feed and make a dash from wherever they may be, directly to the mouth of the river in which they individually were hatched. This is perhaps the most remarkable feature of the whole sequence, though the manner by which they subsequently find their way up exactly the right tributary of the main river and then up a branching maze of lesser tributaries to just exactly their own home stream is little less extraordinary. It has now been demonstrated that they accomplish this in the fresh-water phase of their homeward travels by a completely uncanny and to us really incomprehensible ability to distinguish from all others the exact mineral content and balance of the waters of just one tiny stream. While it seems to have been scientifically demonstrated that this is so, it is not known how the fish does it, though it is suspected that the organ concerned may be the lateral line (which is a sense organ supplied with nerves stemming from that basal pair to which our auditory organs are attached). However, the fish do not "hear" these minute chemical differences but apparently may be more properly said to "smell" or taste them. We really do not know; we have no homologous sense organ.

Often the last stages of this great journey are fraught with all manner of mechanical difficulties—not only the multitudinous nets, traps, and weirs men lay to catch them, but also waterfalls and other barriers (in many cases rendered worse by artificial dams—around which, however, fish ladders are now sometimes constructed to aid them on their way). The jumping abilities of salmon in negotiating waterfalls and rapids are known to everybody, but the sheer swimming power entailed cannot be appreciated until you try just to stand in some of the more modest rapids that they negotiate. The height to which they can jump is great, but more amazing is their ability actually to *swim* up a waterfall. Many salmon have to battle a long succession of such falls before they reach their appointed spawning grounds. Then, once the roe is laid in the safety of the slow-moving shallows, the wan and tired fish turn about and start downstream again to the sea. Among these Pacific species of the genus *Oncorhynchus,* none of them ever makes it; spent with the long journey and the effort of spawning, all of them die before completing the seaward trip. The cycle is complete.

All in all, this province is, from the point of view of wildlife—apart from the Sierras of Mexico—the richest and most lush in the whole North American continent. It is also, perhaps, the least known but one of the richest in many other respects; and, unless progress such as we know it stops, it seems destined to become one of the great centers not only of recreation but also of agriculture and other permanent human residence. The climate is not too rigorous even in winter today, and it is said to be ameliorating. Almost anything can be grown there—even wine grapes.

The Heartland

The Great Lakes, Central Lowlands, and Interior Highlands

6 In accordance with our plan of travel we approach this province from the far northwest, from the region of Fort Nelson in British Columbia. Having swept to the farthest west through the sub-Arctic provinces, and then dropped down, as it were, south into the temperate woodlands on the west coast, we must now follow this major vegetational belt back to the east. Because of the extent to which the prairies push to the northwestward, the parklands, temperate woodlands, and even the transition belt of mixed deciduous trees and conifers are compressed into a strip so narrow as almost to disappear in northern Alberta. They do, however, persist in their proper sequence in a narrow belt across the center of the continent from that point to Minnesota, by which time they have together widened out to some 250 miles in depth from north to south.

Here, as you can see from the map, they then fan out like a great funnel directed to the southeastward, spreading from the middle St. Lawrence valley in the north, all along the west face of the Appalachians, to the southern face of the Ozark Plateau. And they funnel out in three streams—the Transition Belt across the Great Lakes to the St. Lawrence; the Deciduous Woods to the feet of the mountains; and the Parklands first south and then west again, making a great curve round the Ozarks to flow into the Southern Pinelands.

This great triangle, taking Minnesota as its apex, is today the most highly developed part of our continent from the human standpoint. I do not like to introduce the works of man, especially of industrial man, in this survey of our continent, since my primary intention is to try to depict it as it was before the advent of the latter and to describe those parts of it which still remain unsullied. However, the greater part of this province has now been so completely altered by non-native people that it is almost impossible to see what it was originally like.

The east coastal strip between Boston and Washington, D.C., is today even more heavily populated and industrialized, but there this "blight" is far more concentrated and there are still (as we shall see in the next chapter) numerous extensive areas, often hard by the most populous districts, that are not only completely wild but may in some cases be truly virgin territory. In this Heartland Province, on the other hand, apart from its periphery, the whole land surface has been cleared and either put to use for agricultural purposes or built over with sprawling cities, towns, and industrial plants. The industrial areas are almost confluent and are concentrated precisely in that portion of the triangle originally covered by the Deciduous Forest Belt with an extension down the St. Lawrence Valley, but they avoid the uplands of the Interior Highlands and the Appalachian Piedmont. What is not therein built over is devoted to intensive agriculture. Around the northern half of Lake Michigan and around Lake Huron, woodlands still hold considerable sway, and along the Piedmont and on the Boston and Ouachita mountains and the Ozark Plateau they still predominate, though agriculture is everywhere steadily creeping inward to the bases of the steeper slopes. In the central western area, which was originally a huge parkland enclave, we now have the great corn belt and widespread stock-raising. The trees that originally dotted this land were cleared when it was colonized; now other and often non-indigenous trees are being planted but by a different formula to that employed by nature. Though still isolated for the most part, they now stand around farmsteads, along roads, or between fields as windbreaks. This province is rich in oil, iron, and copper, and its soil is highly suitable for all manner of crops and especially corn.

It is interesting to note that the rainfall of this triangle in summer (average ten to twenty inches) is lower than that of the areas immediately adjacent to both the east *and* west, where it averages twenty to thirty inches; in winter (still at ten to twenty inches) it is intermediate between a wetter zone on the east and a drier one on the west. Moreover, the limits of this stable rainfall area are almost precisely those of this province as defined on the basis of vegetation. This Heartland is, in fact, in almost every respect a mean of all the varieties of climates, floras, and faunas of the whole continent—neither hot nor cold, dry nor wet, densely forested nor barren, and astonishingly equable throughout the year. It is ideally suited to European man and in many respects partakes of features identical to his traditional environment. If we may regard the white man simply as another species of fairly large mammal—an introduced species, in fact—that migrated to this continent from Europe, the biologist would expect the majority of its individuals to gravitate toward and settle in just this triangle. The eastern seaboard is perhaps better suited to—or should we say more easily adapted by?—people from the seagirt western fringes of Europe; the damp, warm southeast by Africans; California by Mediterraneans; and the dry southwest by Middle Eastern folk or those from the arid uplands of the Iberian Peninsula. Man *is* a species of mammal and, despite the great changes he is now able to bring about in his surroundings, he is still—as we shall constantly observe before our travels are over—to a very considerable extent governed in his actions and place of abode by the nature of his ancestral environment. In other words, even modern man likes to dispose himself and his activities in new places in accord with the underlying pattern of the different types of vegetation to which he has been accustomed.

There is a very interesting example of another animal doing exactly the same thing in this province. This is none other than the Ring-necked Pheasant, which was introduced as a game bird from Europe—to which continent it is, incidentally, alleged to have originally been introduced from Asia either by the Romans or in Roman times. These birds were at first hand-reared and then released at the appropriate season, and this was done more or less haphazardly all over the eastern states. In many areas this practice has had to be continued, as the released birds die out and do not breed successfully in the wild. In other areas, to the contrary, they immediately adapted themselves and multi-

The Sparrow Hawk or Kestrel (Falco sparverius), *a small falcon and not to be confused with the European Sparrow Hawk, nests in holes in trees and is common in this province.*

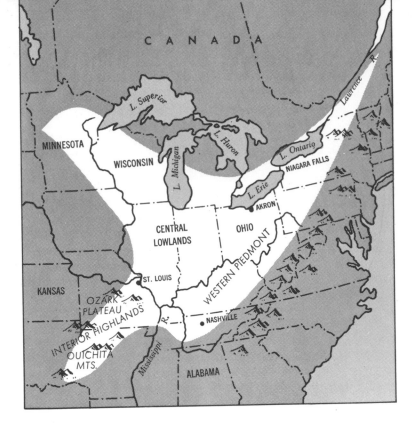

If we take a super-rocket's-eye view of this continent, we may note that it forms a quite compact unit lying across the hundredth meridian and centered about the point where that line crosses the fortieth parallel on the border of Nebraska and Kansas. By way of analogy we may liken it to a body, with Greenland as its head, Alaska and the Labradorian peninsulas as arms, Baja California and Florida as little hind limbs, and Mexico as a tail. Looked at in this light, and as though it were lying on its back, the South Montane Block would be its stomach, the Rockies and Appalachians its lungs, and the province under discussion here its heart. Indeed, the Great Lakes District and its associated lowlands and subdued southern mountains form the heartland of this continent.

This province is hard to define although in both phytogeographic and physiographic respects it is clearly

distinguishable from all the surrounding provinces. Perhaps it is therefore best defined by explaining how it adjoins surrounding areas.

This continent is shaped like a great V formed of peripheral mountain chains that converge to the south. The area between the arms of the V is filled in with an immense plain, some three thousand feet high at the south and sloping gradually downward to sea level at the Arctic Circle. The only feature that interrupts this formation is the penetration of the bottom of the right-hand arm of the V by the wedge of lowlands or "bottoms" of the Mississippi valley. Somewhat off center, to the east upper side of the central plateau, lies a vast depression filled with the Great Lakes, the largest body of inland waters in the world.

This province is roughly triangular and is bordered on the north by the Hudsonian, Boreal, or Coniferous Forests— actually, the Pine-Spruce subbelt. Its western face is the limit of closed forest abutting onto the Prairies. Its southeastern edge follows first the eastern face of the Interior Highlands and then, crossing the Mississippi, the western face of the Appalachians. Although it is predominantly a lowland province, two of its four subdivisions are uplands, mounting through foothills to modest mountains. These subprovinces are the Great Lakes, the Central Lowlands, the Western Piedmont of the Appalachians, and the Interior Highlands composed of the Ozark Plateau and the Boston and the Ouachita Mountains.

Actually, the major vegetational belts athwart which it lies, extend eastward through the entire Appalachians and to the northwest in a long, narrowing tine to the region of Fort Nelson in British Columbia, by which point they are compressed almost to nothing between the Prairies and the Boreal Forests proper (see general map). The belts are, considered from north to south, the Transition or Mixed Coniferous-Hardwood; the Deciduous, closed-canopy, temperate woodland; and, between this and the Prairie, the Parkland. The dimensions of this province are considerable, its three faces being 1200 miles on the north and west and 1700 on the southeast, giving it an area of no less than 720,000 square miles.

plied almost prodigiously, spreading far and wide. Yet, in a land that appears to be highly suitable to them both as to climate and food and where predators are no more numerous than in their homelands, and with no natural physical barriers that they could not surmount, these birds spread only just so far and in certain directions. In fact, they spread throughout this province to its east, south, and north borders precisely; only in the west did they march on to cover the whole Prairie Belt north of Oklahoma. Their containment south of the Transition or Mixed Forest subbelt, the southern edge of which cuts across Lakes Michigan and Huron, is remarkable because there is no physical barrier along that line—merely a subtle change in vegetation.

The distribution of our indigenous game birds (or gallinaceous fowl) is just as precise. The eastern form of the Wild Turkey (Meleagris gallopavo silvestris), for instance, was once distributed all over the eastern United States from the hundredth meridian to the east coast, except for Florida, where another subspecies (M. g. osceola) held sway. However, it too ranged north exactly to the southern edge of this same Transition Belt. So also did and does the Bobwhite. The Sharp-tailed Grouse, on the other hand, stays north of that line; while the Ruffed

Grouse, which once covered this province plus Appalachia and all the Boreal Forests to the north of it, has now departed therefrom except for a string of isolated "islands" stretching along the Interior Highlands. The Spruce Grouse is even more precise, venturing south precisely to that same line from its Canadian homelands. Here we have no less than five birds of a single group, plus an introduced species, whose ranges are delineated by a "line" or border that is virtually invisible to us. It is one of the most notable demonstrations of the maxim that the distribution of animals is primarily circumscribed by that of vegetational forms. And, just to add a final note of conviction to this maxim, let me add that the Prairie Chicken, which once ranged over the whole Parkland belt, is today confined to just those areas wherein either parkland or prairie conditions have been retained or created by agricultural needs.

THE AMERICAN BIRD

I would like to say a few words, in passing, about one of the above-mentioned birds which, in the opinion of not a few, would be more suitable as the national emblem of the United States than the one now used. This is the Wild Turkey. There were originally seven races or subspecies of Wild Turkey apart from the quite different Ocellated Turkey of southern Mexico and Yucatan *(Meleagris ocellata)*. These were the Eastern *(silvestris)* found from the hundredth meridian to the east coast and south of the Transition Belt, exclusive of Florida where it was replaced by the race named *osceola;* the Rio Grande race *(intermedia)* ranging throughout central and eastern Texas and south down the east side of Mexico to the twentieth parallel, which is the bottom of this continent as defined in this book; Merriam's *(merriami)* in Colorado, New Mexico, and parts of Arizona; the Sierra Madre form *(mexicana)* from Arizona all down the mountain ranges of that name on the southwest side of Mexico to the state of Durango; and the Mexican *(M. gallopavo gallopavo)* in two isolated areas to east and west, south of the twentieth parallel, around Colima and Vera Cruz respectively. The seventh form is known to have existed among the coastal ranges of California, but it is now extinct and has no scientific name; it has been replaced by stock of other breeds brought in from outside. The range of these birds today is by and large the same (with the exception of the Vera Cruz form, which is also now extinct) but is everywhere spotty. They have been reintroduced

to many areas and are generally doing well; but, strangely, no turkeys appear ever to have lived in the desert or scrub belts even if well vegetated, and they will not survive there today. In this province they are now found only on the Piedmont and the Interior Highlands.

These races of turkeys are all quite distinct, having not only noticeably different plumage but also quite differently formed and colored wattles and other naked facial adornments. The Ocellated Turkey is quite another animal, having, as its name implies, prominent eyelike spots shaped somewhat like those on the tail of a peacock. There is still debate as to whether the domestic breeds are derived from our bird or the Ocellated. It seems pretty certain that the first turkeys that were taken back to Europe were obtained in Yucatan and would thus be of the latter species. It is interesting to note that just about the one country they did not reach until quite recently was Turkey, and in this connection there is an interesting story told about the origin of their English name. It is said that the specioneer (equivalent to purser on a modern ship) on Cortez's flagship was from the Levant, and when the Yucatecans brought the first of these birds to the ship he, seeing their spots, called them *tok-qai* or a word of similar sound meaning "peacock" in his own Arabic dialect. This the Spanish sailors are said to have

Of the swans of North America, the Mute is introduced, the Whistling and Trumpeter are indigenous. The last (below) is Western but has been introduced elsewhere as an ornamental bird.

reproduced as something like "tocái," which the British converted to "turkey." In point of fact, the first of these birds were carried to Spain, but it was found that they bred better in the Low Countries—then Spanish—and Belgium became the great center for raising them. The blue and the white varieties were developed there in very early days. They were then imported into England, where their stock was greatly improved; and from there they were finally shipped back to America to the colonists in New England. There are statements of early date in the latter region affirming that these imported turkeys would not breed with the wild ones.

ORIGIN OF THE HEARTLAND

The position and configuration of this triangular heartland is not due entirely to physiographic features of the land surface nor even to its particular and unique climate. Initially, it has a much deeper origin and cause. Once again, this is the recent (or current) "ice age" and its long-term pulsations of temperature and precipitation. Its past influence on this province is neither obvious nor even apparent until it is pointed out to us by geologists. Yet these influences *were* paramount, and it was an icecap that created the whole physical structure of the area.

Four major advances and retreats of the ice took place. Beginning with the most distant past, these are named the Nebraskan, the Kansan, the Illinoian, and the Wisconsin. Between these the ice vanished completely from this province; and these intervening or interglacial periods, as they are called, have been named the Aftonian, Yarmouth, and Sangamon respectively. The ice did not come down exactly the same way each time, though on the whole it spread over much the same area and tended to follow the same routes between the major land surfaces. The Illinoian reached farthest south, almost to the junction of the Mississippi and the Ohio. At one time or another an icecap seems to have stretched from the eastern face of the great barrier of the Rockies in the region of northern Montana, all the way to New Jersey and northern Pennsylvania.

The effects of these inland ice advances were very profound, not only over that portion of land which they actually submerged but for a great distance beyond, and all the way down to the Gulf coast. The proximity of a large icecap means those terrible idiabatic winds of which we spoke in connection with Greenland (see Chapter 1), and in this case those blowing south from this icecap were confined between the great mountains on the west and the Appalachians on the east. The air could, in fact, be almost viscous, it was so cold, and it literally poured off the ice and down over the Mississippi valley. However, some interesting facts have been discovered lately which set for us some real conundrums.

The ice must have advanced at a really terrific rate (or alternatively, according to one current theory, the crust of the earth must have slipped up under the polar region at an astonishing speed) because, rather than pushing all the major vegetational belts southward before it, the ice seems to have ridden roughshod over them, bulldozing everything south to regions where such southern woody plants as oleanders grew. Evidence of this is the wood of several southern temperate trees which has now been found in the icecap's terminal moraine. These trees must have been growing at lower latitudes, for they needed mild temperatures and a certain annual quota of sunlight merely to exist. Moreover, unless the ice moved south—or, conversely, the crust moved north—in less time than it takes oleander wood to rot, those trees simply could not have been there, because either

the extra-cold adiabatic winds would have killed them, or they would have been transported too far north on the shifting crust to regions where there simply was not enough sunlight annually for anything but a few specialized alpine-Arctic plants, mosses, and lichens to grow.

This is a very important feature of this province's recent history: it means that, even when a vast icecap covered its northern half, the southern half, although chilled, could have been and probably was initially wholly forested, so that oleanders grew in cracks along the ice front itself, just as flowering shrubs grow at the very feet of glaciers in Alaska, Norway, and Switzerland today. Nothing is more surprising than to be pushing your way through a dense oak-elm-and-beach forest under a flashing summer sun, plagued by mosquitoes in the shade, and trampling on orchids, and suddenly to break out from the undergrowth upon a towering peacock-blue wall of ancient ice. Yet there are many places in the world, in both northern and southern hemispheres, where you can do this at the feet of mountain glaciers. Could ancient man have experienced similar conditions at the edge of this ancient icecap? It seems from the evidence of buried woods that he could have done so, and this can only mean that man and animals could have camped and hunted all across what is now the United States throughout at least the preliminary phases of all four ice advances. This puts an entirely different complexion upon our concept both of an ice age and of the status of interglacial man and animals in North America. In fact, whoever the people were who dwelt on this continent before the Amerindians—and left such quantities of beautifully made stone tools—they could quite well have been hunting egrets on one side of the Mississippi at St. Louis while ice cliffs towered skyward on the other.

However, the icecap in the north had a profound effect upon the south of this province, due both to winter snow and summer rain and to the vast quantities of water that issued from the icecap every summer when it melted along its front. The southern part of the province was then very lush and much of it swampy or flooded; and, since the presence of open water tends to equalize the air temperature, that part of the land, though close to the ice, was somewhat warmer than it would otherwise have been during the autumn.

MECHANICS OF AN ICE AGE

An icecap may be as much as two miles thick. Ice is really a kind of rock and a heavy kind at that. A two-mile thickness of it piled up on land causes the underlying rock to sag. The result is that the ice can thicken some more, for its surface is thus lowered relative to sea level and if more snow falls, more ice is formed. The ice sheet becomes thicker, and thus heavier, and exerts more pressure upon the rock below, causing it to sag further. However, there comes a time when the weight of the ice is so great that it begins to render its own lower layers plastic so that they begin to flow. Then the ice begins to move outward in all directions. This may produce some very odd results because, while the bottom ice may be locked in a valley, the upper layers may glide over it and ride over mountains or even run uphill.

The last icecap spread all over the Laurentian Shield—that

Facing page, above: The Long-tailed Weasel is the commonest of this clan in the Heartland and the East, but is rarely seen, being nocturnal and wary. Below: The Mink ranges almost all over the continent except for deserts.

The Great Blue Heron, one of the commonest waders in the East, has a wing span as great as an eagle's. It winters in the South but individuals may stay about the Heartland all year round.

great domed slab of most ancient and almost non-compressible rocks that spreads all across eastern Canada; the whole of the Quebec–Labrador Peninsula; the Gulf of St. Lawrence; Newfoundland; Nova Scotia; and the whole of New England. To the west it spread over the Canadian Lakes District (see Chapter 3) from the Keewatin Peninsula. A great part of this, notably the Laurentian Shield, Labrador, and the lands about the mouth of the St. Lawrence, did not sink to anything like the same extent as surrounding areas. The greatest sag was under Hudson Bay; the next greatest sag occurred in the area south of the Laurentian Shield over what is now known as the Great Lakes.

Evidence that all this territory was once covered with ice is plain to see, once the things to look for have been pointed out by geologists. These may be divided into two lots: those produced on the land actually covered by the icecap, and those to be seen on lands beyond its farthest extension. The first is of two kinds: that produced while the icecap was growing and advancing, and that left as it retreated or melted away. Of course it is not yet certain whether the land slid in under a permanent polar icecap, whether the icecap crept south over the land, or whether it developed *in situ*. There was obviously a southward movement of ice, but this need not have been a gradually expanding cap having its origin far to the north and pushing its edge slowly outward like a vast gob of molasses. To the contrary, a change of climate that caused winter snows on the Laurentian Shield to accumulate without melting in summer could have started the process; or excessive snow could have blanketed the whole country. Then, if the snow did not melt, it would be converted to an ever increasing mass of firn that finally compacted to ice, which, growing in thickness, would eventually initiate those movements mentioned above. The edge or front of the cap may in fact not have moved at all although enormous volumes of ice moved outward from the inner areas of the cap to its periphery. In either case, the movement was massive and produced most noticeable effects.

The first of these was that the entire surface of the earth was bulldozed, not only of all vegetation and surface soil but of subsoil and, where the land rose above the general level, of whole hills. Whether the ice formed *in situ* or flowed in from outside, it froze everything beneath it unto itself in one vast permafrost, with the result that the bottom of the ice mass consisted not so much of ice but of all manner of rock fragments, from boulders weighing hundreds of tons to fine sediment, like the abrasive granules on a monstrous sheet of sandpaper. As this was shoved over the face of the earth it ground everything flat, while itself being fractionated; and one may gain some idea of the power of this abrasive machine by calculating the downward pressure exerted by two miles of ice. This works out at about nine billion tons per square mile of land surface. The ancient Egyptians cut the enormous blocks of stone to build their pyramids with saws made of soft copper or even of wood, simply by moving sand and water back and forth in grooves under their modest weight. The really remarkable thing is that anything except a sort of rock soup should remain under the terrific pressure of the ice.

Vast quantities of such "soup" were produced, which finally seeped out from under the edge of the ice or were left after it melted. This was washed away by the meltwater and deposited in lakes and swamps, or at the bottom of the seas and oceans, as extremely finely particulated silts. The highly sticky clays that cover large areas of the surface of Canada, the Yukon, and Alaska today are composed of this material. A lot of coarser material also survived, ranging all the way from fine sand to enormous boulders. These have all their corners rounded off, and when they are deposited along with clay, sand, and other materials, and compacted, they form a monumental hodgepodge or "conglomerate," as it is so aptly called by geologists. Considerable areas on the land surface of this province are covered with this ground-up and rolled material left by the ice. Where the land surface was mountainous enough to cause the ice to break up into separate tongues between the peaks, moraines were formed on top of the sheet. These are long lines of broken rock, gouged out of or knocked off the containing mountain sides, or fallen down upon the ice surface from above due to frost action. These snaking lines of material are then carried forward on top of the ice and finally dumped off the front of the icecap. Sometimes, however, this material sinks down into the ice and gets carried along in its midst, or it works its way right to the bottom and gets ground up along with the other material down there. If it stays on top of the ice it may be dumped without having been rolled; it is then readily recognizable due to the angular edges of its component rocks.

In addition to these various types of moraines left at the edge of the icecap (which result in typical country such as is seen over the greater part of the north of this province, with hummocky low hills scattered in haphazard manner and with de-

A *tree frog*, or *tree toad* (Hyla). *Billions of these inhabit temperate and tropical areas. They have clinging disks on their toes, are adept tree-climbers, and eat insects.*

pressions between them from which there is no outlet), the ice left other distinctive things. Two of these are *drumlins* and *eskers*. The former are also isolated low hills, but they have one longer axis and they lie in roughly parallel lines, these lines following the direction of the retreat of the ice so that they slowly converge upon its final point of departure. The method of their formation is not known; nor is that of the strange eskers. These are long, narrow banks, looking for all the world like abandoned railroad beds, that may run perfectly straight for miles or wander about like vast snakes. One suggestion as to their origin is that they were formed in long, tunnel-like caves under the ice, through which meltwater flowed during the "retreat" of the icecap when the ice itself was no longer moving. Another theory supposes that they were formed on top of the ice but also in stream beds, and were then gently let down to earth as the ice rotted away below them. Since they look as though they were man-made, they are rather startling when first seen.

THE GREAT LAKES BASIN

The theory that the enormous basin of the Great Lakes is initially due to a sagging of the crust of the earth is viewed with disfavor by some. These critics note that before the first ice advance the whole area was manifestly well above sea level because it was amply drained by large river systems of which there is still geological evidence, whereas now the bottoms of the lakes themselves, but *only of the lakes,* are in some places as much as three hundred feet below sea level. This school of thought supposes that these huge troughs were bulldozed out by the ice. There is possibly as much to be said for one theory as the other, but it is observable that the area as a whole is now rising, and it appears to have been doing so steadily since the icecap went away. The Hudson Bay basin has also been rising, but there is a contrary proposal about its past history too: namely, that the central dome of the icecap never did lie over it but was, rather, divided into two, one centered on the Keewatin and the other on the Quebec–Labrador peninsula; and that the ice flowed *into* it—rather than out of it—from both sides, meeting along a line down its center that then extended south from James Bay by way of Niagara to and down the Hudson River Gorge.

It does indeed seem that two opposed ice sheets from the northwest and the northeast met in the Great Lakes area, spewed on side by side for some distance, and then separated, one turning east to reach the Atlantic at Long Island, the other continuing south to form the great sheet that reached the region of St. Louis. As this combined icecap retreated for the last time, an ever changing series of huge lakes was formed along its front. At first these drained south to the Gulf, but, as the land was progressively released northward, outlets broke through to the Atlantic via the Hudson and St. Lawrence valleys, and finally to the north into Hudson Bay. As the land sprang back from its overload, the lakes contracted until they took up their present conformations. Finally, Lake Ontario broke through to the St. Lawrence and its waters drained off suddenly to a depth of nearly two hundred feet, causing the waters of Lake Erie to start spilling over a great bluff, thus forming Niagara Falls.

At the present time the lip of those falls is cutting back at an average rate of about four feet a year; but the rate of cutting in the past has changed, as may be seen from the variations in the size of the gorge below. The time since this cutting began has been estimated at a minimum of ten thousand years; however, other evidence appears to indicate that the icecap still covered the falls at that time, which brings the date of the end of the last "ice age" very much nearer to the dawn of our history than had previously been supposed.

The Western Piedmont and the Interior Highlands were not apparently glaciated, but there is scattered evidence of the existence of morainic and other glacial-type deposits in both areas, which suggest that considerable snowfields with glaciers might have formed on their higher levels for short periods. The Western Piedmont, which forms a wedge lying between the Ohio and the Cumberland rivers, is composed of the foothills of the Appalachians, the eastern flank of which merges with this prov-

ince. This strip runs from the region of Akron, Ohio, south to Nashville, Tennessee, and may be extended to include the Nashville basin. It is an extremely fertile belt, second only to the Central Lowlands in this respect, but it remains much more heavily vegetated, with closed-canopy forest over large stretches.

ANIMAL IMMIGRANTS

All of this gives us a new view of this province as it is today and goes far toward explaining the appearance of the land, its vegetation, and its animal life. It is a new province, repopulated from the northwest, the south, and to some extent from the uplands of Appalachia to the east, where a temperate flora and fauna seems to have been able to survive all four ice advances. This was once a land of continuous forests, and it must have been exquisitely beautiful. There lived forest bison, elk, great droves of white-tailed deer, black bear, puma, bobcat, and all the lesser folk like raccoons, skunks and, above all, beaver. We must say once more, though we will repeat it again and again, that the latter animals have probably had more to do with the landscaping of our continent than any other animal. They were the first animals to move in the moment that the land was freed; they will work right up to an ice front; and, above all, they *do something,* and that of a nature that produces profound physical results. Much nonsense has been written from time to time about the beaver, but they literally move mountains, dam whole water systems, and, by stemming the natural processes of erosion, build fertile land; thus, they alter the composition of vegetation by changing the water table, and perform many other works on a vast scale. However, they categorically do not do this "by taking thought upon the matter." To the contrary, they appear to do it all in a kind of bumbling and entirely unimaginative manner—just digging and ditching all the time by some kind of built-in compulsion, whether the results be satisfactory to themselves or not. Simply by the law of averages plus the fact that failures are automatically eliminated, the results of all their activity are, on the whole, in accord with what their species most needs to get along. And it just so happens that these results are also highly advantageous to man, particularly to agricultural man. If the beaver does the right things, he obtains a better living environment—ponded water, flooded land, good pastures, hardwood trees with the right bark to eat, and so forth—and all these things are just exactly what modern man also wants. All over this province, as in large parts of Appalachia, you will see either such useful activities being currently prosecuted or the good results of the past industry of these remarkable animals.

Large parts of three of the subprovinces are still well forested. This is the land of maples, oaks, and beeches, and it was once that of the American Chestnut, now virtually eliminated as a result of a disease that spread all over the country with extraordinary rapidity between the years 1904 and 1914. There is still some true wilderness in the Interior Highlands, and in northern Wisconsin and Michigan. Its vegetation as a whole is very much like that of Appalachia and the eastern seaboard; it lies in the same world belt as most of Europe, and it is usually regarded as rather ordinary but somehow "proper" by a high proportion of visitors, both American and foreign.

Overleaf: A flight of teal over a marsh dotted with muskrat lodges. These lodges are like those of the beaver but are made of rolls of grass and sedges.

The Lesser Canada or Cackling Goose is mainly an Alaskan and Pacific coastal species but is found and may even breed on the Great Lakes.

These mandarin ducks, introduced from Asia, are close relatives of the American wood ducks, which are considered by many to be our most beautiful wild ducks.

After being nearly exterminated in the United States, Beaver are making a tremendous comeback everywhere. Through their everlasting dam-building and ditching activities, they are the animals most responsible for the landscaping of the country.

QUEER "FISH"

I have often been asked if there is any particular group of animals that might in any way typify this province, in view of the obvious fact that all creatures normally seen there seem to be equally typical and even better known in one or more of the surrounding provinces. From the point of view of the naturalist, I would suggest that it is the denizens of the fresh waters that are here most outstanding. Apart from the game fish such as trout, bass, and sunfish, fresh-water fish as a whole do not seem to offer the nonspecialist much novelty or excitement. However, if a visitor goes to the aquarium in the Toledo Zoo, even if he is a Midwesterner he will get a surprise; and even if he is not a fisherman he will find himself spending much more time than he expected staring at the really fabulous-looking inhabitants of the Great Lakes and the Mississippi and its tributaries that are exhibited there. There is one fish with an elongated spoon for a mouth that defies description, known as the paddlefish (*Polyodon spathula*) or the spoonbill, which most people don't even know exists, let alone in our own midst. Then, in the mountain streams of this area and particularly of the Interior Highlands, dwell those enormous, sacklike salamandrids called Hellbenders, a type of animal otherwise known only from eastern Asia; while in the weed-covered ponds and ditches of the lowlands, there are huge populations of the almost equally preposterous-looking Mud Puppies, with paddle tails and plumose external gills that look like feathers. Then there are also the Sirens, snake- or eel-shaped creatures of the waters with a single tiny pair of limbs up forward. Frogs are also extremely prominent in this country, and there are a plethora of tortoises and turtles. This is most notably the country of fresh-water animals.

WORLDS BENEATH US

It is water, too, that has brought into existence another outstanding feature of this province. This is caves. Much of the surface of the Interior Highlands, the Piedmont, and other areas are covered with limestone strata. These rocks are soluble in acid waters such as rain (which contains carbonic acid derived from the carbon dioxide in the air) or waters filtered through plant roots that gather humic acid.

A cave is basically just a hole in some otherwise more or less solid material. Yet a cave is like a living entity, although actually a purely negative one. It is born, it grows, it has a mature life and maybe a long old age, but ultimately it dies. However, unlike an animal, any one of these phases may be arrested for any length of time; and growth, maturity, and decline may take place not just once but many times. Short of complete dissolution, erosion, or other form of mechanical transportation of the medium in which the cave exists, it appears to be virtually immortal. It can never be filled up with the exact material in which it is formed, but it can collapse under extreme pressure during earth movements; and then, if it does not contain any extraneous material, it may be totally obliterated by rock flow. Otherwise all that can happen is that it may fill up completely with some deposit and then be buried. In this case it becomes a fossil cave. Fissures and veins that are completely filled in abound, and most of these seem to have been filled as they grew, solution and deposition taking place together.

Stalactites and stalagmites in Mammoth Cave, Kentucky. Such structures result by accretion from dripping water.

Some limestones, notably some of those in this province, are just about as ancient as any sedimentary rocks can be, having been laid down under a sea in what is called the Cambrian Age, which is estimated to have started about 550,000,000 years ago. Now, unless surface waters are completely acid-free, caves start forming in limestone immediately it is raised out of the salt sea where it originates. There is a vague theory that prior to the evolution of land plants there was no carbon dioxide in the atmosphere, and if this is so, caves first started in Devonian times, 350,000,000 years ago, and some from that age are (as geologists can demonstrate) still in existence—and as caves.

Caves have a fascination all their own, and that which is to be seen in them is very worth while, for most caves have great natural beauty. The formations that have grown in them over the ages are of wide variety, from towering columns measured in hundreds of feet to tiny flower-shaped clusters of crystals and beautiful little pearl-like concretions found in limpid pools. The floors of caves also often yield bones and other animal remains, and the dejecta of primitive and early man. So far the caves of this continent have not given up anything like the treasures of this nature that have those of the other continents, but this does not mean that there are not important discoveries of this nature still to be made. No two caves are alike, so that you can go on visiting new ones for a lifetime and still find something novel in almost all of them. It is in this province, however, that one may probably best be initiated into this subterranean world; and there is probably no better place to start than Mammoth Cave in Kentucky. Well over 150 miles of passages have been mapped in this vast complex of corridors, rooms, deep pits, crawlways, and a great variety of other-shaped holes. Yet anyone may walk through many parts of it in perfect safety today and see examples of many of the principal things to be found underground.

In 1952 a man was drilling a well in Alabama and had gone down just over a quarter of a mile, when, to his utmost surprise, up came a five-inch, blind, colorless salamander. Now you cannot have any animal living in solid rock, so there must have been water down there. Further, you cannot have just one animal (even of a kind that has been until then entirely unknown and unsuspected) existing anywhere: it must have had parents, have a mate, and produce youngsters. Also, all animals must eat, and as there cannot be any plants in the total absence of light—apart from parasitic or saprophytic ones—these salamanders must subsist for the most part on other animals. But those in turn must eat too, and we would like to know where their food comes from. It must be washed down from above; but in the immediate area of this first discovery, no caves are known. The only other suggestion is that there are down there certain specialized bacteria that actually eat rock, such as those that cause the "rotting" of old buildings like Notre Dame Cathedral in Paris.

Several kinds of salamanders and also fish have now been brought up from deep well drillings all over a huge area from western Texas to the Atlantic coast. Their distribution has been plotted, and it has been found that when laid out on a map, the distribution of each species forms a pattern like a river system. Further, these networks overlay each other but without any apparent reference to each other, and they are found to be at different levels; so that, while the waters of all of them must presumably come down from above and must be confluent, the animals of one level cannot get into the next below or above. These weird creatures must have been evolved down there from primitive surface-living species that somehow penetrated into the very bowels of the earth eons ago, and they must have been there ever since despite great movements of the earth's crust.

Many Green Mountains

The Appalachians from Maine to Alabama, and the Eastern Piedmont

7 Although much of this province today still looks, from the air at least, like a mountainous green wilderness, and although a great deal of it back from the highways *is* a wilderness, its surface covering of vegetation is not, except in very limited areas, what it was before the coming of the white man. We would like to know what it did look like in that bygone era. This is synonymous with inquiring what the Pilgrim Fathers saw when they landed at the rock they named Plymouth, and it must be to a very great extent a matter of reconstruction, for most of Appalachia has been altogether changed not once, like the other countries of North America, but twice in the three hundred years since that eventful day.

The activities of this continent's new inhabitants who came mostly from Europe and West Africa are not of any concern to us, but it must be emphasized here that almost the whole face of Appalachia was once completely altered by those people through deforestation. This was done for the most part to create pasture land for the raising of sheep, and it extended in many cases in the northern areas to the very tops of the fairly high —for the area—mountain ranges, so that all the way from Maine to Tennessee stone walls and homestead foundations of colonial age may be found right up to, and even on, the summits of some of the highest ridges. Also, this country was the source of iron ore, as well as bog iron, and the forests were slashed and cropped to the ground in vast swaths to make charcoal for the smelting furnaces. Then, later, there was a mass exodus of rural New Englanders; the upland sheep pastures were depopulated of their ovine hordes; weeds and scrub took over; and eventually a secondary forest, for the most part unprepossessing, grew up. Despite the wildernesses of Maine, the vast preserved forests of the Adirondacks, and the allegedly backwoods lands of the Alleghenies, there are few places where truly pre-Columbian nature has been preserved. Nonetheless, there are such places; and from them, from early records, and from the results we can see today of nature's own efforts to reproduce or re-create the face of her postglacial youth, we may gain some idea of what Appalachia looked like before our ancestors arrived.

THE REFUGE

We can see from the map that this land is a mountainous one and that it has a limited coast line, rocky and steep in the north,

sandy, pebbly, or muddy and gently shelving in the south. It was once clothed in an almost endless blanket of greenery; a mixed forest of hardwoods and pines, the latter predominantly of one species *(Pinus strobus)*. It is a continental, not a coastal, land, and it forms the eastern or right-hand tine of the great V of highlands that forms the framework of this continent.

The vegetation of the northern half of this province extends south almost to its southern extremity along the highest ridge of the Blue Ridge Mountains, forming a narrow tongue. Wrapped around this tongue from Kentucky on the northwest side, south through Tennessee to Alabama, thence east through Georgia and northeast to about the southern border of Virginia, on the lower slopes, among the foothills, and filling the valleys is another type of forest of considerable luxuriance. This is the true Woodland Deciduous, broad-leafed forest. The bottomlands are mostly rich pastures, but the rivers are lined with woods and marshes; the hillsides are clothed in closed-canopy forests of many kinds of oak and hickory, walnut, some birches, alder, hazelnut, hornbeam, willow, poplar, elm, magnolia, tulip trees, laurels, sassafras, planes, maples, ash, horse chestnut, and a few acacias. Beneath the canopy and in more exposed places an equally luxuriant undergrowth spreads. This contains many magnolias and numerous species of rhododendron, kalmia, and related plants. This undergrowth extends high up the mountains and may spread also under the pines or even form an almost alpine type of growth without trees but with open grassy glades between the bushes. When the rhododendrons are in bloom the hills look as if they had been painted, and photographs of them are reminiscent of old-time, hand-tinted picture postcards.

It is this horseshoe-shaped swath of foothill and piedmont country that is the real "South," rather than the pine-covered lowlands and coastal plains. It is here that the richest soils are to be found, and it is this portion of this province that enjoys the most abundant rainfall, combined with moderate temperature and winds, all year round. It was not recently glaciated, and to it retreated both the fauna and flora that were driven out of the north by the ice: in turn, that same fauna and flora acted as a reservoir from which the lands released from under the ice were restocked, most of the animals and many of the plants spreading north as the climate ameliorated. But other plants and some animals stayed behind, either because they had been initially indigenous to more southern latitudes or because the winters farther north were still too rugged. It is important to appreciate this fact, for the fauna and flora of the eastern side of this continent is—and apparently has been since very long ago—isolated from that of the west side by the great intervening prairies and steppes. Its only connection is around the top of the prairies via Canada, and when this route was cut off by icecaps, the plants and animals of the east had nowhere to go but south into southern Appalachia. Had the ice gone only a little farther south, both would have been driven out into the Caribbean and extinguished forever.

Appalachia has its quota of oddities, ranging from isolated patches of spruce forest in western Maine and in the central Adirondacks to the shifting sand dunes of southern Maine. Throughout the parallel ranges of the Alleghenies and the Appalachians proper (often called the Blue Ridge), there are many beautiful though—to the eyes of those from more moun-

The Chipmunk, a small ground-living squirrel, helps landscape the country. All summer and fall it buries nuts which it often forgets to eat, and which then sprout, creating new woodlands.

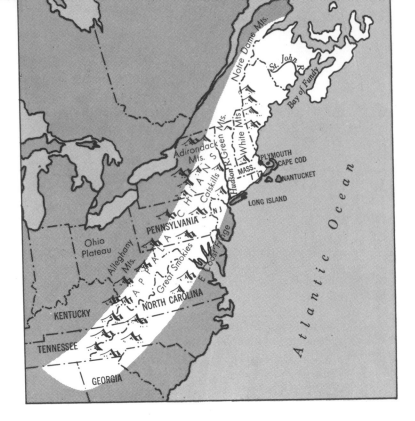

The province of Appalachia extends somewhat beyond the limits of the Appalachian Mountains and coincides more closely with what geologists term the Appalachian Fold. It is all mountainous or at least hilly; it spans 1300 miles from New Brunswick in a southwesterly direction to the northwest tip of Georgia, and is on an average some 200 miles in width. It has a short coast line of about 400 miles length between the Bay of Fundy and the mouth of the Hudson.

Its northwestern boundary is fairly well defined, being the foot of the mountains—in some places actually an escarpment—bordering on the lowlands of the Heartland or Great Lakes

district, though the junction between it and the western piedmont is in many places not an abrupt line. On the southeast—that is, from the neighborhood of the Hudson River to the border between North and South Carolina— its boundary is the "fall line" (see Chapter 8), and this then cuts inland and west to northern Alabama. In the northeast this province merges with the Gulf of St. Lawrence in that, from a phytogeographical point of view, it is really a southward extension—resulting from its altitude—of the Transition Belt that runs through that region.

Just as the mountain ranges of the Far West overlie the major vegetational belts, so also to a certain extent does Appalachia, but in other respects it produces quite contrary side effects. This is because it lies alongside a "trough," or major swing to the south, of the belts rather than athwart a "peak" or acute swing to the north, as do the Rockies. Thus, while the Rockies carry boreal forest right down into the Desert Belt at higher altitudes—as in the upper slopes of the Sacramento Mountains in New Mexico—the Appalachians merely push the Transition (mixed coniferous-deciduous growth) and the Deciduous Woodlands somewhat south into the Parkland, in the form of a tongue of uplands.

The vegetation clothing this province is confluent with and fundamentally similar to that of the St. Lawrence valley and the northern part of the Heartland or Great Lakes district. Throughout this whole area the typical conifer is the Eastern White Pine (Pinus strobus). Its presence clearly marks the limits of the province, especially in the south and east, where it abuts onto the Coastal Fringe Province and on the Great Southern Pine Belt (which are actually parklands) where the Longleaf (P. palustris) and the Loblolly pines (P. taeda) hold sway.

Appalachia consists of a series of mountain ranges located in echelon in the north and more or less parallel in the south.

tainous countries—subdued vistas of great magnificence. There are still forests everywhere, ranging from the veritable "rain forests" of Maine, with their soft flooring of ferns and fungi, to the dry, brittle valley sides of Pennsylvania and the considerable upland forests of Tennessee and North Carolina. There are also endless lakes in the north and lush natural valley bottoms everywhere, many of which have not even now been obliterated by clearing for agriculture and man's settled community life. There are a few places—though fewer than many suppose—where the land appears really to be still as it was when the only men around were as much a part of nature as the raccoon or the deer. These are very lovely, and when you stumble into one of them you immediately know, unless you are a quite insensitive person, that you are in something of the olden times. Let me describe one that is typical of the central block of this land.

A PRE-COLUMBIAN VISTA

This place is tiny. It is held at an elevation of only some seven hundred feet above sea level in the embrace of a circle of cultivated fields, cattle pastures, and apple orchards. It is only about four square miles in area and, most surprising of all, it is just seventy miles from Manhattan Island. As you travel the dirt roads that envelope it, on an average of only about five miles from its secluded center, you would never suspect that it

existed just over the hills. There is not even a footpath leading into it, and you must trudge across the fields to get to it; and from there it looks like a most nondescript wood ahead. I first found this place when a visiting friend's dog took fright at an accidental gunshot and ran away. Following her large tracks, we entered this almost holy place, referred to, we later learned from its laconic owner, as "that worthless swamp." Swamp it may be; yet it is covered by a real forest where some of the poison-ivy stems are as thick as one's leg.

Happily, my companion that day was an Amerindian and knew every plant and animal in this, his land; he had the proverbial eyes of a hawk, and much knowledge of the now no longer extant medicine men of his tribe. Following the dog tracks we descended a gentle grass slope, climbed a deteriorated stone wall, and entered a pure stand of alder bushes. Immediately the air was permeated with a mingled aroma reminiscent of the loading platform of a perfume factory. The sun shone brightly, and hoverflies—those black-and-yellow-banded insects that helicopter in filtered sun shafts—were all about us. We trudged into waist-high sedges that crunched and gave off most delectable aromas; pristine black-and-white flycatchers eyed us brightly from the bare-fingered tops of the bushes; and somewhat surprisingly, a crested kingfisher let out a screech and whirled away ahead. Then we struck a small winding path that had no discoverable beginning. Suddenly it was just there, clearly defined and rapidly clearing, and its muddy center was churned by the passing of what could only be an endless parade of deer.

Following this path, winding between the giant, billowing alders, we presently came upon something that I had not seen previously outside of forest Africa—a genuine and completely natural dew pond, perfectly circular, filled with limpid, clear water looking like a black mirror, and surrounded by a gently sloping muddy verge completely mosaicked with tracks of the local white-tailed deer. Among these were also tracks of raccoon, opossum, muskrat, many mice, some larger water birds, and some fair-sized creature with a strange leaping gait. These latter most nearly matched the prints of one of our rarest carnivorous animals, the fisher marten, but I frankly did not then believe this possible since the animal was alleged to have been extinct in this area for a long time. (About a month later a pair were caught in traps by a licensed trapper who took them to the game warden, not knowing what on earth they might be.) From this pond, which was about twenty feet in diameter, four paths meandered away almost exactly to the four points of the compass and were so laid out among the great bushes that you could not see more than a few feet along any of them.

Just beyond, very ancient oaks unexpectedly towered above us and, as we went in under these, almost all undergrowth faded away. We found ourselves in a sort of natural cathedral with a true forest canopy above, a carpet of mosses at our feet, and a few spindly saplings balancing like giant green feathers in the gloom. From the great trees there hung genuine creepers—not the finger-thick vines that entangle our shrubbery if we neglect to tend it, but great liana-like ropes of poison ivy, lode vines, and wild grape. In some places the trees that once supported these monsters had completely vanished and the creepers

A common red fox in full winter coat. This is one of the most widely spread of all mammals, and one that manages to survive and thrive alongside human settlements. Cross and silver foxes are natural mutations of this species.

Below: A pair of long-tailed or New York weasels, among the better known of the numerous weasels on the continent.

themselves grew like trees, their acres of foliage held aloft on neighboring heads. There was a small rocky bluff from which several ferns burst in pale mops, and there were tiny forest flowers that I have never seen anywhere else. And there were birds somewhere up above.

Here, suddenly, was a glimpse of the kind of environment that the first refugees from Europe must have encountered just beyond the oceanic verge where salt air may be driven over low headlands—the kind of forest that once stretched for a thousand miles. This small secluded spot happens to be in the foothills, and there were none of the conifers so typical of Appalachia. Even if it had once been cleared in colonial times—which my

prising a distinct mountain complex. In the northeast there are the mountains that lie athwart Maine and Notre Dame in Quebec; due south of these the two parallel north-to-south ridges in New Hampshire (the White Mountains) and Vermont (the Green Mountains); to the west of these the Adirondacks; and then a considerable upland area stretching from the Catskills to Jamestown in New York and on into northern Pennsylvania. Southeast of this extend the curving parallel Alleghenies and the mighty Blue Ridge, which leads south to the Great Smokies. Each, in a way, has its own distinctive floral make-up and noticeably distinct faunal composition. These differences are slight as between adjacent areas, but even a few hours' drive

A beautiful and most remarkable butterfly, the Monarch (Danaus plexippus), *just emerged from its chrysalis and drying off. This insect migrates to Mexico.*

Above: A caterpillar of the Black Swallowtail Butterfly. Facing page: A caterpillar of the Spicebush Swallowtail Butterfly.

Amerindian friend doubted as much as I—that was so long ago that what is called a climax forest had had time to grow again, and to maturity. And here in the moss and under rotting logs were tiger salamanders, and odd snails that you don't see in newer woods, and shrews which are more than hard to find all about that area. Here they were everywhere in the deep leaf mould. This, moreover, is in New Jersey. Those who have visited the northern part of that state will know that it is splendidly wooded, but to stumble into a real forest there is more than just surprising.

FERNS AND FUNGUSES

We noted above that Appalachia is divided into a number of separate ranges. These are actually seven in number, each com-

is sufficient to reveal the change, especially if one travels in either direction along the spine of Appalachia.

The block of territory which is normally called "the forests of Maine" actually is a fairly small pocket, centered around a southern outlier of typical boreal spruce forest, in turn centered around Lake Chamberlain. It is separated from the St. Lawrence Gulf area by the St. John River and from the valley of that river on the west by the long ridge of the Notre Dame Mountains that runs almost north to south from Cape Gasparie through Quebec to Vermont, and thence, as the Green Mountains and the Berkshire Hills, to western Massachusetts and Connecticut. This was once wholly—and today is still to a considerable extent—a land clothed in pure pine stands of the same ubiquitous northern species, but about the center of the massif these give way to a solid stand of spruce. This area has, in fact, several aspects of a true outlier of the north, not a few of its plants and some of

its animals having been left there after the ice retreated for the last time, cut off from their brethren to the far north by the St. Lawrence valley and the escarpment of the Canadian Shield.

To enter these woods, especially in early summer, is to step into a world of long ago. Away from present cleared land, the surface of the earth has never been desecrated by man since it was released from the mile-thick icecap. It is a climax forest *par excellence,* as any botanist can tell by examination not so much of the trees, which are not, comparatively, of any great variety, but by looking down upon the ferns, mosses, and above all the funguses. I do not know of any comparative statistical survey having been made of the fungi of Maine specifically for comparison with those of any other region of this continent (or any other), but to an ecologist, it is these plants that, in this area, impress one above all others. Their species and forms seem to be endless. They grow on all kinds of trees, alive, dying, or dead, from their roots to their summits; they proliferate on all fallen wood, on the earth itself, on the stems of bushes, and even on stones. They spread their fleshy masses in all manner of forms and in almost every color of the rainbow—purples, magentas, bright blues, reds of every shade, oranges, jet-black, yellows, and all manner of browns. There is even a bright green species, an anomaly if ever there was one, since fungi do not manufacture chlorophyll. The color in this case, however, is due to commensal algae that grow in special pits on the surface of the fungus.

The matter of funguses has connotations of several kinds other than the aesthetic. Although plants, these "things," like animals, live exclusively on matter; they are called saprophytes, and they play a most vital role in the whole economy of nature.

Without them, the rest of the plant world would come to a dead stop on land. It once used to be thought that the growing threads, or mycelia, of funguses found infecting the roots and stems of other plants indicated some sort of horrific parasitical infestation or "disease." It is now appreciated that, without these, most of the plants so "infected" would be unable to carry on their essential life processes. Then again, moulds—which are only funguses—were once also thought to be invariably unpleasant. It is true that they are almost always engaged in destruction through the process that we call "rotting," but we have now at long last come to realize that this is a most essential procedure in the great cycle of life and one upon which we are wholly dependent for our food. If the funguses did not get to work and break up all the dead things that fall to the earth, their lesser brethren the bacteria would be unable to digest them, and we would, eons ago, have been submerged under a stratum of ammoniacal debris.

ANIMAL LANDSCAPERS

Here again, as in the other northern lands that we have visited, there have been other special factors at work to rebuild a ravished country. Beaver, for instance, did as much here as they did across the wide swath of the center of the continent. Northeastern Appalachia is a checkerboard of lakes. These are mostly glacial in origin, due to the changing of watersheds, the damming of valleys by moraines, and the gouging of gutters by the ice. However, there has been time for the industrious beaver to alter many of these into lush meadows, to drain others, and generally

A beaver with a freshly cut stick for its winter food supply. After he has built dams to raise the water, and constructed lodges, he anchors masses of food under the water for the winter.

to initiate new watercourses and even river systems. Even if they did not actually produce such comparatively major topographical changes, they completely altered the vegetative cover of enormous areas simply by raising or lowering the level of the water table.

If you will climb the mountains and look down upon almost any of the valleys leading northwest from the central massif of Maine on a clear day, you will notice that they descend by a series of gigantic steps, clearly defined by a difference in color between the hardwoods that grow on the steps themselves and the darker softwoods that grow on the surrounding slopes. A great deal of this pattern is the work of beaver and has been accomplished in a few thousand years. These animals, as we have already described in more detail, require both standing and running water, and the closer to the Arctic the more precise are their requirements. By damming a stream here and cutting a sluice or canal there, they tend to make the water flowing from the heights proceed in a series of jerks. But once they have brought part of it to a halt at any point, the water pushes out into the surrounding soil and even into the rocks—for even granite has a considerable free-water content—and thus raises the water table even on steep slopes. Some trees and bushes cannot grow with their tap roots in water; others not only can but need to do so. Thus, when beaver make a dam, a large area surrounding the resultant lake is apt to change its botanical face. And it can do so in a surprisingly short time. I have carried on a minor and haphazard experiment of this nature in northern New Jersey by building two dams across a bottom pasture of black earth underlaid by clay. In five years I have, instead of a pasture, a twenty-foot forest of small trees and large shrubs, and

Overleaf left-hand page: Dogwood in the spring in a typical temperate broad-leafed woodland of Appalachia. Right-hand page: The glory of early autumn in the same province.

some acres of swamp. What is more, the dominant trees all around the periphery of both have changed—those that predominated before having become sickly or even died, and others having sprouted phenomenally.

The speed at which vegetation can change is often, in fact, grossly underestimated, and although crops are divided into four classes—algae which you can harvest daily; leafy crops, once a month; cereals and tubers, once a year; and trees, once every half-century—all may proliferate at a multiple rate if the amount of daylight, the temperature, or the water availability is increased. There is an experiment, now in its tenth year, on the eastern seaboard wherein a square mile of sandy soil previously supporting only scrub pine and some holly has had its annual rainfall artificially raised by means of sprinklers from 43 to 143 inches. It now supports a dense forest well over fifty feet tall, containing all manner of animal life from worms and snails to birds that were never seen in the area before, and some of them not previously outside the subtropical belt. Water alone can perform miracles.

SUBURBAN ANIMALS

It is in Appalachia perhaps more than anywhere else that we see the direct evidences of the last ice advance or crustal slip,

Beaver can fell almost any tree and lay it in any desired spot, despite the tree's inclination or the slope of the land. They then cut it into logs which they roll to water.

The Lake Placid area in northern New York. This is a land of numerous lakes, left mostly by the bulldozing action of the last great icecap.

and the wonderful changes that have followed its "retreat." It is for this reason also that the northern areas of the province have such a strangely agglomerate fauna. As you roam about this country today the wildlife is more notable for its profusion than its variety—at least at first sight. There is said to be more game per acre in Pennsylvania than in any other state in the union, and despite Appalachia's almost fungoid growth of farmland, industry, and towns with their sprawling suburbs, there is no doubt that some mammals and many birds and amphibians appear to thrive in the new conditions. Deer swarm literally everywhere, even wandering into suburban areas. On a main highway not more than twenty miles from New York City, I once witnessed a game warden count 127 head in one herd grazing peaceably by the roadside while cars roared by.

There are raccoons that beg for scraps on a restaurant veranda overlooking Manhattan, and the police in Harlem have orders to eliminate both raccoons and opossums that occasionally turn over trash cans in the city streets. A pair of red foxes were found breeding in Central Park, there are wild mink in Van Cortlandt

Park, owls were discovered in the towers of the American Museum of Natural History, and peregrine falcons have nested on more than one famous midtown New York hotel and have molested the pigeons in Wall Street.

Wherever you drive in Appalachia you will see fat ground-hogs chumbling away on grass stems at the very edge of the blacktop roads, skunks wandering blissfully about, and cottontail rabbits bounding in and out of hedgerows. Cats bring moles and shrews to your doorstep on Long Island, and there are gray squirrels everywhere, and chipmunks toting nuts around many houses. I have taken a nest of flying squirrels out of a restaurant within greater New York, and a weasel out of a drainpipe in Brooklyn. There is a group of youths in that same borough that collects snakes and destroys thousands of black widow spiders in vacant lots. Even more bizarre, full-grown finner whales are beached within city limits, a harbor porpoise got stuck in a sewer in the Bronx, and a brook trout was found swimming in a midtown gutter flooded by a broken water main.

And then there are the birds. They are everywhere. Sea gulls bring bits of dry bread to be softened in city fountains, crows turn up to eat food put out for pigeons, and thousands of migratory birds have slammed into the Empire State Building. Moving only a little way out of the city, you will find wild ducks breeding on the marshes, hawks on the cliffs, and all manner of perching

birds in parks and gardens. Although the white man has "wrecked" the original ecology of this continent, enough time has now passed for the wildlife to get over its initial shock and to bound back. A new balance is developing, and it is nowhere more obvious than in Appalachia, the first area to be ravished and the one that has been most hardly done by.

There are still what used to be called "rare" things in this province. I mentioned the occurrence of fisher marten in New Jersey. There are unseen ones like the fabulous star-nosed mole and the anhinga or snakebird, which is popularly thought of as being a denizen of Floridian swamps but which has bred in that same state. Appalachia is a great place for black bear, and they are downright numerous in many parts, even appearing within thirty-five miles of New York, to the considerable astonishment of Westchester commuters. There have also been repeated rumors of mountain lion in Maine, the Adirondacks, the Poconos, and even in the Alleghenies. It was not long ago that the idea of porcupines in Connecticut was considered ridiculous, but now they are quite common in many areas. The fauna is really very varied if you dig for it. What is more, many forms seem to be spreading steadily north and east. Mourning doves, opossums, and turkey buzzards have all moved into New England within the past twenty years, and coyotes have been reported in upper New York State.

The lesser creatures are also numerous though less obvious. The chorus of the spring peeper frogs is notable, as are the basser compositions of the bull, green, and leopard frogs. Snakes are fairly abundant, and a foreigner may well see black, hog-nosed, and garter snakes any day, while copperheads and timber rattlers are extremely numerous in some parts. I know of one place in northern Pennsylvania where they congregate for hibernation in enormous numbers. Tortoises, both box and wood, and snappers are very numerous, and the newt and salamander population is enormous, though mostly known only to specialists.

There are insects all over the world, but in Appalachia there are some that come as a great surprise and seem to be especially outstanding. Most notable are perhaps the vast, pastel-green Luna Moths that sometimes just appear out of the night and freeze to the side of the house under a light. Then there are the huge Cecropia Moths, the large praying mantises that sometimes invade the skyscrapers in cities above the four-hundred-foot level, and those terrifying creatures the giant dobson flies, the males with their inch-long pincers snapping menacingly in front and their flat bodies and dusty-looking wings raised behind. People see these; but there are many other smaller fry that have to be looked for but which are altogether fabulous. I have in mind certain carpenter and wood-boring bees that drill perfectly circular holes into fence posts with a noise like a radio

Above: The Scarlet Tanager, one of the most colorful birds of the East, and, right, the Blue Jay, also beautiful but a robber of the nests of other songbirds, and generally rather a pest.

Below: Taken in the Adirondacks, this shows mosses and lichens, including Polytrichum, Cladonia pyxidata *and* C. constella, *of the forest floor at higher altitudes.*

Above: Fall among the southern Appalachians. The Great Smokies of North Carolina in which stands Mount Mitchell. 6685 feet.

Right: Coltsfoot, a common flower of the area, and, far right, Painted Trillium, two of the endless variety of gentle flowers that bloom in this province from early spring to late fall.

One of many fungi in the woods of Appalachia, Urnula craterius *is sooty black and leathery in texture. It appears in spring in secluded places.*

with a defunct tube and some of which then proceed to perform miracles therein. This is not to suggest that such creatures do not exist elsewhere—they live in almost every country in the world—but in Appalachia with its furious spring, fairly long summer, and prolonged fall, one seems to notice their activity more intimately. If you trouble to open up their works you may find, in certain cases, the most marvelous series of thimble-shaped structures, one above the other, made from perfect oblongs or circles cut from rose leaves, each containing an egg and a supply of food for the hatching larva. However, in this land you need not resort to the labor of sawing up fence posts to disclose miracles of insect life. All you have to do is sit on the front porch and rock, while the wasps labor back and forth from some mud patch with loads of clay with which they will build wondrous upside-down skyscrapers on your ceilings and walls, in which they will stash away a larder of spiders, in a state of suspended animation, for their young.

FOOTPRINTS ON THE SNOW

But these are all wild things of the warmer months. What of the colder months? During this season of the year, Appalachia for the most part looks as if it had been seared by a passing comet

and would never grow another green thing. Only in the north and at higher elevations where the conifers predominate does the land seem to maintain any virility, and this is a somber dark green indeed. Strangely, conditions appear to be even more depressing the farther south one goes along the narrow ridge of true Appalachia. South of the thirty-sixth parallel of latitude, which is in northern North Carolina, the foothill forests of the coastal area or of the northeast are a little greener, but those of the western flank leading down to the Ohio Plateau are even more lifeless in appearance. Apart from the pine forests, what appears to be a luxuriant land in summer and early fall becomes in winter a thin and rather scrawny brown stand of paltry trees and shrubs. Looking through these stunted woods one wonders where on earth the deer can find enough cover to get out of the wind, let alone out of sight of hunters and their other foes.

Of course there are endless hidden places of the utmost charm to be wandered through during this northern winter, but, despite all the claims made about this land at that season, it is really for the most part a dreary-looking place. Nevertheless it is a fine time for geologists and rock-hunters because the bold features of topography are then laid bare and not a little of the ground itself is more than just accessible—it is positively naked.

But then, after the first snows, which start early on the uplands in the north and last long into the spring, all manner of new things come to the surface, as it were. Strange birds congregate where any food is available, and all manner of foot tracks appear on the snow. The hosts of spring, summer, and fall have gone, and the vegetative cover has gone, but now one sees places where creatures like otters, moles, and mice go about their business, clearly typewritten on the glistening surface. The snow on the surfaces of ponds is crisscrossed by rabbit tracks and the plunged hoofs of deer. From somewhere come all manner of living things that are not otherwise seen. Every so many years huge pure white owls appear, wandering south from their tundra fastnesses due to a sudden shortage of lemmings, their natural food. They sit on fence posts and glare menacingly with vast yellow eyes.

But there is one part of Appalachia that never folds in upon itself with the coming of the cold. This is the short coastal strip from the St. John to the Hudson rivers. Winter life is much more active from the latter south to Georgia, but that is another province which we will visit later. (The outstanding part of what is otherwise the coast of Appalachia—namely, Long Island, Martha's Vineyard, Cape Cod, and fabulous Nantucket—is really a northern extension of that province, which we call the Northeast Coastal Fringe.) That part of Appalachia which borders the sea is heavily indented, low in the south with reed-filled marshes between gentle rocky headlands, and almost fjordlike in the north with steep cliffs, sandy or pebbly coves between, and not a few craglike islands offshore. It is the abode of typically northern coastal oceanic life, and was once that of a now extinct giant breed of beachcombing mink and of galaxies of wading and diving birds. Endless schools of right whales, porpoises, and some dolphins used also to migrate up and down this coast.

Today, we have regretfully to tell the outsider that he will be hard put to it even to get to the seashore from the land and may be either arrested or shouted at for daring to put a toe into salt water. Almost the whole coast is "enclosed," barricaded, or contaminated in one way or another. Instead of whales you see an endless parade of small craft, and in place of the delicate little wading birds and the diving ducks you may more likely see human youngsters, and instead of the great beach mink there are pet dogs and stray cats. This is a sad picture, but let us face the fact; it is an ecological fact and is, we can only presume, a natural phase in the history of this land. And yet, despite this singularly uninteresting present-day fauna, one may still find all manner of delights if one can get onto the shore. Thus I have a remarkable friend who, with his growing son, spends a great deal of time beachcombing, even today, and who brings back from every one of his overnight expeditions bags full of natural treasures, as well as coins of colonial vintage and other human artifacts, and endless rolls of film showing wild animals that the average New Englander has never seen and few New Yorkers have ever heard of.

PASSING HORDES

At this point we may introduce a particular marvel of nature that will occupy much more of our attention in a later chapter. This is the mystery of migration, a phenomenon in which the wading birds of Appalachian shores and estuaries play a key role. Migration is an annual process, not to be confused with either immigration or emigration, both of which occur in the

An oyster fungus (Pleurotus ostreatus) *growing on an aspen trunk. Many fungi, such as this, are edible.*

world of animals as well as among men. However, migration does not mean just a going to one place at one time of the year and a coming back to the first location at another time. It is enormously more complicated, as we shall see when we come to meander along the coastal inlets of the southern part of the east coast. Nevertheless we have one of the major "flyways" of the migrating birds running down the east side of Appalachia, where countless hosts from great eagles to tiny warblers struggle back and forth twice a year between the far north and the tropics, navigating—as is now known in the case of some warblers at least—by the stars. But also there is an all-year-round passing of other millions along the coast. Here all kinds of birds—and fish, for that matter—move constantly north or south, at all times of the year, often in contrary streams, while others come to rest here and some go all the way south to Argentina. These multitudes we shall meet presently, but the outsider must not forget that, if he can get to the coast of Appalachia today, he can spend the rest of the year just sitting and watching a stream of life passing by as it has done throughout the millennia since the mile-high barrier of ice departed this section of the earth's crust.

Sand Dunes and Sea Gulls

The Northeast Coastal Fringe

8

This is a country where the gulls laugh as well as mew and where the waves swill instead of bumping upon the shore or crashing against the rocks. It is a coastal land bathed by cool water pouring down its shores from the north. This cool stream is pressed against the coast by a much more powerful warm ocean current that flows in the contrary direction only a little way offshore. Once it was a country of lonely strands, forests of miniature pines sighing in the wind, and endless reed-filled creeks. Today, much of its strand is littered with debris. We have come now to the southern edge of the great northern forests, and we step down onto the first of a series of provinces that constitute the Parklands. These describe a great S, lying on its side, first down the east coast, thence round into and up the Mississippi valley, then south and west around the Ozarks and on again north of the great Prairies to the Canadian Rockies. There they "duck under" the mountains to appear once more on the Pacific coast, where they extend south to southern California. The Parklands are a transition zone in which the trees open out, and grass, herbage, and shrubs appear between them, slowly gaining the upper hand until the trees have totally gone and pure prairie pertains.

This Northeastern Coastal Fringe Province is at the same time the most northern tip of an extensive biotic zone called the Atlantic Fringe. This, with pine trees predominating, extends from the island of Nantucket down the coast to Florida, thence around the Gulf of Mexico to Tampico; and it actually crops up again on the peninsula of Yucatan and around the Bight of Honduras, though there it is the Orchardbush of the subtropics.

Reviewed as a whole and with regard to its endless sandy soils, sand dunes, mud flats, shallow swamps, and stunted vegetation, it forms a unique province. Nevertheless, it is almost impossible to differentiate it from the two hundred miles of coast that stretches south of its lower limit (which runs from the source of the Tar River to the point of Cape Hatteras) and reaches to the phosphate plains immediately south of Cape Romain. Yet there is a noticeable difference between this little triangle and the rest of the province, as anybody who specializes in the study of reptiles, frogs, salamanders, snails, ferns, and a few other animal and plant groups will affirm, and as any keen bird-watcher could demonstrate in any one month of the spring or fall. There is a distinct "break" or change-over about the Tar River which runs from east to west and extends westward to the piedmont of the Appalachians, about fifty miles inland.

This point is on the so-called fall (or fall-off) line which backs the coastal lowlands at varying distances from the coast all the way from New England to the delta of the Mississippi. This marks the first cataract or drop of the rivers that run off the continental plateau and that therefore call a halt to landward navigation. It may be noted in passing that, apart from a few resorts such as Atlantic City and a few ports like Norfolk, there are no large human establishments on the coastal plain of this province (New York lies in Appalachia) and very little settlement throughout its area, whereas many of the greatest cities, such as Philadelphia, Baltimore, Washington, and Richmond, are perched on the fall line.

The reason for this change-over is clarified by a glance at a map of the ocean currents that run along its beaches. From the north and down to Cape Hatteras a cool current hugs the beaches, while from the south a warm current, in the form of the concentrated upper layers of the Gulf Stream, swirls along against the coast. These meet head on off Pamlico Sound, and several most interesting things happen. First, two air masses, carried along over the currents but varying considerably in temperature, meet, so that there is a sort of perpetual aerial disturbance here that results in unexpected storms and thick fogs. Second, both currents are constantly shoving along countless billions of tons of beach materials, from considerable pebbles to fine sands. These also clash, and since there is a fairly wide, shallow, submarine coastal shelf at that point, they meet head on and pile up in a ridge running seaward to form Cape Hatteras.

CREEPING BEACHES

The study of beaches and beach formations warrants a volume in itself, and some of the things that have been discovered by marking thousands of pebbles (once done with paint but now by spraying with radioactive substances) are almost beyond belief. Items you would not believe even a heavy storm could shift have turned up miles away on the other side of fairly deep channels in a surprisingly short time during which no strong winds were recorded—and these sometimes in directions contrary to the movement of the pebbles.

The whole length of the Atlantic Fringe is noted for its sandspits, sometimes of enormous length, such as seventy-mile Padre "Island" off the southeastern coast of Texas. Those of the Cape Hatteras region are outstanding. Their apex—Cape Hatteras itself—actually lies over twenty miles off the coast proper, and that is a poor imitation of a coast, being hardly above high-tide point and subject to all manner of annual fluctuations. The cape is a V-shaped, sandy ridge backed out into the Atlantic. It is less than a mile wide at some points and about thirty miles long, with its longer tine going north. It is a menace to almost everybody, especially human coastal navigators, but it is a delight to some creatures, notably the lesser whales or dolphins.

The Gulf Stream wins the battle of the waters here, stopping, turning, partly absorbing, and otherwise pushing the cold stream from the north down below. But, instead of battling westward into the curve of the coast, it then barges merrily off almost due north and turns east outside the cool stream swirling round Nantucket. Thus two completely different kinds of water, one

The Northeast Coastal Fringe is marked by shore-line sand dunes, many of them bound with coarse grasses. These dunes are unstable, their material moving inland.

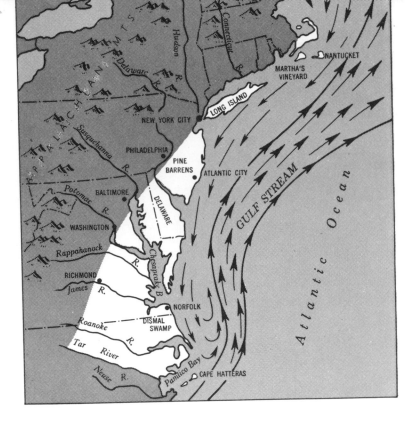

The Northeast Coastal Fringe Province extends south from Montauk Point on Long Island to the Tar River valley and Cape Hatteras at the eastern point of Pamlico Sound and has northern outliers in Cape Cod and its associated islands. It is 600 miles long from northeast to southwest as the crow flies, 850 miles in length along its landward or western curve, and about 100 miles wide at its southern extremity. Its coast line is enormously indented, measuring on ordinary land maps at least 5000 miles and on ocean coastal charts over 14,000 (estimated). Its high-tide level edge varies all the time, as sandspits shift and storms move mud banks. Its total area is about 45,000 square miles, but almost a third of this is covered by waters either fresh, brackish, or salt. It is North America's most indented stretch of coast, surpassing in this respect even the coasts of British Columbia and the Alaskan Panhandle.

This province is almost wholly enclosed by the province here called Appalachia. On its southern border it meets the Great Southern Pine Belt and this, in fact, at only one point about midway between the headwaters of the Tar River and the city of Raleigh, North Carolina. A subsidiary, triangular slip of coastal territory, covered with pine barrens, muddy estuaries, and sand dunes, extends south from the Tar River to about Cape Romain. This is not a part of the Northeast Coastal Fringe from an over-all ecological point of view, but it is a physical extension of it. The province as a whole is really an extension to the far northeast of the Parklands Belt. Thus its tree growth is in the form of an isolated facies, and only shrubs make a closed canopy. Its height-growth can be increased by added rainfall but its over-all facies cannot be changed to a closed canopy.

The province may be divided into seven major parts, namely: (1) Cape Cod, with Nantucket and Martha's Vineyard islands; (2) Long Island; (3) the southeast New Jersey pine barrens; (4) the "shore" section of Delaware and Maryland between the mouths of the Delaware, the Susquehanna, and the Potomac; (5) the three peninsulas between the Potomac and James rivers; (6) the Dismal Swamp area between the estuaries of the James and the Roanoke rivers; and lastly, (7) the headland between the Roanoke and Tar rivers that runs out to Pamlico Sound and Cape Hatteras.

This province is bounded on the east by the open ocean but on the west and north by the "fall line." This line is the escarpment marking the real border of the continent; it is the point at which rivers running from the Appalachian uplands finally tip off the edge of the continental piedmont and old coastal plain, onto the newer beach deposits laid down since the last ice advance. These deposits were first raised from and are now again being slowly lowered into the sea on the continental shelf.

The province has a fairly high annual rainfall (fifty-three inches) and a modest temperature gradient—much more so than nearby Appalachia—so that snow hardly ever falls even on Nantucket, and if it does it quickly melts. Although the soils of the strip bordering the fall line may freeze in winter, those of the coastal area never do.

---

from the Davis Strait and the Arctic and the other from the Gulf of Mexico and the tropics, each with its own fish and fish food, meet here. All kinds of sea animals also gather off this cape in a frenzy of gustatory delight, salt-saturated and vitamin-starved southerners gorging on oil-filled morsels from the cold north, and vice versa. There come also to this feast the pelagic or open-ocean rovers to feed on both. And to this roiling mass of assorted life come the dolphins by the tens of thousands, rushing and leaping through the races and darting almost onto the beach in pursuit of prey.

The commonest is the Bottle-nosed Dolphin (Tursiops), erroneously called "porpoise" in the South and especially in the great sea aquariums of Florida. Also coming there are the real or Common Dolphin (Delphinus delphis), a denizen of the open blue water on this side of the Atlantic, and the Spotted Dolphin (Prodelphinus), the champion jumper, while the superdolphin known as the Blackfish (Globiocephalus) may be found a little offshore but sometimes comes rushing onto the beaches in droves. (Strangely, when they do so, even if they are hauled back into deep water, they invariably turn right around and bumble ashore again.) The true porpoises (Phocaenidae) are not found here or ever south of this point. They are quite different, cold-water animals with blunt noses and strange trident teeth. The fish called the Cory or Dolphin Fish—sometimes even simply "dolphin"—is a deep-sea, warm-water creature but does sometimes get mixed up in the Cape Hatteras merry-go-round.

The low coast to the south of this cape reflects the incidence of warm as opposed to cold water, even to the extent that massive phosphate beds have formed thereon, a material that is not precipitated by cold waters. Naturally the beach material moves slowly northward from the south and southward from the north, but in both cases it tends to build both wide beaches and offshore spits, though much more noticeably so to the north than to the south. The reason for this is that the spin of the earth causes the water in the northern oceanic basins to turn—

To landward of the sand dunes this province is edged by wide marshes. These form natural wildlife refuges and provide breeding grounds for many kinds of birds.

and rather rapidly—in a clockwise direction. The Gulf Stream jets out of the narrows between the south tip of Florida and Bimini Island at the rate of 2.75 miles per hour and 6 billion tons per second, day and night, year in and year out. Baby eels hatched in the depths west of Bermuda swim into this stream and get carried to Europe in three years. A lumber ship, itself made of wood, foundered off Long Island late in the last century, and was washed ashore on the Outer Hebrides off the west coast of Scotland two and a half years later, and some of its cargo finally lodged on the coasts of Portugal, Madeira, and the Azores.

Things go round and round, but only one way, in the North Atlantic, and a current moving beach material against this pre-scribed direction has a hard time and is apt to drop its load in ridges extending from the existing south-pointing capes; and so a spit soon forms. But if a cape happens to point north, the wind, the waves, and the major ocean drift may win; and the

siderable height on a perfectly flat beach where all the little sand grains should logically be blown away into the neigh-boring inland swamps. The slightest impediment, such as a shell, a pebble cast up by a high tide or a good blow, or a piece of beached seaweed may start a dune; and then, if a lull in the wind follows, some seed may sprout in the little piled-up mass and put out roots and a shoot. This anchors the ridge, and more sand piles against it on the windward side. As a result, the immature plant tries harder, and if rain or even salt spray accompanies the next blow, it grows faster, both binding the sand below and arresting more of it above. The little ridge begins to grow, steep on the windward side, tapering gently off on the leeward. If the plant wins this struggle—for in-stance, by finding enough nourishment in the form of a roll of rotting seaweed—other debris will accumulate around it and the ridge will extend and grow upward; the plant, often a grass,

The Horseshoe Crab, a notable inhabitant of this coast, is actually related to the scorpions. It comes to the beaches to mate and lay its eggs in early summer.

whole, like Sandy Hook at the northern tip of the Jersey coast, may grow to the north, creeping part by part over itself on the ocean side and always turning inland until its tip gets to the left of the inshore current, after which things proceed rapidly until one has a real "hook" or crook, like Cape Cod.

On the coast itself, there are endless sand dunes. Dunes are most contrary things that may build up while being blown down and disappear while being built up. You can get dunes of con-

will proliferate and arrest more sand; and so on. Sand dunes up to four hundred feet high are known, but before they die and become a part of the land they go through a strange life cycle and sometimes do many odd things. They can march along like waves, or they can stay put, retaining their form but never being made of exactly the same material. This is contrary to ocean waves in which the individual drops of water just go up and down but the crest moves along.

Sand dunes may give way under gravity, set off by minute changes in temperature, and start "singing." This is a most frightening noise, coming as it may do altogether unexpectedly in dead calms, by day or by night, and sounding like bells, gongs, agonized animal wails, distant gunfire, or an avalanchean roar. There are singing sands on the coast of New Jersey, and some that I encountered near Toms River made "boing-boing" noises like those unearthly electronic musical instruments that were tried out some years ago. As you walk quietly and gently over them in dead silence, they respond with eerie ululations.

SUNKEN LANDS AND SWAMPED RIVERS

The little natural country of which we now speak has a strange history. It is actually the bottom of a shallow sea that was once

Starfishes are very common all along the coastal shelf of this province. Most of them dwell on sandy bottoms, but some, like this sun star, frequent rocky places.

Right: This shore shelves gently out to sea and has a sandy bottom that forms the habitat of many bivalve mollusks and their natural enemies, the starfishes.

Overleaf: The sand dunes support a meager flora of succulent plants that can thrive in an excess of salt. Their roots finally form soil. Few animals live among the dunes, but the adjacent shores abound with sandpipers and sea gulls.

part of the continental shelf. However, although it is an emergent or raised bit of land, its major features today are caused by subsidence or "drowning." Its almost numberless creeks and inlets are old river systems engulfed by the encroaching sea, either as the ocean rises or as the land sinks, or both. As to just what has been going on along this coast recently, there is much debate, though it can be shown by annual measurements of tide levels that this part of the coast is definitely sinking. In fact, the whole eastern seaboard of North America, from Nova Scotia to southern Florida, currently has a tendency to sink.

On the modern coastal plain of this province there is as much deposit derived from the land as there is marine material. While the ocean currents are ever bringing sand, pebbles, broken shells, and a certain amount of silt and dissolved mineral matter slowly along the coast from both the north and the south, the rivers are spewing forth volumes of mud and organic matter. The latter tumbles over the fall line all the time, especially in flash floods, but it falls into almost still water and, even if it does move seaward, it soon encounters the tides. Still water does not carry solid matter: it drops it. The faster a river flows, the bigger the items it can move; the slower it moves, the faster it drops its load; and it does so progressively and qualitatively, the bigger bits first, the finest silt last.

The amount of material washed off the land into or at the sea is almost beyond comprehension. In the delta of the Mississippi, where the flow of fresh water is more powerful than the paltry tides of the Gulf, this material is tipped right *into* the sea, building the land at a rate of some two to four hundred yards seaward per year. Along the northeast coastal seaboard the rivers are not powerful enough, there is a much greater tide—some six to ten feet—and there are strong currents immediately offshore hauling even greater loads of debris. These factors combine to stop almost completely the flow of even the big rivers so that they jettison their loads. Their water, however, still has to go somewhere, and since it can neither flow back upstream nor "pond," it finally moves out into the sea. The riverine material along this coast is brought *to* the sea but dropped before it gets there. This fills up the estuaries.

Thus, all along this coast, we get a neat succession of belts, starting inland at the fall line with modest gorges; then entering muddy, meandering, flooded river mouths; next turning to flood plains on which silt is laid down; and finally coming to the innermost of the beach deposits. These last are of two kinds: old beaches with pebbles and heavier material that have been left inland by the piling up of more stuff to seaward by the currents, and wind-blown sand that has jumped over this and got stuck on the outermost flood plains.

Since flood plains are particularly fertile, all manner of vegetation tends to spring up thereon, starting with aquatic plants in still creeks, followed by sedges and grasses, then by bushes that can grow in saturated soil, and finally by a woody growth of limited stature. All this vegetation seizes blown sand and holds it, though the plants are ultimately smothered by it. This is the result to be seen in many places but not on this coast because the prevailing winds here do not blow off the sea. This is a factor in favor of the rivers, the fresh water, and the sodden-soil plants, and it tends to make the beach deposits back up or ridge up, which in turn produces a series of shallow lagoons strung along the coast just inland of the sand dunes. The great

The Beach Plum is a typical dune plant that, like the mangrove of the tropics, can take root in such sterile places as salt-saturated sands.

Dismal Swamp just north of Pamlico Sound with its innumerable waterways is a good example.

Between the larger rivers, however, something else has happened. Here the sand has piled up or been raised up from the old, but not so very old, sea bottom. Some of it is still very saline, the rest wind-blown and sterile. It forms low, rolling ridges and depressed domes or superdunes. Only a limited flora will grow on it—stunted pines, some hollies, dwarf sumac, sassafras bushes, a little white poplar and cottonwood, some dwarfed black cherry, and, near the coast, beach plum and catalpa. Grasses do not do well, are coarse, and tend to be clumpy; an almost tundra-like growth of bayberries, groundsel bushes, briars, and fox grape takes over in drier areas; while blueberries, cranberries, and the like mass in the swamps. The only trees that can really take hold are stunted pines, notably *Pinus rigida,* and these grow in comparative isolation, become twisted and gnarled, and lend a rather dreary and somewhat faraway aspect to the land. But then this province is, after all, an extension of the Park Belt, and so closed-canopy forest would not be in order even if the soils and climate favored it. As a whole, these coastal pine barrens are not a markedly favored land, but they have great charms uniquely their own.

It is perhaps small wonder that the Anglo-Saxons and the Hollanders elected these shores to land on first. There was much here that they understood and a lot they recognized. The Celts and Scots, coming from more rugged and rocky coasts, chose the Appalachian and Laurentian seaboards, where the breakers crash themselves to green surf amid the cliffs or pound into sandy coves. The refugees on the *Mayflower,* hailing from exile in the Netherlands or the bland south coast of England, almost selected Cape Cod, the northern tip of this sea country, as the birthplace of the modern nation but by mere whim moved on to Plymouth Rock on the coast of Appalachia just beyond the northern end of this province. Sir Walter Raleigh's colony and the other colonies attempted on the southern plains failed; the Spaniards, on the other hand, also failed on the coastal lowlands and on the Park-lands but fared well among the arid mesas and wind-blown, dusty, near-deserts of the extreme Southwest, which were so like their equally grim homeland. It was the Hollanders and the fenland English who understood the endless sandspits, mud flats, flood plains, marshes, and barrens of this coast which so much resembled their homelands. Ecology applies to man as well as to other animals and plants, and phytogeographical tradition is far stronger than any mere cultural or ethnic whim. People always prefer to stay within the vegetational belt of their ancestors.

OUR LIVING FOSSIL

There is a curious animal indigenous to this coast but otherwise found only on the extreme east coast of Asia. This is the so-called Horseshoe Crab. It is a most ancient animal, not a crab at all (although, like the crabs, it is a member of that vast group called the Arthropoda, the "jointed-legged ones") but a member of the scorpion group. This group includes the insects; the spider types or arachnids; the crustaceans, such as lobsters, crabs, and shrimps; the millipedes and centipedes; and other hard-shelled but jointed creatures. In the eons of geological time the arthropods have evolved in almost countless ways, until today they greatly outnumber all other forms of animal life put together. But in this vast proliferation, the Horseshoe Crab has remained almost unchanged since the earliest times.

At the end of May and in the early part of June, these strange

Among the marshes are many wading birds. One of those not often seen but often heard is the Least Bittern, which raises its gawky youngsters in the reed beds.

tank-shaped animals come mincing out of the depths on their array of two-fingered feet, to the shoal beaches of this coast. There the little males meet the much larger females, to whom they attach themselves for an extended period in the shallowest water possible. The eggs, which are laid in huge masses, are tiny, spherical, black things, and are deposited in clusters just at low-tide level among gravel or on mud flats. From these hatch minute ovate creatures that do not look at all like their parents: in fact, they look very much like those most ancient of all arthropods called the trilobites, and they behave accordingly, going to the bottom and clinging to things, all facing into the prevailing tidal stream or current. These tiny larvae are tailless and go through several stages of different shapes before developing into the adult form. The countless tons of eggs laid by these animals every spring along the shores of this province are a great attraction to birds, which are plentiful enough in any case. The birds congregate in such vast numbers to feed upon the eggs that one wonders how the Horseshoe Crab has combatted extinction for so long.

Many land, shore, and sea birds are always to be seen on this coast. The little Fish Crow is very prevalent, squawking and clearing up messes on beaches, in marshes, and even on the dry sandy barrens where there are hosts of small mammals and a plethora of amphibians that, dead or alive, make fine food for these birds. Frogs abound because of the marshes, which are filled with Peepers and Bullfrogs, and there are also arboreal species such as the beautiful Anderson's Tree Frog on the New Jersey barrens. Red-winged Blackbirds are typical denizens of the reed marshes, perching audaciously on the wind-blown stems. Catbirds are very numerous too, and the somewhat over-balanced-looking Brown Thrasher makes the drier ridges its home. The woodpecker known as the Flicker is very common and is here almost entirely a ground-feeding creature. Robins are everywhere, even on the beaches. The Common Starling has now invaded this territory too, as it has almost all others, and it may be seen in the spring tramping about in great armies, stabbing at the larvae of the noxious Japanese Beetle—a trait that has gone far to compensate for its overfecundity and its annoying habit of roaring around municipal buildings all night in our cities. In the spring all manner of little warblers come through on their way north, and there can hardly be more vividly colored creatures than some of these. The best that modern color printing provides can in no way reproduce the brilliance of the contrasting blacks, whites, and above all the yellows of their plumage. But most ubiquitous are the sparrows that typify the landward side of this province. They come in all manner of varieties that chip, chirp, and pip, and also in some cases sing most exquisitely, but they are modest little folk, hopping about in and under things and pecking away at their tiny seed foods almost unseen.

Of the shore birds there are a multitude. Even to do them the most rudimentary justice would call for a large volume. There are the dull-coated Clapper Rails that lurk in small patches of reeds and drive one frantic by their elusive "clapping"; there are Great Blue Herons, and Night Herons, and Egrets that stand about in shallow waters and just look; there are Double-crested Cormorants that like to go fishing on the sea but spend a lot of time sitting in pairs on chosen bare branches over creeks; and there is even the Anhinga or Snakebird, a rather colorful creature with checkered black and white wings and a neck like that of a snake, armed with a long, thin bill that is capable of destroying an eye if held too close. But it is when we get among the ducks and their kind that we really come upon the avian principals of this region.

Most spectacular is perhaps the Greater Snow Goose, a glorious creature that passes over the heads of sleeping New Yorkers twice yearly, to the number of some 100,000, but absolutely unbeknownst to them. It is a great white bird with black wing tips that was once almost exterminated. It breeds on marshy lagoons, in June, in western Greenland, Baffin and Ellesmere Lands, and on Bylot Island, and winters for the most part on Pea Island (now a national wildlife refuge on Cape Hatteras), but some of them settle down for the winter in the salt marshes of Virginia, Maryland, and New Jersey. These birds have an assembly point at St. Joachim on the St. Lawrence River, where they gather each year in the fall until wintry winds send them off to the south. They are delightful creatures in many respects. They mate for life and are devoted congeners. If the mother dies while eggs are setting or goslings are still in the nest, the father takes over and raises them with infinite patience and care. There is a delightful anecdote by Langdon Gibson, ornithologist on the 1891 Peary Greenland Expedition; he relates that after he had accidentally killed a nesting female, he was, on passing through the same valley some time later, "happy to see the male proudly marching at the head of his family of six at least ten miles from the nest." The Greater Snow Goose must not be confused with the Lesser, which nests in the northwestern part of the continent and in northern Asia and which uses the Pacific and Mississippi flyways to migrate. There come here also countless Brant Geese and the ubiquitous Canada Geese, and occasionally a stray Blue Goose. The ducks are too numerous to recount in detail, apart from the common but magnificently proud Mallards with their discrete lady-folk. There is a vast literature on the ducks, most of it abundantly interesting as well as informative.

But it is surely the true sea birds that, above all, lend the distinctive flavor to this province. It may sound ridiculous to inlanders and to the natives of other coasts, but to a northerner, born amidst the wailing winds and drifting mists of the colder North Atlantic, the mewings, anguished cries, and defiant shouts of the larger gulls is not only music but somehow a symbol of all life and of its contentious struggle. Along the sandy wastes of Nantucket Island and Cape Cod, all along southern Long Island even to the human conglomeration of Brooklyn, and again from Sandy Hook to Cape Hatteras, the Herring Gull and the Black-backed Gull howl and yell and mew and scream, while the smaller gulls laugh a bit, and the terns chink away at the passing wind, ever flapping up and down like jointed kites but very seldom going anywhere in those winds, and always looking, looking downward in the ceaseless search for their agile food. The sounds of all of these waft in to you on land by night and day, rain or shine, and even out of the dense blankets of noisily silent mists that so often enshroud this coast. They proclaim everlastingly that the raucous struggle for life goes on and that tomorrow the same gulls will be still sailing, floating, swooping, fighting, gliding, and living.

There is a great difference between the various major parts of this province, as we have already said. This is due to several factors. The first is that the great icecap on its last "advance" south just reached the line that divides this province from Appalachia. This mile-high bulldozer brought with it inestimable tons of boulders including gravel, chewed-up rock, sand, silt, and dust and huge rocks called *erratics*. There is one of these behind a large department store in Manhasset, Long Island, that was thus brought all the way from Canada by the ice and is estimated to weigh over a hundred tons. This it spewed forth from its margin in the form of moraines and boulder drifts. The whole north coast of Long Island is formed by a ridge of such material. Much of Nantucket, some of Cape Cod, and parts of Martha's Vineyard are also so littered. This gives these areas a solidity not found in the area from Sandy Hook to Cape Hatteras. In the latter, the land is composed of low, slightly rolling sand hills, varying from glistening white to a rich red (notably east of Washington). These sand hills are clad with scattered gnarled pines and hollies, and there are intervening estuaries with endlessly proliferating tributaries and side creeks filled with mud and reeds. Along the whole coast the interminable sand dunes with their offshore sandspits and shingle beds continue.

The sands form most glorious phenomena on Nantucket Island and on Long Island from Montauk to the Rockaways, and all down the rest of the coast to Hatteras, while they extend south beyond that to Cape Romain and resume again in a slightly different form in Georgia. Sometimes they form a steep, tall cliff, as along outer Nantucket; sometimes they stretch for miles inland as flat, wind-blown deserts. Usually they have, backing them up to landward, great marshy lagoons filled with reeds. Only in a few places do they march directly and quickly into grass-covered ridges stippled with pines.

Within the compass of this province as a whole there is too much to be seen in an average lifetime. It is enormously varied, and, where modern man has not blighted it, it has an ineffable charm. But always, whether the summer sun shines bright, a frosty winter sun sparkles over it, or it is shrouded in gray scud, half-hidden in rolling mists, or lashed by a cyclonic wind, it has a certain air of desolation about it. There are flower-carpeted sandy acres and dense tall blueberry scrubs on Nantucket, piny dunes with shoreward-leaning clumps of grass on Cape Cod, and steep grassy downs facing the ocean on Martha's Vineyard. The grim pine barrens of farther south and the muddy estuaries and sand-blown coastal strips are the same. They have neither the roaring boisterousness of the more northern rocky coasts with their Valkyrian strength, nor the sun-drenched pallidity of their more southern counterparts. The Northeast Coastal Fringe Province lies athwart and between the North and the South, and it is unique.

The Great Southern Pine Belt

The Coastal Lowlands from Cape Hatteras to the Mississippi and the Western Timberlands

9

We now enter a land that contains, among other things, what the average North American calls the Deep South, or at least a fair share of it. But on the whole it has very few of what are popularly considered the essential attributes of that area. The real land of magnolias and belles, tobacco and cotton and stately tradition, is the eastern Piedmont of Appalachia, since the best land, which was first settled, lies there on the old continental plain above that slight escarpment known as the fall line. All the great centers of culture and now of industry lie along that line—Raleigh, North Carolina; Columbia, South Carolina; Atlanta, Macon, and Columbus, Georgia; Birmingham and Montgomery, Alabama; and so on. With the exception of Tallahassee, there are no big towns within this vast area, all that there are being coastal ports—Wilmington and Charleston in South Carolina; Savannah and Brunswick in Georgia; Jacksonville and the

Above: The Carpenter Frog (Rana virgatipes), *common in the bogs of this province, makes a noise just like two carpenters driving nails a little off beat. Left: The Suwannee River, part of the border between the great Southern Pine Belt and peninsular Florida, is banked by lush forests.*

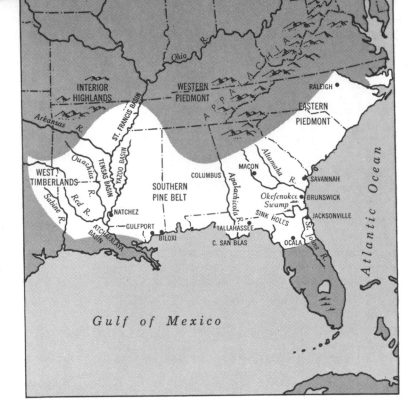

When the southern limits of the Northeast Coastal Fringe, of Appalachia, and of the Heartland or Great Lakes provinces have been defined, we are left with a sickle-shaped territory lying between these boundaries and the Atlantic on the east and the Gulf on the south. From this territory two peninsulas extend to the south—Florida to the east and the delta of the Mississippi to the west—which are treated separately later on.

To put this province in perspective, let us repeat that between the Prairie Belt and the Temperate Closed-Canopy Woodland or Forest Belt there lies the intermediate belt known as

the Parklands. Such country is primarily clothed in grass and trees, but the trees do not form a closed canopy. This province is predominantly of this nature throughout, and lies between the woodlands on the north and the prairies to the south. However, there is in this huge province a considerable variety of subsidiary types of vegetation. These are of two principal kinds: First, there are the areas where the trees, in this case almost exclusively pines, are so massed—often due to the prevention of fire by man—that their interwoven heads do form a closed canopy and exclude the grass. Second, there is the extensive and generally near-coastal swamplands wherein numerous broad-leafed deciduous trees are intermingled with the conifers. These may also form closed canopies and sometimes even of two layers, constituting veritable "jungles" in the wider sense of that term.

The province must also be divided into three major and three minor subprovinces. The major ones are (1) the Southeastern Coastal Plain, from the Tar to the Apalachicola Rivers and south to the St. Marys–Suwannee River barrier with its associated swamps; (2) the East Delta region from the Apalachicola to the Mississippi; and (3) the West Delta region or West Timberlands (confusingly called the East Timberlands in Texas). The minor subprovinces are (a) the northern third of the peninsula of Florida south of the St. Marys–Suwannee swamp barrier to the "neck" of the peninsula, roughly a line between Withlacoochee Bay and Daytona, which we include in Chapter 14; (b) the Mississippi valley from the confluence of the Ohio south to about Natchez; and (c) the delta itself—but this is so different that we give it separate treatment.

This province measures about 1200 miles around its curve and is about 200 miles wide on an average, excluding the area described above in (b).

---

resorts of North Florida; Mobile in Alabama; and the Biloxi–Gulfport complex in Mississippi.

To learn that the greater part of this area, and of this whole continent for that matter, is predominantly clothed in a blanket of pines and other coniferous trees comes as a considerable surprise to most of us. Because of intensive agriculture, the ornamental planting of exotic trees and shrubs, and the extensive clearing of land, we have the impression that this is a wide green continent blooming with hardwoods and lush grasses. In point of fact, other than some parts of Appalachia, a narrow strip spanning the central plains north of the prairies, and some patches in British Columbia and among the Pacific coastal ranges, all our woodlands are composed of coniferous trees. Apart from these, most of this continent is actually a very dreary, brown, and seared land for six to nine months of each year. It is flat and mostly uninteresting.

The province under discussion is certainly flat, and quite a large part of it is frankly uninteresting, being nothing but mile after mile of pine trees of very modest proportions with at most a little grass and a few scraggly bushes beneath. But it is never leafless, brown, or apparently dead, as is most of the rest of the continent either all year or for a substantial part of it. Pines are conifers, and most conifers are evergreens; so also are the oaks and several other non-coniferous plants of this southern region. It is therefore always green, though of a rather somber tone.

This sprawling province actually is a rather compact unit apart from the Bottomlands of the Mississippi valley, and these

form a sort of filigree pattern following closely the river, streams, and other waterways, while typical parklands continue right across them on the higher ground between. However, the latitudinal and thus the seasonal temperature range within this province is considerable, more especially between the northern end in the vicinity of Cairo, Illinois, and the southern end in Florida. There are sometimes frosts all over, but those in Illinois are more frequent, profound, and lasting than the occasional light and overnight freezes of southern Florida. From east to west this land is astonishingly homogeneous; yet it has marked subdivisions, as defined in the legend accompanying the map.

We now move through this province from northeast to southwest, then due west, then up the Mississippi valley, then southwest again to the West Timberlands, and finally northeast once more around the Interior Highlands at the edge of the Prairies.

CANEBRAKE TRAPEZE

South of the Tar River, there stretches along the coast of North Carolina a triangular area some two hundred miles long by about fifty wide that is very closely related to the Northeast Coastal Fringe. This is marshland and is really a continuation of similar country that lies between Albemarle Sound and the Tar River estuary. Its coast between Cape Lookout and Cape Fear is low and lined with dunes, and there is an almost continuous island sandspit off and parallel to the beach. Back from the dunes is some magnificent country and a paradise for ornithologists, with extensive canebrakes covering acres of standing water. These at first sight appear almost sterile but on closer inspection prove to support a wonderful life all their own.

All you see at first are the ubiquitous red-winged blackbirds dancing about at the tops of the waving cane stems, often offsetting the gusts of wind and the waving of the stems by opening their wings. A friend of mine, an engineer, who is not partial to bird-watching, occupied his leisure some years ago by trying to work out a formula for this performance by the birds. He rapidly got into higher mathematics and came up with an idea that seemed to excite him. He got the notion from these blackbirds that there was still a lot of important information about flying machines of all kinds to be derived from the study of flexible models, attached to freely movable and flexible bases or stems, in infinitely unpredictable and varying winds. This proposition did not sound particularly inspiring, but one unexpected fact did emerge from what he said. This was that the blackbirds managed to preserve their equilibrium mechanically and apparently solely by reflex actions. Therefore, he argued, a mechanical device could do the same if it had a built-in "nervous system" of a special kind designed along the reflex-motor circuits of these birds. This was many years ago, and the thought germ seeded and bore fruit; for my friend ended by designing a system that, by a complex arrangement of electronically controlled feedbacks, kept a model on an erratically agitated pedestal quite stable even when subjected to equally erratic wind pressures from any angle. It is a comparable system that guides self-guided missiles.

Among the stems of the canes are to be found a whole galaxy of interesting little creatures. Birds of the rail family, designed for going through things, abound; and bitterns that have the habit of standing stock still with their long, thin beaks pointed skyward, thereby giving as perfect an imitation of a cane as any non-botanical body could. There is a small mouse—a variety of Harvest Mouse, *Reithrodontomys,* a name almost exactly the length in typescript of the animal's head and body—that builds a cozy, spherical, and tiny nest around three or four reed stems above the water, in which it lives all year round. These nests may be miles inside the hearts of perpetually flooded reed beds or canebrakes, and their minute inhabitants spend their entire lives—and have spent quite a part of their more recent evolution—in a sort of endless acrobatic, semiaerial gymnastic, for they loathe water and are bad swimmers. They feed on the flowers, seeds, and shoots of the reeds, grasses, and canes; but they also eat many of the multitudinous snails that live in or just above the water and lay their eggs on the stems, as well as many insects—and, it is alleged, the eggs and young of small birds, and even each other on occasion.

LO! THE GRASS

The main body of this southeastern coastal plain appears to be absolutely flat and level, but it is really composed of a series of broad terraces mounting by very slight elevations toward the fall line. It is clothed in a more or less continuous blanket of pines with meandering, open fields of short grass. There are two schools of thought regarding the original nature of this country. One is that grass is man-induced by the felling or burning of

The Southern pine forests stretch for hundreds of miles, sometimes as closed stands, sometimes as parklands with short grass below. There is almost no other vegetation.

timber and that therefore, by inference, this whole country was once a continuous forest. The other regards the grassfields as indigenous, and believes that they were maintained and the tree growth controlled by naturally induced fires. It is interesting to note that the lower reaches (i.e., coastward to east and south) are more typically parklands, with the trees isolated and an almost continuous carpet of grasses beneath, while as one approaches the fall line and the deciduous woodlands of the Appalachian piedmont, the trees become more closely packed and segregated and the grass forms wandering belts or lakelike pockets. This succession is typical of all parkland belts: isolated

The great Okefenokee Swamp in southern Georgia swarms with life dependent on vast quantities of fish; these in turn live mostly on insects and their larvae.

trees in grass on the prairie side and copses of massed trees amid grassfields on the woodland side.

This somewhat monotonous scenery stretches all the way from the Tar to the Apalachicola—Chattahoochee rivers and back to the fall line. To the seaward side it gives way to dunes and marshes on both the Gulf and Atlantic coasts, but where it abuts onto the base of the Floridian peninsula it runs into a singular phenomenon. This is a dual interlocked river system, with bogs and swamps, that actually renders that peninsula an island, since one can travel by water from the Atlantic to the Gulf via the St. Marys River to the Okefenokee "Swamp," and from this down the Suwannee River to the Gulf.

THE WOBBLING BOG

Before we go any further into this, we must investigate the difference between a swamp and a bog. The Okefenokee is a

splendid "guinea pig" for such investigation as well as a marvelous place. It is now a reserve, combining a large federal preserve and an area administered by a remarkable private citizens' organization known as the Okefenokee Association, Inc., which leases its area from the state of Georgia and calls it Swamp Park. The total area of this vast bog, for such it is, is between 650 and 700 square miles.

It is a most exceptional bog in that it looks like and is to a large extent covered by a very fair forest. In this it may be classified with similar areas in equatorial regions rather than with typical bogs of the temperate, sub-Arctic, and Arctic regions. A bog (as opposed to a swamp) may be said at the risk of oversimplification to be an area that collects water, rather than one that is simply flooded by an overflow from elsewhere. Northern bogs are usually composed mostly of masses of moss with either tundra or muskeg-type plants that hold water and sometimes cause this to pond around its edges, notably on the upward grades. This water is held above the general water table in apparent defiance of gravity and hydrostatic principles by processes that we cannot describe in detail here; such bogs may, moreover, actually creep slowly uphill. Bogs of the tropical type have in common the fact that they also are, so to speak, domes of water. The Okefenokee is just this.

In order to understand this place you should visit it in winter when the cypresses are leafless. Only then is it possible to see that it is not really a very tall forest but rather a sort of open wood, growing for the most part in water (often *through* water, as explained below) but elsewhere in saturated soil. Besides the dominant cypresses, its timber consists of the rather scruffy-looking Loblolly or Black Pine and the clean-looking Short-leafed Pine, with a sprinkling of other larger trees. Beneath these grow catspaw briars with flaming red berries, red and white bay—the bark of the former was once used for tanning—and a delightful bush with little pink clusters of blooms called locally and cheerfully the hurray or fatta bush which, though smelling sweet and giving nectar, is strictly shunned by all bees. There is also the pretty red-leafed bush called the Virginia willow, and the climbing heath vine and a spiny smilax or bamboo vine that reaches fifty feet or more. This forms a fairly dense mass under the trees, but the area is divided up into flooded forest, open "prairies" that are either flooded or saturated, and islands of shrubby growth dotted about in the latter. In the depths of the main swampy area the trees reach a respectable height, and in summer the place has an eerie enchantment that is unique. Everywhere there is a patchwork carpet of scrub palmetto.

The name "Okefenokee" is said to be a Seminole word meaning "the Place of Trembling Earth." Though I am a bit suspicious of "native names," there is little doubt about the accuracy of the term since, though the earth here does not actually tremble, it does wobble or bounce up and down. And here we come to a really bizarre note.

Persons born and raised in this country who call themselves "swampers" and who have come to love and, comparatively recently, to protect their country, tell of sudden tremendous noises like prolonged gunfire that often can be heard in this great bog at night. Nobody has ever been present at the point of origin of one of these outbursts, and outsiders have failed to explain their cause, though several suggestions have been made.

The Southern "Cypress" is a deciduous conifer, Taxodium distichum, *but is not a cypress in the popular sense. It prefers swamps and its roots send pillars, called knees, upward out of the water.*

Both Liston Elkins, the savior of this priceless American heritage, and his present head guide, Will Cross, concur in the theory that they are produced by uprushings of enormous amounts of marsh gas formed deep in the bog. Mr. Cross told me that he has several times gone by a place in the early morning that he had seen the day before, and found there great new "holes" in the bog, like circular ponds, as much as a hundred yards across and filled with mangled bog debris. I once witnessed a similar event at the junction of three rivers in West Africa, and it shook the very ground like an earthquake and brought up a seething mass of rotting tree trunks, many alarmed crocodiles, and a family party of somewhat hysterical hippopotamuses.

You get "boils" in swamps, as we shall see in a minute, but these explosions are more typical of bogs. The reason may be that bogs, unlike swamps, are often—even usually—domes of water that rise not only above the general water table even in flat territory but also above the surrounding water-surface level. This may sound exaggerated, but consider a sponge. This you can saturate to a point where, if it is fine enough in structure and if its holes are small enough, it will hold standing water at its top even if placed on the board beside the sink. A bog is a vast natural sponge, and the Okefenokee does demonstrably (as proved by the use of sensitive surveying instruments) form a distinct dome. How the water gets into it when all the surrounding area is in drought and its water table low would be a complete mystery were it not for the phenomenon called "suction pressure" discovered by botanists studying the way water can rise or be pumped to the topmost leaves of a four-hundred-foot tree. The matter is too complex to go into here, but is a combination of air pressure, capillary attraction, and evaporation, and these are just what a good bog employs to maintain its water-surface level.

In doing this, the Okefenokee—and some bogs in the tropics—do something even more remarkable. In cross section there is found, far down, a layer of impermeable clay forming a shallow basin. In this is a layer of organically formed muck going up to the general level of the land. This usually has an extremely firm surface—strangely enough—but then, on top of it, there is a stratum of pure, limpid water. Finally, over that again and actually "rising into the air," is a layer of surface soil, usually composed of a tangled mass of roots and other vegetable matter. In and on this last grow the small trees, shrubs, bushes, vines, grasses, sedges, palmettos, and other plants. Only the bigger trees break through it and proliferate their main roots into the deep, firm muck below the water stratum, which is about eight feet deep. If you are not too heavy and have fairly large feet, you can step out of a boat onto this upper layer that is floating on the water below, and either walk carefully about on it or bounce up and down or rock and roll as if on the finest spring mattress; and all but the largest trees around you will in time pick up your rhythm and start swaying crazily. When one of the gunfire explosions takes place this same earth does indeed tremble, sometimes for minutes on end.

ALLIGATORS AND PUMAS

The Okefenokee has a rather strange and specialized fauna. The whole area is swarming with gars and other fishes such as the

Typical of the South and the Gulf coastlands is the Spanish Moss (Tillandsia) that festoons trees. It is a flowering plant (of the bromeliad family) but is covered with tiny scales.

127

Bowfin, and it is alive with alligators—the largest obtained by the head guide measured fourteen feet nine inches. The alligators eat a great amount of the lily roots and other vegetable matter, as well as gars and other fishes and a lot of fresh-water snails and mussels. On the hummocks, or "islands" as they are called, there are many rattlesnakes, and the waters are full of cottonmouths. Besides these, there are many banded water snakes, green water snakes, mud snakes, and innumerable smooth green tree and rat snakes. "Turtles"—i.e., water tortoises—are everywhere. Strangely, there are no mink here, but there is a special small breed of muskrat, some opossums, and raccoons, and there are now estimated to be between thirty-five and forty-five pumas residing here. There are also black bears, and these two carnivores are even becoming a little too numerous. Birds are ubiquitous, including egrets, several species of herons, and the Sandhill Crane, a delicate and a noble bird that calls for some of the attention now given so profusely to the poor Whooping Crane. Red-shouldered hawks are also prevalent. Among the mammals we must not forget the Otter, which abounds, the Gray Fox, and the Fox and Southern Gray Squirrels.

Despite the fact that the Okefenokee is a vast sponge and sucks up moisture from all around, it does develop an excess of water and thus has to have overflows or outflows. These are the St. Marys River and the Suwannee River, down the latter of which we will now travel to the best Southern Pine Belt example of a swamp. And a most remarkable one it is too!

DOWN UPON THE SUWANNEE

It is a great shame that the estuary of the Suwannee River has not been set aside as a national preserve; the move appears to be not even contemplated. It is unique and it is still almost perfect, but the bulldozers and shack-builders are already creeping into it from the north, and the resort promoters and station-wagon fishermen from its glorious coast, while the state, county, and federal governments are aiding and abetting its destruction by laying down good roads along its edges. There is one road all down the west side already: another on the opposite bank will doom this lovely natural enclave to extinction among a welter of expensive split-level hovels, gasoline stations for power boats, and the all-pervading beer cans. Here is a bit of America left almost as it was when Ponce de Leon came looking for the Fountain of Youth. And he could well have believed that he had found just that in any of the great "boils" that line the banks of the Suwannee.

Boils, also appropriately called springs, as found all across northern Florida, are a most remarkable phenomenon. They occur in quite a range of sizes from a diameter of only about ten feet to circular areas on lake bottoms up to a quarter of a mile across. The most impressive are the isolated ones of smaller size, up to about fifty feet in diameter, especially those hidden away alone in the forest. I have one in mind that I shall not name, since it is a natural curiosity that should be left in its own isolation with but one wire-fenced walkway to and from it, whereby its owners, the public, may view it.

This is about fifty feet in diameter and about ten feet deep, is almost exactly circular, and is completely arched over by cypresses festooned with Spanish Moss. Its waters are just as clear as the air above it, and its bottom is absolutely pristine, pure, white sand. Its surrounding bank is about a foot high at normal water level, and it is about three hundred yards from the Suwannee River, with which it is connected by a slightly winding, narrow channel, also sand-bottomed and crystal clear. If you submerge in this pool at its edge and slowly lower yourself until your eyes are just level with the top of the water, you will see to your amazement that the water in it forms a slight but distinct dome rising highest in its center. If you then start to swim toward that center, and even if you are a very strong swimmer, you will find—if the big river is normal or low—that it is almost impossible to attain, and that the moment you stop your efforts you are washed back to the bank at an ever increasing velocity. If you then just float you will find that, in a few minutes and very slowly, you will be propelled along clockwise until you come to the outgoing channel, into which you will be sucked.

This strange phenomenon is not unique to Florida, but it is very nearly so. It represents a water-discharge device equivalent to the gas discharges of the bogs but on a continuous system. There is always too much water in and on the great swamps, and as it cannot run off because of the natural levees thrown up by the creeks and greater waterways, and since it cannot go down because the ground is saturated already, it just lies there and presses downward. This forces the waters below to go away sidewise, or anywhere; but, as they have great difficulty in getting out of the swamp into the surrounding moisture-resistant soils and strata, and since they cannot get into the rivers because these are already full and actually stand above them, they burst out onto the surface. The water keeps coming, and it long ago washed away every scrap of vegetable detritus, fine silts, and sands, so that there remain only the coarser sands, the individual grains of which are just large enough not to be pushed away by the force of the upflow. Through these grains the underground water is filtered to absolute blue-white purity and then, having gained the upper hand, as it were, drains rapidly away "down-hill" to the nearest big river.

STRANGE BEASTS

The Suwannee River estuary and valley from its wide delta to some fifty miles inland is dotted with these boils. Some are filled with water lilies, alligators, and the monstrous Alligator Snapper, a water tortoise or turtle that may grow to a length of nearly four feet; others are pure and pristine; still others are murky and have no precise outlet, just respilling their endless waters onto the forest floor to be redistributed among the cypress knees.

The Suwannee River valley has another distinction. It marks the change-over point from peninsular Florida to the true continental land mass, and it partakes of both of these as well as of a coast-fringe aspect and of some oddities of its own. It forms a long wedge with the meandering river wiggling about its center on its way to the sea. Its main channel is lined by perhaps the most magnificent tree growths, outside of the great western conifers, in the continental United States. Cypress predominates all the way, but the two banks are curiously different at all points and for long stretches, and one type of broad-leafed tree after another comes to the fore, with various oaks predominating, giving the water front a continuously different aspect. Its beauty is quite beyond words, especially in spring.

Starting about thirty miles from the sea and continuing to it, side creeks lead off with increasing frequency for miles in every

One of the commonest animals in this province is the Opossum, a most competent creature that has persisted almost unchanged for some seventy million years.

129

direction. Up these the trees often meet overhead. They are the abode of innumerable birds, such as the White Ibis, the Wood Ibis, the fish hawks, and the Osprey, which need both water and trees. A dormitory of white ibis on one of these creeks is an unforgettable sight if the evening is clear and the cypress is in its first spring flush of delicate chartreuse green. The place is alive with all manner of mammals, from muskrat and otter to still a few puma, bear, and many deer. Although the razorback hog has got loose here, it does not seem to do much harm to the natural economy and even these feral pigs have gone nicely "back to bush." It is also possible that the little weasel-shaped cat called the Jaguarundi is also indigenous here. It is the home of the giant River Frog *(Rana heckscheri)*, a rather lovable great brute that, unlike its brother the Bullfrog, apparently cannot understand artificial lights and so just sits on the road until you pick it up.

Of some significance in the area are two aquatic mollusks: a river "mussel" that provides much of the food for younger alligators and a large water "snail" found in the swamps and boils that sticks neat packets of globular, white, hard, but brittle-shelled eggs to twigs and tree boles just about high-water mark. Now this is a very sore subject, since the ability of animals to prejudge, seemingly by months, the top level of floods for the coming year is and always has been held seriously in question, though it has been claimed for all sorts of animals from all over the world. Here, however, you can see where the highest water reaches by a very clear wash mark on all the tree boles; and, sure enough, the snail eggs are all just about three inches above that mark whereas there are none below—and this we know because when they lay their eggs these animals cement them firmly to their anchor with a pure white platform of calcium carbonate or "eggshell." There are never any such of the current year below the flood line, though all are laid before the flood season.

The featureless lowland plains of the east coast extend west all the way to the Mississippi, covered with interminable pine flat-

woods on the coast side and with low, rolling hills of reddish earth nearer the piedmont. But at the Apalachicola River, which runs south to Cape San Blas, something really impressive happens; quite what, nobody has so far been able to say, and none of the risings or sinkings of the land about these parts in any way explains the phenomenon. If you drive across this "break" and have been forewarned, you will notice quite a change in scenery from one side of this river to the other; but if you are not watching, nothing much will seem to occur. This is one of those strange barriers that nature erects, apparently haphazardly, which take considerable study, sometimes of very small details, even to recognize.

What happens here is that not a few animals and particularly aquatic ones—for instance, the population of one species of amphibians known as the Siren—suddenly stops on one bank of the river, while other related but quite different species start immediately on the opposite bank, only a few hundred yards away. One would think that, whereas terrestrial animals might sometimes not be able to overcome even a small water barrier, flying animals like bats and birds and insects should be able to do so, and that there would be no difference between the water-inhabiting creatures of the two sides of such a divide. Yet, time and again, all over the world, most especially in the tropics, a modest river will form a complete barrier to both flying and swimming creatures—though sometimes not to land-walking ones—whereas a fairly wide gulf or even a sea will not do so. This is not only odd but highly significant, since it demonstrates that our ideas of why things are as they are, and the criteria by which we prognosticate what they should be, are as yet by no means fully established. Nature's particular forte is the exact placement of her *oikoi,* or houses, for her children. If one kind of salamander is adapted to one kind of vegetational zone, it will thrive therein; but if it wanders out of it, it will be eliminated. This goes for species as well as lone individuals. For some reason still unclear to us, nature ordained that there should be a faunal break from north to south about the Apalachicola River; and there it is—a fine lesson in the principles of ecology.

Just to the west of the Apalachicola also there is the first of many great swamps, now constituted a national forest and bearing the name of that river. This is a very interesting place, since it first introduces us to a number of new phenomena. All the way from the northeast boundary of the province we have been seeing the famous, gray, waving, Spanish Moss, draped from trees of all kinds as well as from many human devices such as telephone lines and even laundry cords. It becomes quite excessive farther on in the delta and bayous, as we shall see, but it is not till we get here that its real significance becomes apparent. This place is low-lying and grown with a massive stand of cypress, some oaks, and various pines which seem quite happy growing in standing water.

TREES WITH KNEES

This is really a vast "river bottom," being sandwiched between mile after mile of pine-covered flatlands to west, north, and east. Its basis is a filigree of muddy and placid small waterways lined by modest stands of Swamp Cypress *(Taxodium distichum),* which is a rather nondescript vegetable thing when without its feathery, delicate leaves. It specializes in growing in water.

Normally this tree has a tall, straight trunk that may reach as high as 150 feet, a few rather straight side branches, and a bulbous base where it enters the water. It also has the curious

Another very common mammal of the Southern Pine Belt is the Raccoon, shown here carrying its young (above) and nursing (facing page). It has managed to adjust to modern man and has even invaded cities.

habit of sending upward from its roots woody protrusions that stick out of the earth and the water. These are customarily called "knees." They are extremely light in weight and almost pithy, and are covered with bark that can be peeled off them after boiling. They then make extremely fine living-room ornaments, either as lamps or just standing about after being oiled or slightly polished. This so-called "cypress"—actually another in the long list of misnomers, since it is in no way related to the true and original Cypress of the Mediterranean, or even to our true cypresses (Cupressus)—grows fine timber, and the best of its stands were logged out from all this area during the past two centuries. Nevertheless it is almost ubiquitous and is slowly coming back, so that some very fine specimens are to be met with in protected areas such as this.

There is a profusion of other trees that stand about in this swamp, some of them coming as quite a surprise—like certain pines such as the Scrub and the Slash, which would normally die promptly if one tried to grow them in water or saturated soil. Then the festooning of these same trees with Spanish Moss and even with small, spiky bromeliads—epiphytes looking like small pineapple plants—somehow seems quite irregular.

TEN BILLION GRAY BEARDS

Spanish Moss (Tillandsia) is undoubtedly the chief characteristic of this whole province, as well as of South Florida, including the bottoms and bayous, considerable parts of the Western Timberlands, and the extreme north of the Eastern Chaparral. The mere volume of it is quite inestimable, and a not inconsiderable industry is now founded on collecting, drying, and packaging it. It is used for stuffing such things as cushions and as packing material, and for this it is almost unsurpassed. But you do have to be rather careful about it when untreated, for it often harbors untold numbers of a certain kind of mite (a relative of the ticks), which not only abounds but has remarkably resistant qualities and amazing powers of reproduction. Untreated, it should never be used for bedding for animals.

Spanish Moss spreads and proliferates simply by being broken (which is not nearly so easy to do as you might suppose because it has a fine central strand of about the consistency of a horsehair) and then blown from its point of origin to the first snag it encounters. It can be blown considerable distances above the ground; on the ground it rolls about in neat spindles. Its central strand is an extremely tough black fiber, so strong that even a modest twist of these fibers can support the weight of a man. One experimenter, at the time of this writing, thinks he has found a way of extracting these long, thin fibers; if he has, he may find himself with a new industry on his hands, for they not only match but surpass nylon and many other chemical fibers in tensile strength. You can do all sorts of things with Spanish Moss. Fresh and mixed with any clay or claylike mud, it serves as an excellent binder for fashioning pottery objects which can then be fired directly. Dead and dried, it can be used as tinder

The Rice Rat (Oryzomy palustris) *is a long-tailed, rat-shaped member of the vole family common throughout the South. It sometimes swarms in enormous numbers.*

and blazes like high-octane gasoline. You can make lines from its threads, and you can make a horrible broth out of it that will prevent you from starving if you can swallow it. It is actually a flowering plant related to the pineapple.

FLATLANDS AND BOTTOMS

The pine flatlands, as they are called, continue west right to the Mississippi valley in the neighborhood of Natchez. Their southern border sometimes fringes the Gulf; otherwise it stands a little back from the coast, which here supports a rather luxuriant mixed forest of oaks, oleanders, and other broad-leafed trees, a variety of conifers, and many introduced palms and acacias, flowering shrubs and bushes. Off this coast are many long, sandy islands, some of which support masses of sea grapes and buttonwood trees of a stunted variety. At the mouth of the Pearl River one "drops" out of this forest and down onto the deltalands, while the pine parklands continue onward to the north side. From this point also they swing due north, bordering the Western Appalachian Piedmont. In that direction, they appear originally to have continued uninterrupted to the confluence of the Ohio River. This is a flat plain of modest elevation bounded now on the east by the continuing fall line, and ending on the west along the bluffs overlooking the Mississippi River and its tributary the Yazoo River.

The pines start again west of the Mississippi valley, south of the Interior Highlands, and reach to the Grand Prairie somewhat west of Dallas, Texas. Their southern limit in this area is the edge of the deltaic flood plain west to Port Arthur and thence northwestward. The parklands increasingly give way to open prairies both to the south and west, and in those directions junipers, live oaks, and even some mesquite gradually replace the pines. This area is commonly known as the Western Timberlands (but Texans call it the East Timberlands). These are a series of low uplands of what is rather delightfully called, in geotechnical parlance, *subdued relief*, comprising some 70,000 square miles of landlocked territory. This is today for the most part cleared of its original vegetative cover, but it still supports some pine stands and fairly extensive, meandering belts of scruffy live oaks and other hardwoods that follow the water-drainage channels. It is comprised of the drainage basins of the Red, Sabine, and Trinity rivers; the upper waters of the Brazos River; and the western drainage of the Ouachita River, which joins the Red to make a linked but subsidiary effluent of the Mississippi. To the northwest it has fairly extensive prairies of a blackish color, and the eastern strip is very appropriately called the Red Rolling Lands. The southeast is an almost pure stand of typical pine "flatwoods." The area has little faunal significance, being a transition zone between the Prairies, the outlying Ozark Plateau, the Bottomlands of the Mississippi valley, the southeastern Chaparral, and to some extent the muck of the delta.

There remain within the general compass of this province the great Bottomlands of the lower Mississippi valley, comprising the St. Francis, Yazoo, and Tensas basins lying between the eastern bluffs and the foothills of the Interior Highlands, and the narrow Atchafalaya Basin, which debouches onto the delta. This is a land of multiple rivers, creeks, and lakes, great and small, including almost countless numbers of bow-shaped ones; these are old twists in the rivers that were silted up at either end when the river cut a more direct channel. The waterways and lakes are surrounded by extensive swamps covered with thick, tangled growth ranging from fields of tall sedges to semiaquatic brush and dense forests with massed undergrowth, most of it flooded. Between the waterways, the higher ground seems to have been originally typical parkland, either dotted with isolated trees or bestrewn with copses interspersed with grassfields. This country merges with the foothills of the Interior Highlands to the west and with the Timberlands to the southwest. This subprovince has an exceedingly rich, varied, and abundant flora and fauna, which in the Bottomlands is of a specialized nature. This we will meet later when we explore the delta itself.

White Mists and Emerald Hills

The Central Pacific Coast Ranges and Parklands, the Sierra Nevada, and the Cascades

10

We have noted that the Parklands lie between the open grasslands or prairies on the one hand, and the closed-canopy forests of the temperate regions on the other. Further, we have noted that the Parklands thin out in eastern Texas, swing north around the Interior Highlands, and then veer northeast to cover the Illinoian drift plain. We have also stumbled upon the prairies away up in extreme northwestern Alberta near the Yukon border, and again in isolated, low-altitude patches in British Columbia. Since the Parklands must lie north of the prairies, they too must appear in these places; and they do. Moreover, if we should fly a plane north from Dallas, Texas, to the region of Springfield, Illinois, and then follow from there what is almost exactly a great-circle route to the northwest, we could remain all the time over parkland until we reached a point about 57 degrees north and 120 degrees west—though this belt would narrow to only a few miles for certain stretches along the United States—Canadian border. From that point the Parkland Belt, as we may see from the general map, turns almost due south and "plunges under" the Rockies—to reappear first ringing the little, isolated, valley-bottom prairies in southern British Columbia, and then on the delta of the Fraser River. On parklands there is grass, while the trees may be anything from mesquites, junipers, and live oaks (as in Texas) to firs, pines, or maples (as in the lower Fraser valley).

If all the mountain ranges of the West were to be swept away, the distribution of the vegetational belts would doubtless not be exactly as it is today, but it might be substantially so. The whole of the coastal plain would then be clothed in parklands from the Fraser River south to the region of San Francisco, while inland from this prairies would stretch from Kamloops to the Sacramento valley and San Luis Obispo. As it is, all the lowlands of this province are thus clothed, there being parklands down Puget Sound and along the coast of Washington, while a "lake" of prairie fills the Willamette valley from just south of the Columbia River and then continues through the volcanic ranges east of the Klamath Mountains via the valley bottoms to link with the great grass-covered valley of the Sacramento. Prairie also covers all the low inland coastal ranges of California (numbered I to III on map) from north of San Francisco, inside the Redwood highlands, all the way south to the Santa Maria River, while isolated trees or clumps of trees (i.e., parkland conditions) occur on the upper slopes of these.

Today, the Willamette and Sacramento valleys are extensively and intensively cultivated, and the latter, which contains large marshes, is widely irrigated; but there is still considerable acreage around their peripheries that is relegated to stock-raising or is simply left virginal. These regions I have always found to be exceedingly beautiful, with a coloring all their own. In the summer when the sun is bright and the temperature high, the grass (mostly wild oats) turns a glowing golden color, while tiny clumps of brilliant green bushes and small trees sometimes nestle in the shallow gutters that intersect the rolling surface where there is some water at or near the surface.

It is recorded that the wild turkeys once ventured out from the nearby copses to feed on the grass seeds. Today one may see in some places considerable flocks of peacocks, which appear to be quite feral and to breed successfully in the wild. They are, of course, introduced birds, and they or their parents have simply wandered away from private gardens or parks. Their presence is a most notable example of how "nature fills her (ecological) niches," that time-honored truism of biological literature. The turkey is a gallinaceous bird of large size, spending much time and feeding on the ground but retreating to the woods or forests to roost. When it vanished from this area, an ecological niche for such a bird was left empty. The peafowl, also a large gallinaceous bird of similar habits from a similar environment in Asia, fits into that niche and may, in time, fill it.

These prairielands appear at first to be sterile and lifeless, but if you will go out upon them and spend time quietly observing, you will be rewarded far beyond your expectation, for they swarm with small creatures both by day and by night. By day, most of these are birds, many of which come out of the surrounding parklands or even from the woodlands beyond and above them. The most obvious are western meadow larks, which are everywhere, and great clouds of house finches (also called "linnets"). Less conspicuous are numerous sparrows of half a dozen species—savannah, grasshopper, lark, chipping, and song—flocks of goldfinches, some pipits, and white-winged doves. Lines of little California quail march about usually in single file, and there are horned larks, and sometimes a plethora of robins. Nearer the trees, mourning doves and band-tailed pigeons are everywhere, the introduced pheasant may often be seen, and there are enormous numbers of the ground-feeding red-shafted flickers busily pursuing ants. Both Steller's and the scrub jay make their appearance, and Brewer's blackbirds are seen in the evening. In any moist place the ubiquitous red-winged blackbird appears, and its close relative the tricolored redwing is indigenous to these areas only.

At night the mammals take over, though by day a ground squirrel and a chipmunk may be seen along with the desert cottontail rabbit, the black-tailed jack rabbit, and the little brush rabbit in suitable localities. Never seen but widely spread on these lowland plains are pocket gophers—a giant form in the Willamette and a smaller one in the Sacramento valley—and there are quite a lot of moles. On the driest parts to the south are kangaroo rats; on the open plains grasshopper mice; in the taller grass, harvest mice; and among what shrubbery there is under the trees on the parklands, white-footed mice of several kinds, and woodrats. There are also many voles (called "field mice"). To feed on these lesser folk come both striped and spotted skunks, badgers, gray foxes, and in some areas even coyotes. There is a weasel on these prairies too. With few

Squaw Grass is a prominent feature above the tree line of the higher alps in the Cascade Mountains. Such uplands reproduce conditions found on the Arctic tundras.

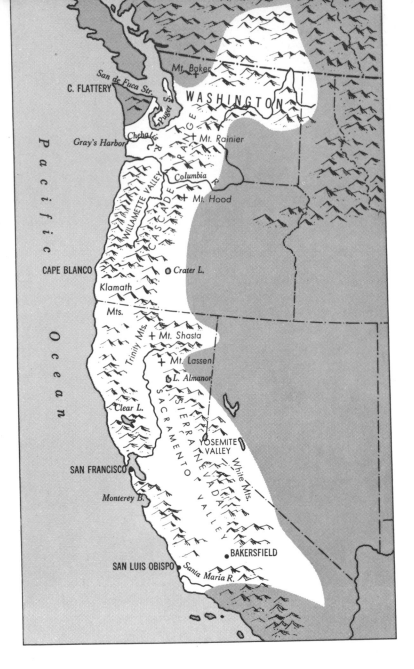

it has such a wide range of latitude, while the major vegetational belts that it covers run almost exactly from north to south instead of from east to west, and are six in number. Further, it supports two huge chains of mountain ranges with very different composition, climate, and other features; and finally, it lies between an extremely "moist" ocean and an extremely dry desert. All the major belts, from icefields to hot deserts, are also represented herein as montane zones.

The boundaries of this province are fairly simple and precise except in the north and northeast. To the north, we notice the slight complication of the Olympics, an outlier of the Northwest Pacific rain forests but south of the Strait of San Juan de Fuca. Also, as we pointed out in Chapter 5, the northern limit of the Cascades merges with the coastal, range-forest type of vegetation but is primarily defined on phytogeographical principles. Nonetheless it is quite definite.

Ignoring the mountains, this province lies in the Transition and Deciduous Forest Belts in the northwest, then in the Parklands, and finally in the Prairies down to about 35 degrees north latitude. As almost all its lowlands are basins among mountains, they are ringed by zones of Parkland with broadleafed, temperate Woodlands above these, and above those again, the Transition and other Boreal zones. The true temperate woodland belt just shaves the northwest.

The two tremendous mountain ranges stretch through the full length of this province in the form of a kind of bent ladder. The outer or western is composed, from north to south, of the North Coastal Ranges; the very ancient and curious Klamath—Trinity Complex; the Redwood Forests of northern California; the Santa Cruz Range; the San Blas; and the three blocks of hills inland of these (I—III on map). The inner or eastern chain is composed in the north of the mighty Cascades, and in the south of the Sierra Nevada, with the volcanic peaks around Mount Shasta in the center. Between these chains of ranges lie Puget Sound, and the Willamette and Sacramento valleys. All the ranges run substantially from north to south except the Klamaths, which have a more nearly northwest-to-southeast orientation.

The southern end of this province is the north face of the south Californian Block of mountains, the Santa Maria River on the west, and the southern extremity of the Sierra Nevada on the east.

Apart from Mexico, this is by far the most complex province on this continent and the most difficult to describe in a limited space. It is not just that it is some 1600 miles in length and only some 200 miles wide, an awkward shape in any case, but that

---

exceptions, all these small creatures inhabit the prairie and parklands alike, though there are some that stay in either one of those belts or the other. And there are other hosts that live in the adjacent closed-canopy forests but come out onto the grasslands either by day or by night to feed.

MIMA MOUNDS

The prairies of this province in many places display one of the most remarkable features to be seen anywhere on this continent, called "mima mounds" after a small grassland area of that name just south of Puget Sound. These consist of acre upon acre of land that is raised into regular oblong or circular mounds of subdued contour, which are scattered over all the coastal prairies and grasslands as far south as Mexico. Their appearance

is very singular, especially on level ground and when seen from the air or after a heavy rain. When these mounds were dug through for railway or road cuttings, or merely out of curiosity, it was found that they were really huge lenses, each lying in a depression the proportions, area, and dimensions of which were almost identical to those of the part raised above the base level of the plain. Moreover, from the bottom of this depression long, dark "fingers" extended downward and outward in all directions, meandering hither and yon. Usually these great lenses are composed of a dark, silty earth with a capping of sod, and they rest upon underlying, harder, more stony subsoils. Speculation upon the origin of these mounds continued until 1947—with not a few contending that the most likely agency of their construction was human—when Dr. Victor B. Scheffer, then of the United States Fish and Wildlife Service, undertook an investigation of the phenomenon. His report is one of the most fascinating expositions of what is called "biotopography" or the forming of land surfaces by animals, for he demonstrates that these thousands of square miles of mounds were all built by the small, burrowing rodents called pocket gophers. The method they use in digging and the result this has on certain types of terrain alone seem capable of producing these mounds. Dr. Scheffer produces evidence that these animals had been at work wherever such mounds are found, but he cautions that the exact method of their construction has never yet been observed in action—by pocket gophers or any other agency, biotic or physical. It seems, however, that in areas where the subsoil is very firmly compacted or very rocky, or where the surface soil lies on rock, these mounds appear. It is assumed that the animals burrow down as far as they can and throw the detritus up out of their holes. Then as they extend galleries radially underground, they cause a hollow in the soil but a low dome above it, each animal family working a limited area. Rain water then collects in the gutters between these areas, while different plants grow on the slopes of the mounds and on top of them; so that by addition of soil on top and by washing away at the bottom, they form these domes, which are on an average about six feet high at the middle.

FROM ALPS TO DESERTS

These prairies are, as I mentioned above, ringed by a ribbon of parkland, and this in turn closes up so that the trees form a closed-canopy temperate woodland as you go up the sides of the encircling mountains. Then, if you continue upward, the composition of this deciduous forest changes and the conifers begin to appear, while the hardwoods thin out. Eventually one enters the pure northern coniferous forest with all its belts (as seen at sea level as one travels north) neatly arranged horizontally in zones one above the other. On the higher peaks the spruces open out just as they do at the southern edge of the Arctic tundra, and true montane tundra appears in the form of tiny dwarf willows, mosses, and all the rest, to form a zone that has been locally called the "Hudsonian." Above this the tundra creeps up near the peaks but finally gives way to true barren ground with nothing but lichens. There is no better place in the world to see for yourself the rigid zoning of vegetational types and the invariable succession of these belts. Moreover, if you start your ascent up the Sierra Nevada from the Sacramento valley near its southern end, you will pass through all the major belts found on this continent north of the Mexican border.

Though this province is by no means the largest on the continent it is, apart from Mexico, by far the most varied. To describe it as a whole requires two separate expositions. First is that of its "basis," which is to say its lowlands as they may be seen today and as they would cover the whole of the area if the mountain ranges were not present. Second, the mountain ranges have to be described; but these are all so different that they cannot be treated as a whole. The best procedure, therefore, is to start at the north end of the coastal string, proceed south to the San Blas, and then come back up the inland chain. This has the added advantage of leading us back up to the appropriate edge of the next province to be discussed. We may therefore begin with the Olympic Peninsula.

This, as we have seen, contains a central mountain range of

A mule deer fawn pauses at the foot of a great Jeffrey Pine in the upper montane forest of the Sierra Nevada.

the same name which is clothed in the Northwest Pacific type of rain forest. However, these highlands are surrounded by a lush growth of broad-leafed forest at lower levels, and at sea level on the east side by typical parklands. This vegetation follows the coast line south for some way, while the parklands lie in a narrow strip to the east in the Willamette valley.

Along the coast from Gray's Harbor to Cape Blanco there stretches a long mountain range clothed in a luxuriant growth. This strip lies along the border between the Deciduous Forest and the Transition Belts so that broad-leafed trees predominate at the lowest levels and conifers take over at higher altitudes. The coast from Cape Flattery to the estuary of the Columbia River is sloping, with offshore bars and a coastal plain that widens out about the Chehalis River mouth. The southern part is cliff-bound and at the south end flanked by mountainous sand dunes, which we shall visit presently.

These mountains are also clothed in a veritable "rain forest," so moist in some parts that foresters call it "the asbestos zone" because it will not burn, with a lush bedding of ferns, delicate huckleberry, and a few other woody bushes beneath. Under these is a ground cover of sorrel and various beautiful mosses. The canopy is dominantly composed of magnificent hemlocks and spruces, but wherever these are eliminated, by falls or fire or today by clean logging, a seething mass of mountain alder springs up. Among this the seedlings of the conifers struggle up to eventually take over again. Also, various other interesting plants grow under the great trees, notably one that has the appropriate name of the "devil's club." This is a herbaceous plant growing to some six feet, with large leaves covered all over with a tight fuzz of sharp needles. In these forests are some very large trees, two especially—to be seen south of Astoria—being reputed to be exceptional. One is a Sitka spruce, 15 feet 9 inches in diameter as measured at a height of four and a half feet from the ground, 195 feet tall, and estimated to contain 60,000 board feet of lumber, enough to build six two-bedroom houses. Its age is believed to be about seven hundred years. The other is a Douglas "fir" that has a diameter of 15 feet 7 inches, is 225 feet tall despite the fact that a large portion of its crown has been broken off, and contains 100,000 board feet of lumber. This is thought to be at least a thousand years old. It is an awe-inspiring tree to look at, possessed of a sort of magnificence and an ancient placidity. I lay on my back—the best way to look at such a tree—gazing up at it in the shafted sunlight of the forest in which it stands; and I got a great thrill thereby because on this tree—mostly on its first limbs, which are over a hundred feet above the ground—there were growing four other kinds of plants—several licorice ferns, two red huckleberries, a vine maple, and several (of all things) little hemlock trees, most of which were growing out of its slightly leaning side.

The stately conifers in this forest stand close together but are not too tightly packed, and the sunlight plays all manner of light effects upon the filigree of delicate green-leafed little things below. The earth is soft, moist, and loamy and smells of aromatic rosins. There is silence and stillness, but for the now-and-then subdued roaring of a wind passing overhead. And there is life here. There are deer and great herds of elk that, although mostly keeping to the more open areas and the broad-leafed bottoms and gulleys, may be seen passing majestically through. There is a tiny chipmunk (Townsend's) that "chips" at you and plays

A mule deer buck in velvet in the Sierra Nevada. The typical deer of the West, it is the common form found along the Pacific coastal ranges.

about in the low bushes, feeding on berries; and there are innumerable coyotes that wander hither and yon unseen but leave their tracks everywhere. The most outstanding bird is the Pileated Woodpecker, a magnificent creature almost as big as a crow with a metallic red topknot; this bird shrieks at you and makes the gallery of the forest echo with its riveting—and it really can make the chips (as big as your thumb) fly. There is also a tiny wren that skips about among the low tangle with its tail held erect, making a noise like two pebbles being tapped together; and there is the colorful Black-headed Grosbeak, a finch that putters about on the outer foliage of the conifers.

This is a lovely, ancient world that, alas, modern man has to a great extent destroyed. There were always fires due to lightning, but we have made them more frequent and more destructive; also, logging produces horrible spectacles, though it is in many respects as beneficial as it is harmful, for it promotes new growth of the conifers. Today, led by the governments of the states and the union, this practice is pretty well regulated, and there are several big companies that have gone beyond the minima of care and conservation laid down by officialdom. The results are apparent in magnificent young and immature stands of healthy trees everywhere. Fire, under certain circumstances, can be not only beneficial but essential to some forests, and its curtailment may produce odd effects by allowing certain trees to predominate when others that would naturally do so are smothered. Then again, unless proper steps are taken to aid the conifers in coming back after clearing, alders and other non-conifers may take hold and grow so densely and quickly in this land of warm fogs and much rain that they completely blanket the conifers.

SEA LIONS AND SEA PIGEONS

The coast of this subprovince is glorious to behold. The great Pacific rollers undulate forever upon the rocky cliffs and thunder into sticky-looking foam. Between the cliffs and rocky headlands are curving sandy bays, their beaches piled high just above tide mark with a rampart of driftwood of gargantuan proportions. In this sea there is a great deal of life. All down the Pacific coast from Alaska to Baja California there are immense kelp (seaweed) beds somewhat offshore, and southward through these the gray whales again pass every year, just as they did before the white man more or less exterminated them in the latter part of the last century. There are also a great many seals and sea lions along this coast, and there is one place—now a tourist attraction and one of the most worth while on the entire continent—just north of Florence, Oregon, where the latter assemble in great numbers. Here are both the little southern species (*Zalophus*) known to almost everybody as the trained "seal," that adept comic of so many acts, and the vast, lumbering northern form (*Eumatopias*).

Together, there are several hundred of them that spend more than half the year either on ledges at the bottom of a three-hundred-foot cliff, or in an adjacent series of gigantic sea caves, where they breed. These (or this—for it is really one great tunnel entered from the sea at one end by a vast archway and then exiting via a long tunnel and a small hole to the south) are filled with tumbled boulders upon which the huge waves break deep inside the cliff. Upon these rocks the seals lounge about, belching and snoring. Above, in the eerie damp shadows, many strange birds called sea pigeons or pigeon-guillemots (*Cepphus columba*) make their nests; they have black plumage, bright red feet, and vivid white wing patches that are only seen

in flight. When their young hatch, the parents' life is hard, for they have to fish perpetually, returning about every half-hour to feed the chicks. They make their nests in crannies in the most impossible places, and they are not very good navigators, landings being their weak point, so that they usually crash onto the cliff, toss their load at their youngsters, and then fall back into the air and take off again to the high seas. On the cliff above, which is clothed in a mat of stunted firs and shiny bushes, gawky cormorants maintain breeding colonies and many gulls wheel and wail or squat, heading into the everlasting winds and mists with ruffled feathers.

THE FORGOTTEN LAND

All down the southern stretch of this coast as far as Cape Blanco, there are miles of incredible sand dunes; in fact, they are veritable sand mountains which at some points extend for more than two miles back from the sea and rise to a height of some three hundred feet. The sand is forever moving inland and tailing off to the northeast. It follows the normal behavior of dunes, but on such a grandiose scale that it produces some astonishing results. First, low down by the sea, there are just normal dunes, but behind these are vast masses of sand sculpted around outlying blocks of vegetation that have somehow been able to withstand their onslaught and that now lie in smoothly curved bowls and funnels, the tops of their tallest trees being below the level of the sand all around. Landward, the sand spills into solid stands of large conifers and broad-leafed trees, swamping them in a soft beige mass like superfine grain spilled from an elevator. Some of the trees are more than half buried but still growing staunchly. But more astonishing still, these marching dunes have in some places wallowed over the steep coastal ridge and spilled down into a string of lakes that here parallel the coast. These lakes themselves are a very odd feature of the area, constituting a kind of false shore line but separated from the sea by a few miles of timber-clad hills and dunes. Normal topography is reversed here; for, going away from the sea, you can walk out of a tall, closed-canopy forest into the deep water of a fresh lake and find yourself confronting a sand beach on the opposite shore, extending away inland and rising into massive dunes. Immediately south of Cape Blanco the coastal ranges bifurcate to form two parallel chains of ranges which reach south, hugging the coast, to the neighborhood of San Luis Obispo. The North Coastal Range actually flows into the inner or eastern chain which starts with the Klamath complex. This is perhaps the most fascinating region in the United States, as yet incompletely mapped and unsurveyed and to a large extent unexplored. It is 250 miles long and on an average about 75 miles wide (some 18,000 square miles), and although surrounded on three sides by major modern highways, is crossed by only two first-class (one, as of writing, still incomplete) and two secondary roads. It is wholly mountainous, embracing the Siskiyous and the Klamaths that rise to seven thousand feet in the north, and the Trinitys that rise to Mount Yallo-Bally, over eight thousand feet, in the south.

These mountains rise precipitately in dozens of parallel ridges. The valleys and the lower reaches are clothed in the most wonderful conglomeration of both broad-leafed and

The central Pacific coast is strung with beaches and coves interspersed with vast dunes and towering cliffs. Warm mists roll in from the Pacific Ocean almost daily.

coniferous trees, with the former predominating at lower levels. There are here huge maples and oaks, elders and willows, mixed with the coppery-barked madrones of the south and the pines, spruces, and other conifers of the north. The lowest valleys are parklike, even having incipient prairies in the form of open grassfields. The main northern block of this subprovince is only now slowly and tentatively being penetrated by tedious road-building operations in order to get at its rich, primeval lumber resources. Therein grows timber that is quite beyond description—enormous, clean-limbed, almost all rigidly straight and vertical, and almost clear below but for a blanket of rhododendrons. This is mostly Sitka spruce, but there are also immense Douglas firs and some pines that must surely top any found elsewhere.

In these forests there is a large and varied fauna; but, like all primeval forests, it guards its inhabitants so well that you have the utmost difficulty in seeing them at any time. I have sat absolutely still for more than an hour and never seen anything more sizable than an insect—not even an unidentified movement—though there were some tiny twittering bird or squirrel noises going on high above. Nor do you see much at night unless you adopt professional jungle-hunting techniques and stay near the watercourses, when otter and mink may be encountered and numbers of rodents seen. Yet wherever there is soft ground (and springs and streams line every slope in every gulley) you can hardly put a finger between the tracks left by all sorts of animals. This is the mark of the truly virgin forest, which immediately distinguishes it from that which has been inhabited by man or hunted over by him since time immemorial; and this forest was apparently shunned, even by the Amerindians, on account of certain legends and beliefs. Curiously, the local men who are currently cutting into this wilderness building roads, timber cruising, or surveying, assert that, while there are many black bears around the edges and while there are some deer in the forest itself, larger game is not plentiful and bears do not seem to exist there.

There are many fascinating things to see in this isolated country, but to me the most surprising was on the beautiful Klamath River in a forest-choked gorge deep in the wilderness, with towering spruce and fir on either hand and the nut-brown river rattling along among smooth boulders, with huge trout and salmon stationary between them like miniature submarines. On the boulders sat sea gulls, and every now and then they soared into the air and pealed with laughter just as if they were crying at the winds of the ocean. Somehow this did not seem right from an ecological point of view. Almost as unexpected are the multitudes of quail (the California or Valley Quail) that rustle about among the dead leaves in some of these valleys. There can hardly be a more enchanting sight than a mother and father of this species leading a dozen youngsters—tiny, animated balls of fluff, which rush hysterically about like mechanical toys.

The southern portion of this mountainous area, composed of the Trinity Mountains, is clothed in forests of slightly different botanical constitution. Although also wild, it has been more extensively traversed, explored, and hunted over. It reaches to Clear Lake, which is only some seventy miles north of San Francisco. South of that point there lies a series of parallel, much lower mountains and hills that extend to San Francisco Bay. These are clothed in short grass with isolated trees at lower levels (typical parklands), then copses above this, and finally a crown of thick woods of broad-leafed but mostly evergreen trees such as oaks. These continue with narrow breaks caused by rivers leading from the Sacramento valley to the coast, all the way to the Temblor Range between San Luis Obispo and Bakers-

field, forming the inner of the two coastal ranges. Their fauna is that of the peripheral parklands of the Sacramento valley.

THE LAND OF LIVING FOSSILS

Parallel to the Klamath complex and these low inland ranges, and stretching from just south of Cape Blanco to Monterey Bay, lie the great Redwood Forests, clothing a narrow, mountainous strip facing the Pacific. The northern part of this strip is composed of the Pacific slopes of the Klamath Ranges, which run northwestward to the sea in echelon, but it is quite distinct (and unique) as a vegetational subprovince, or rather a zone. This is the last retreat of the mighty redwood trees *(Sequoia semper-virens)* and is maintained by the warm mists and fogs that drift in daily from the nearby ocean. Together with the Klamath-Trinity complex, this land appears to be one of the "oldest" parts of this continent. It has been under the sea, either as a whole or in part, from time to time, and it was somewhat gouged by mountain glaciers during the recent ice age but only to a very limited extent. Yet it has apparently never been completely submerged at the same time as all other surrounding bits of territory, so that it has acted as a sort of refuge for many things from the past.

The most obscure and least impressive of these is a strange kind of smallish rodent known as the Sewellel or "Mountain Beaver" *(Aplodonta)*. It is a very primitive form of rodent with,

as its scientific name states, simple teeth. It has no known near relatives and is unique to this area, having its headquarters in this subprovince but spreading north to the Chehalis River divide; up the Cascades, probably to the Fraser; and south down the Sierra Nevada. It is a compact creature with a large head, small ears, very small eyes, and a tiny one-inch stump for a tail. It is about a foot long and is clothed in dense, hard, brown fur that becomes lighter in summer. It lives in lush growth, from the lowlands to the tree line, and never strays far from water. It digs holes and makes long passageways, some of which often enter water and are flooded. Its food appears to be the leaves of succulent plants and other herbage. It is a sort of left-over beast.

There are also found in these ranges both moles and shrews of distinctive species. Among these is a curious animal known as the Shrew-mole *(Neurotrichus),* an extremely ancient form of mammal that has relatives only in the Far East of Asia. It is intermediate between a mole and a shrew, having wide hands with immense claws and a tail half as long as its head and body, but narrow at the base rather than tapering like that of a mole. It appears, indeed, that there has been land hereabouts for an incredibly long time and that upon it have been preserved certain types of plants and animals from what is called the Mesozoic Age, the period when the dinosaurs predominated. What is more, the nearest relatives of many of its inhabitants turn up otherwise only in the western Chinese region. Some years ago a tree related to the sequoias (and now named *Meta-sequoia* or the "one like the redwood") was discovered in

142

Left and right: Nature as a master stonemason—the Devil's Postpile in California. These amazing structures are formed of basaltic rock or volcanic lavas ten to thirty inches in diameter and up to sixty feet tall and are mostly irregular hexagons. Such columnar strata are also found in northern Ireland and in India.

southern China. The sequoias are themselves a very ancient breed that were once widely spread over almost all the world. Today there are only nine kinds of trees of this family left. Of these, there are three species of one genus confined to the mountains of the island of Tasmania *(Athrotaxis),* one of another kind *(Cunninghamia)* in China, and another on Formosa. Four *Metasequoia* and five other kinds, of which there are only one known species each, come from eastern Asia. The last two genera are American; one comprising the two sequoias and the other the three *Taxodium,* called "bald cypresses" or (quite erroneously) simply "cypresses."

THE LAND OF THE GIANTS

Along this strip where there is much rain throughout the fall, winter, and spring, and where thick, warm mists roll in almost daily from the sea, there grow on the west slopes of the mountains and in the valley bottoms vast stands of these redwoods, their enormous boles often almost touching. Beneath them is a moist mass of ferns and small shrubs, with here and there a sapling squatting full and green just as if it were in full sunlight, though there is none; instead, there is always a filtered green shade, for the heads of the great trees form a porous canopy a hundred feet above. Perhaps the most amazing thing about these groves of huge trees is the closeness of their boles. How they all obtain enough nutriment from the ground is beyond understanding, but there they stand and have stood for centuries, so close that one often cannot maneuver a jeep between them. Another odd thing is the number of double trunks, or "schoolmarms" as they are called, among them; there are groves where more than half the trees are twins. And there is still another odd thing to be seen here, though it becomes even more pronounced in the spruce-hemlock forests to the north. This consists of all manner of trees, from tiny seedlings to monsters, that grow on the stumps of dead trees that have fallen or been cut down. These are no respecters of persons, one species growing on another and vice versa, as well as on their own kind. What is more, there are often far more trees growing on trees than there are young trees growing in soil, and it seems that they derive special nutrient from the stumps. Often these stumps rot away entirely and the saprophyte is left standing on its own but with two or more "feet" that once straddled the stump or log on which it first sprouted from its seed.

Though grassfields and park conditions ring the whole of the lower Sacramento valley on the foothills leading to the surrounding mountains—the southern Sierra Nevada, the Southern Californian Block, and the coastal ranges—the south-central portion of that valley is an arid waste, mostly bare but in some places dotted with tiny clumps of sages and other desert scrub. Here we enter the Northern Scrub Belt and the entire scene changes.

This country will be described later, but now we must turn left or inland and start to climb the mighty Sierra Nevada, which, like almost every other mountain range, is unique in many respects, particularly because it is so isolated and thus

insulated. These mountains stand like a five-hundred-mile-long island in a sea of desiccated grass, scrub, and desert, rising majestically and abruptly all around to forest-clad heights and towering peaks.

In them are vast gorges, canyons, and seemingly bottomless chasms. Between the ribs of this range are flying valleys, lakes, and wind-blown pastures, and clothing its slopes are some of the greatest forests in the world. Much of it is still today inaccessible, but it contains three great natural wonders—the Yosemite Valley, King's Canyon, and, above all, the groves of the giant sequoia trees. King's Canyon has a depth of eight thousand feet—the greatest depth of any stream-cut chasm in the surface of this continent. This canyon is overpowering, the Yosemite is incredible, but the great trees—the giant sequoias—are breath-taking.

To me there is nothing on earth so grand as a large tree. It has the qualities of life, death, and the intermediate which we call time. Personally, I always have a desire to "talk" to an ancient tree, and I have the uncontrollable feeling when in the presence of one that if I did so it would understand. This is not of science; it is of the spirit, and may well be considered out of place. Nonetheless, unless you are completely insensible you cannot fail to feel something similar when you first stand before the great and ancient sequoias.

If you are lucky, you come upon these rather suddenly, for they dwell together in groves amid other towering conifers in only a few places and only on this mountain range, and only between four thousand and eight thousand feet on its western slopes from the thirty-sixth to thirty-seventh parallels. Many of the other trees up there are magnificent, but all of a sudden you round a corner and there before you is a mammoth, its trunk glowing a rich but somber burnt sienna in the shafted sunlight and towering up and up through the lacy greenery above, its base bulging out all around in great, voluptuous udders of bark that then plunge abruptly into the rich, mouldy soil. These trees are scarred by enormous wounds in their foot-thick, corky bark, and these scars are usually black and charred within by fires. But, like deathless sphinxes, they curl their "skin" around the edges of these ghastly wounds and heal them. Their trunks are deeply grooved and seem to be pulled upward like taffy. Right alongside any one may stand an ancient relative or perhaps even a child, and beyond that another and another, dwarfing the two-hundred-foot firs and spruces that somehow manage to wedge themselves in between. The sequoias are magnificent and utterly imperial.

If you can get away from your fellow creatures and just sit among these giants in silence, time drops away; your petty worries vanish; and a sense of unutterable awe envelops you. Then perhaps a delicate deer approaches, or a black-and-yellow fly comes and hovers in front of you. Every now and then a cone drops like a small bomb from the leafy heights above as a squirrel crops it off, and a bright blue jay screeches. But nothing else moves, while the great trees stand silently as some of them have done for thousands of years. This is indeed a belittling thought.

The Giant Sequoia (Sequoia washingtoniana) is said to rank among its numbers on the Sierra Nevada, where it alone grows naturally today, the "largest trees" in the world. This is not so on any count, though it does not in any way detract from their grandeur or interest. Most of them are topped, and the largest—named the General Sherman and the General Grant—are almost bald. In fact, mature trees of this species—whatever the term mature may actually mean in this context—are almost invariably topped. It seems to be the nature of the "beast," for which their great bulk may in some way be a compensation—or a result. If one of the great ones were not so topped it should by mere extrapolation be of incredible height and surpass the tallest specimen of its relative the Redwood (S. sempervirens)—of which, as we have mentioned, the tallest measured was 364 feet, or over a third the height of the Empire State Building. The tallest Giant Sequoia is named the Hart and stands in King's Canyon National Park. It measures only 277 feet. The General Sherman is claimed to have the greatest bulk of all trees (almost 50,000 cubic feet, exclusive of limbs and loss by burns), but this is also definitely not so.

The whole business of the "largest tree in the world" is a frustrating one and has some rather silly aspects. The tallest are often given as this redwood at 364 feet; next a mountain gum tree (Eucalyptus regnans) in Australia at 326 feet; then a Douglas fir in Washington at 324 feet. However, the Australian government claimed another Eucalyptus regnans of 382 feet, and we have seen a Canadian white spruce of 417 feet. In girth, the order goes: a cypress in Mexico with a diameter of over 36 feet, a jequitibá tree in Brazil of 33 feet, a baobab on Christmas Island in the Indian Ocean at 30 feet, and a Kauri pine at 24 feet in New Zealand. Several Canadian trees have bigger girths than any Giant Sequoia, and are of greater volume. The matter is purely academic, but it would still be interesting to know just which are really the "largest" trees in the world in height, girth, and volume. And while doing this it might be worth the investigators' time to go to West Africa and take a look at some of the Terminalia trees that have four buttress roots reaching, in some cases that I have myself measured, over fifty feet from the base of their trunks—which, although usually hollow, measure more than the biggest Sequoia at the base; and which certainly rise over 250 feet into the air. Yet mere size has nothing to do with the magnificence of these particular trees.

Their age does, however, have real meaning. The amazing thing is that these vastnesses start from a seed about the size of a pinhead, and it is three-quarters of a century before a young tree produces any seeds. At that time it is a modest little sapling growing under its giant elders. But once it does get started, it goes on producing cones and seeds until it dies—if it ever does, short of an accident or an ice age. Counts of the rings of large trunks of this species give ages of at least 3200 years. However, even a direct count of the rings of cut or fallen trees is a tricky business. It is quite likely, therefore, that some of the older Sequoias are 3500 years old, which puts their year of "birth" in the reign of Tutankhamen of ancient Egypt, or before the Exodus led by Moses. Not all trees have growth rings but a method of estimating the age of those that have not—such as palms—has been developed by counting the number of leaf bases on the trunk and then dividing by the number of leaves produced on an average each year. By this method certain trees called cycads, of the genus Lepidozamia, growing in Australia, have been estimated to be over 1000 years old. Also the miserable, gnarled, usually almost leafless Bristle-cone Pine (Pinus aristata) of the White Mountains of California have definitely been shown to be over 4000 years old by actual ring counts. This is an almost inconceivable length of time to contemplate for a single "life"; 4000 years takes us back to antiquity and makes our lives seem utterly transitory.

THE GREAT GUTTER

The land of the giant sequoias is contained within that southern half of the Sierra Nevada that lies in the Scrub Belt, whereas that of the redwoods is in the Prairie Belt. This is of considerable significance, for there are plenty of places at the right altitude and with the same soils, amount of moisture, and temperatures in both zones where a characteristic tree of the other could live. Besides, they both grow in the same latitudes. The northern half of these Sierras is clothed in the same vegetation, but the zones gradually creep down the mountain sides as one goes north, while the chaparral thins out and finally disappears below. Here it is the mountains themselves rather than the trees that command our attention.

The enormous size of the Yosemite Valley, despite its present-day somewhat cluttered bottom (near its head it is one vast summer camp), in some ways transcends that of the Grand Canyon though it is of lesser physical proportions. It grows upon you the more you look at it, especially from below, because the moulded gray walls and the vivid greenery seem to lean over upon you. It was carved by a glacier, and, without being awesome or threatening, it somehow seems as if it were poised to strike or, more aptly, to close with a snap like vast jaws.

There is a place on the road into the valley from which a magnificent view may be obtained. The Park Service has made provision for the traveler to drink in the vista from behind a

All down the Pacific coast from Alaska to Mexico the inshore waters grow vast beds of ribbon-like brown seaweed known as kelp. The fauna that dwells in this protective sea forest is peculiar to it.

low stone wall immediately overlooking a steep scree dotted with small bushes and leading abruptly down to a pine forest. The view can hardly be surpassed, but one's interest is inexorably distracted from it and directed downward below the wall, where a sort of zoological pantomime is in continuous progress.

On this slope there dwell several dozen active little ground squirrels, gray in color with a white collar; these are typical of higher elevations throughout these ranges. They have gathered here because tourists tend to drop goodies of various kinds over the edge. However, there are also present a number of well-organized gangs of the colorful Steller's Jay. Between the two populations there is a kind of continuous cold war. The parties intermingle guardedly, while rugged individualists from each may make a limited tour through the territory of the other, but mass travel through "enemy" territory is apparently *verboten*. Both rodents and birds sit nonchalantly about on the boulders or pretend to be at work in the bushes, but if any edible morsel rolls down the steep incline, all sorts of actions, maneuvers, and counteractions are set in motion. Representatives of both parties make determined dashes, each using its particular tactics and physical abilities to the best advantage. If the tidbit comes to rest on open ground, the birds usually win; if it rolls into a hole, the rodents have the advantage; but I have seen a jay go into the ground and a squirrel leap into the air. The whole performance is picayune against the towering backdrop of the ageless mountains but has all the charm of a Disney cartoon.

THE SLEEPING GIANTS

From the geologist's point of view the Sierra Nevadas end to the north about Lake Almanor, which is the headwater of the North Fork River; but from our standpoint they continue to the Pit River valley, which cuts through the mountains from the Great Basin to the top of the Sacramento valley, and so they contain Mount Lassen. This is a volcanic peak, 10,437 feet above sea level, and it was active in 1914 and 1915. It marks the beginning of a long string of volcanic peaks that extend throughout the length of the Cascades. There are no less than 120 of them south of the Columbia River gorge; Mount Shasta and its twin Mount Shastina in the south, Mount Hood in the north, and Crater Lake, Mount Jefferson, and others in between. North of the Columbia River the most outstanding are Mounts Adams, St. Helen's, Rainier, and Baker (which last erupted in 1870). Mount Rainier is now perpetually snow-covered down to 6000 feet, and there are numerous glaciers on all of them, even a small one about two miles long on Mount Shasta.

One of the most colorful places on earth is the famous Crater Lake, which is in the middle of Mount Mazama, another huge, defunct volcano. This is a particularly strange volcano because it must once have been a mountain at least 15,000 feet high in order to have laid down the deposits of which its base is formed Today the rim of its enormous crater stands at only 8000 feet. Thus a pile of material six miles in diameter at the base and rising 7000 feet has disappeared. Where did it go? If the mountain blew its stack, there should be immense fields of its material thrown all around for miles; but there is none. Geologists have therefore inferred that it sank or fell back into itself. Crater Lake is over 2000 feet deep today, and from one side of its floor there

A great tree (Sequoia washingtoniana) *in the General Grant Grove in the Sierra Nevada. Like all Giant Sequoias, it is topped and has an "onion base."*

A baby sequoia stubbornly struggles upward by the side of its gigantic and ancient parent. It will be half a century before it too produces seeds.

arises a little cone with a crater on top that is 700 feet above the lake level. This volcanic activity is, geologically speaking, both ancient and modern, for a lot of it is imposed upon an old land surface that was obviously carved by mountain glaciers during the Pleistocene ice advances.

The Cascades continue north to the region of Kamloops on the North Thompson River in British Columbia. They are clothed, as we have said, in a predominantly coniferous forest—allied to that of the Northwest Pacific Coastal Fringe—composed of Sitka spruce, firs, and an intermingling of willows and aspen.

The whole northern part of the range has been recently and mightily glaciated, so that most of its valleys are shaped like flattened-out U's. The upper slopes are mantled in short alpine vegetation, often with scattered trees, and the tops of the mountains are either bald or snow-covered. All the great volcanic peaks wear a cap of snow and ice. The fauna of the Cascades is quite different from that of the Rockies, many of the larger animals, for example the Moose, being absent. Most of the animal life was pushed out by the over-all glaciation, and repopulation came from the south as the ice retreated northward.

The Great Grass Sea

The Steppes, Prairies, and Bottomlands of the Central Plains and Plateau

11 The whole central portion of this continent is covered by an immensity of grasslands commonly called the Prairie Belt. Today, real prairie of any extent without man-made adjuncts is rare, for much of it has been subjected to agriculture, carved up by a checkerboard of roads, or festooned with wire of all kinds. Its countless bottomlands are also much farmed, and irrigation is making tremendous strides all over its face. Its wildlife has been very largely altered, in that the huge bison herds have all gone and the number of the little prairie dogs has been greatly reduced. This has brought great changes, but only a little greater than those brought about by the creation of new exposed water surfaces; these have introduced or caused visitation by many other animals—mostly seasonal—that were previously scarce or unknown. Some of these, such as the large Western Porcupine, seem passing strange in an environment that appears to be far removed from their normal one.

Prairies appear in the interiors of large land masses and are found in all of these—Eurasia, Africa, Australia, and even South America. They develop where rainfall is lowered due to distance from oceans, and particularly since large mountain masses invariably lie between them and the ocean from which the moisture-laden prevailing winds blow. They are, in a way, temperate deserts and share with such belts both daily and seasonal extremes of heat and cold. They are unsuited to tree growth, and since they are usually covered with porous and uncompacted sediments, they also fail to support shrubs. Perennial herbs make use of seasonal rain but cannot stand prolonged droughts, so that only grasses and certain kinds at that can survive upon them.

Botanists have long debated the true status of grasslands—tropical, temperate, and even those of the polar regions. There have been two schools of thought. One contends that these grass belts are a natural and permanent feature of the vegetational cover of our earth and that their location is the result of fundamental climatic factors. The other faction holds that all grasslands—apart from small glades in woods and forests where the tree growth has, for some reason, been inhibited—are man-made.

The grass family was evolved comparatively late in the

The White River Badlands, carved into the edge of the prairie plateau, are among the most colorful and fantastically formed phenomena on this continent.

148

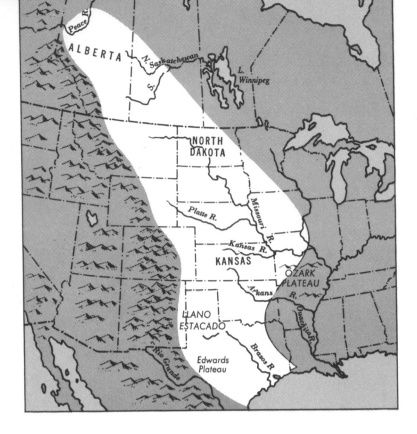

The second-largest province on the continent, this province is over 2300 miles in length from the northwest, starting about the middle Peace River region in northern Alberta and extending to the east Gulf coast of Texas. It is on an average some 500 miles wide. It forms the core of North America and is commonly known as the Prairie Belt—which indeed it is, both technically and popularly. As a whole, it is an immense plateau that descends northward toward the shores of the Arctic Ocean, tilting gently in that direction from an elevation of some three thousand feet in the south. To the southeast it pitches over an abrupt bow-shaped escarpment which runs from the eastern

edge of the Sacramento–Guadalupe Mountains, east and then northeast to the southern fringe of the Ouachita Mountains of the Interior Highlands. Beyond this escarpment it covers the coastal plain of east Texas to the Gulf; then, as a vegetational belt, it crosses the Gulf, fringes the Mississippi delta, and finally appears on the central third of the peninsula of Florida.

The western edge of the prairies lies against the eastern face of the Rockies all the way from the Pecos River valley in the south to about Fort Nelson on the Yukon border in the north. On the north and northeast it marches with the boreal woodlands, from which it is separated by narrow belts of Parkland, North Temperate Broad-leafed Woodland, and the Transition Belt of hard and soft woods. There are long stretches where this change is abrupt and all these belts are compressed into a band only a few miles wide. At other places, the grasses meander into the forest in tongues or the forest breaks up into typical parklands with isolated trees. At still others, dense shrubbery intervenes, giving way to deciduous forests to the north. There are also isolated outliers of prairie deep in the boreal forest between Athabasca and Great Slave Lake. On the east, prairies once made a great sweep over the upper Mississippi into the Heartland area, but this pocket has been considerably vegetated by agriculture. To the southeast, their border bows to the west around the Interior Highlands.

This vast plateau varies from sandy plains and loess to steppes and flat prairies. Upon it stands quite a number of isolated low mountain blocks, and it is cut almost all over by fern-frond-shaped drainage systems, the meandering bottoms of which may be level and heavily vegetated with gallery forest and lush meadows. In other places, they form completely arid "badlands." There is much fertile land following the courses of all the larger rivers. In the past, these supported a different fauna from that of the plateau alongside, and they still do so in some valleys of the southeastern region.

history of this earth. Prior to its appearance there had of course been herbivorous animals—and in large numbers—that fed on all manner of other green things, but it was not till the advent of grasses that vast herds of grazing herbivores could be developed. In fact, the rise of the mammals coincided with the rise of the grasses, and the great herds of mammalian herbivores that flourished in Eocene times were definitely and primarily grass-eaters or grazers rather than browsers, as may be seen from the pattern of their teeth. Now, without the grasslands there would not have been all these kinds of animals; and without vast grasslands there could not have been the enormous numbers of them that we know from fossil evidence existed. And this was millions of years before the advent of man. Thus there must always have been grass belts from at least the end of the age of the dinosaurs. Grasslands must therefore be natural climax growths and must have been in existence long before man.

The reasons for their position globally is the peculiar ability of grass to grow in direct sunlight and withstand hot and cold aridity, combined with their inability to exist in deep shade or under a closed canopy. However, grasslands altogether unaided cannot hold their own against the encroachment of woody shrubs and trees if climatic changes take place. In the case of our Prairie Belt the chaparral of the Northern Scrub Belt would eventually have swamped the grass by moving in from the south, and then parkland and finally temperate woods would have done likewise

from the north, had it not been for certain counterforces. These were animals, notably the bison and the prairie dogs.

Before the arrival of Europeans, man in the form of the Amerindian did not influence the prairies except as just another predator. If he did not set fire to it, nature did so by lightning. The Plains Amerindians were hunters, not agriculturists, and they were nomadic, following the great bison herds. They shared their resources with the grizzly bears and a certain number of pumas. Bison ran by the millions, and along with them were large numbers of pronghorns and white-tailed deer, though the latter stayed mostly in the bottoms. Moreover, mastodons and mammoths were also present in considerable numbers—not nearly so long ago, it now appears, as was previously thought. It was these vast grazing hosts that maintained the grassfields, yet it was not they that held the scrub and the trees at bay. This was the work of certain lesser folk that made up for their small size by their incredible numbers. This lesser fauna was and is typical of and in many respects peculiar to these particular grasslands, and unfortunately it has suffered as great a defeat at the hands of the invading white man as did the bigger game and the native Indian population. Its virtual disappearance has had even profounder effects. This fauna was originally dependent upon the delightful little animals known popularly as prairie dogs.

I should not need to mention that these are not dogs at all, but there is still widespread confusion about their true identity.

They are actually short-tailed squirrels that live in and upon the ground and are just rather extreme forms of ground squirrels or gophers, of which there are numerous species all over the continent west of the Mississippi.

Prairie dogs were once the head of everything on the prairies, and they once inhabited the whole of them. They are singular little creatures, and they display many traits that are particularly endearing to us. They live in "cities" divided very precisely into wards in which the "gardens" of individual families are carefully defined but the homes of all members are connected by means of a labyrinth of subterranean tunnels. In bygone days these cities sometimes stretched continuously for as much as two hundred miles, with burrow entrances about equally spaced a few paces from one another in all directions. Even as late as the end of the last century one such city was calculated to house over three hundred million prairie-dog families. But these vast congeries were not just chaotic masses of animals who had come together simply because there were so many of them and there was sufficient food to maintain them. On the contrary, recent studies have shown that they have a very definite polity, and one that is centered around the ward system.

Prairie dogs eat grass, and each requires just so much to maintain itself, to thrive, and to raise a family; but the supply must be continuous. It is manifest that none but those prairie dogs living on the outermost fringes of one of their "cities"—and one was over 37,000 square miles—can go foraging afar for grass: they must obtain it, all year round, in their immediate vicinity. The really astonishing thing is that this "vicinity" is measured in only tens of square feet, being a very modest circle around the entrance to each family's burrow. The average animal stays within this precinct, though members of one ward may meander about within the limits of their ward. To regulate this, two prairie dogs, on meeting, exchange a sort of kiss. Then, if they are of the same ward, either they go on about their business or they stand up and indulge in mutual actions which have been called coat-cleaning. But if an animal from one ward wanders into the territory of another, the recognition kiss is followed by quite a rumpus, which invariably results in the intruder withdrawing precipitately to his own territory. Sometimes an animal may meander into an adjacent territory and, in his hurry to get back to his own, may rush into a third—where, on being challenged, he may completely lose his nerve and go rushing about in helpless terror. Then everybody rises up on his hind legs and, paddling the air like tiny dogs begging, gives out with a loud, whistling "tee-dee-tit-tee" that is taken up and echoed in all directions. This brings the lost one to a dead stop and seems invariably to give him directions, for he scampers off home while everybody else sits up and waits. It has been suggested that every clan has a slightly different intonation that is recognizable to its members but, of course, quite beyond our powers of sound differentiation.

The Prairie Dog was once the most important animal on this continent next to the Beaver, and did more to create its surface topography than any other. The burrows of these animals are an inextricable maze of passages with little side bedrooms for individual families, community passages, and all sorts of blind alleys, escape exits, and other devices. The animals are great diggers quite apart from the essential business of homemaking, and indulge in the activity to keep their claws trimmed. In captivity they move vast tonnages of earth from one place to another, endlessly making new tunnels every day to no purpose at all. This ceaseless activity over thousands of years all over the Prairie Belt constituted a sort of super-plowing of the whole surface; and, what is more, it was a "deep-plowing," for the animals were constantly at work on the subsoil, loosening it, bringing a quota of it up to the surface, and making it possible for water to percolate down.

Prairie dogs also make little volcano-like mounds around their burrow entrances, so that the whole plain becomes lumpy in a fairly even pattern. When it rains, the moisture naturally runs down into the gutters between the contiguous mounds, which consequently remain moister longer. The result of this is that the grasses grow more readily and luxuriantly there than upon the slopes of the mounds. Each prairie-dog family then manages to maintain itself on a share of the verdure around its hole without ever infringing upon the territories of its neighbors. At the same time, the droppings of the animals are deposited on the slopes, so that the essential minerals are constantly rotated uphill and down dale, as it were. Then again, nothing promotes the growth of grasses like good regular mowing, and this is exactly what the animals do day in and day out. Further, the hope for any other more leafy plant to survive in this sea of grass, even if seeded from a bird dropping or by the wind, is short-lived indeed, for the animals chop it off the moment it shows itself. Thus the prairie dogs tilled and cultivated the prairies, weeded them, and created endless food for endless herds of larger animals as well.

The moment a new breed of men—the white man—entered the land and started killing off the prairie dogs—mostly because horses were alleged to break their ankles in their holes—all sorts of things went wrong. Herbaceous plants began to creep in, led by thistles, and right on the heels of these came woody-

Overleaf top left: Gaily colored chipmunks are as industrious on the prairies as elsewhere, making stores of seeds that often grow and change the whole local flora. Below and right: The true monarch of the prairie and partly its creator, the Prairie Dog (Cynomys). Really a large ground squirrel, it lives communally and once dug "cities" accommodating hundreds of millions of animals.

The American Badger is a denizen of the prairies and once fed largely on the Prairie Dog. It has the reputation of being immensely strong for its size.

The Yellowstone River rises in the Rockies, then descends onto the prairies, loses impetus, and begins to meander and to cut a deep gutter.

stemmed shrubs, followed in turn by hardy trees such as the beautiful, useful, but in many respects almost indestructible Mesquite, which has now moved up from southern Texas as far as Kansas and is being held back only by considerable effort from that area of western Texas called the Llano Estacado. The Prairie Dog was master and part maker of the prairie, but he was not alone.

There was, and still is, another burrower and an even more profound one. This is the Pocket Gopher, a really appalling-looking creature, with tiny eyes, vast front teeth stuck out at the end of a fully furred but bony snout, powerful front legs with huge claws for digging, little trundling hind legs, and a loose-skinned tail that can be used as a feeler when the animal goes backward, which it can do as readily and as fast as it can go forward. Unlike the Prairie Dog, the Pocket Gopher spends almost all its time down below, endlessly burrowing and throwing up small mounds of excess earth. The Pocket Gopher (not to be confused with the plain gophers or ground squirrels) does not live where the Prairie Dog is found, or vice versa. On the pure grasslands there is nothing below the surface but grass roots, and these are not acceptable to the Pocket Gopher. They need bulbs and roots, so they go to work under areas where herbs, bushes, and trees grow. There they do a very effective job of "mowing" all those types of vegetation from *underneath,* thus eliminating them.

The part played by these animals under natural conditions was to hold back, if not actually to push back, the scrub and chaparral on the south and the parkland woods on the north of the Prairie Belt. They did this by cutting off the individual plants of these types at the base of their stems just as soon as they gained a footing, and then toting these treasures down into the subsoil and stowing them away in caches. The efficacy of their efforts may be dramatically demonstrated when a parcel of these animals moves into a young and thriving orchard. They move down the lines of young trees at a surprising rate, cutting them off neatly just below the surface so that, within hours, they wilt, die, and topple. I have seen them completely destroy a thriving citrus plantation in the tropics in one night. The Pocket Gophers had—and still have—few enemies except for certain fungoidal diseases that periodically decimated their ranks, for they are agile at digging, and drill their tunnels deep into the subsoil.

NATURE'S BALANCE

The Prairie Dog, on the other hand, once had many enemies, which is to say—if we would be more biologically precise—it formed the staple item in a large food cycle, for animals do not, of course, have "enemies." Prairie Dogs shared their dominions with a large number of other creatures, notably burrowing owls, which occupied any spare holes. These rather ridiculous-looking birds with gawky legs seem to live on terms of mutual respect with prairie dogs and to gain their living from the multitudes of mice of various kinds that also inhabit the land, though under somewhat servile conditions, picking up the scraps left by the prairie dogs, such as seeds, and even feeding on their droppings. However, the owls were never averse to taking a baby prairie dog if one wandered their way. (The young of these owls are, incidentally, among the silliest-looking creatures imaginable, at least to our eyes, for they are almost completely spherical and tailless, set up upon two parallel slender legs, wear a perpetual scowl, are constantly winking, and seem to have practically no sense of balance whatever.) Next to the owls, which seem to have been merely an ineradicable bore, the most annoying neighbors of the prairie dogs were undoubtedly the rattlesnakes, which appear to have existed in great numbers on the prairies. Being active at night—although with a detectable odor—rather fast-moving, and able to penetrate the burrows, these reptiles appear to have taken a considerable toll of young and even adult prairie dogs. The old tale about their living peacefully in the burrows with the prairie dogs is apparently untrue.

Three other animals were, and still are, much more trouble to the little animals. These are the Badger, the Prairie Falcon, and a large weasel—now said to be almost extinct, but which exists in considerable quantities where there are still prairie dogs in any numbers—known as the Black-footed Ferret. This last is really the North American form of the Polecat of the Old World, known in its domesticated form (when it is usually an albino) as the "ferret." It is a beautifully colored large weasel with an ochreous pelt and a long overcoat tipped with dark brown, black lower limbs and feet, and a black tail and mask. It seems to have been evolved as a natural corollary to the prairie dogs, living by and on them almost exclusively. It is also shaped to enter their burrows and search them out, but even this animal with its keen senses and agility has to work hard to get its food, and it never did more than just control the vast armies of the rodents. The prairie dogs relied on sheer numbers and their tunneling activities for protection, so that even this ferocious little predator could take only a certain quota of the population, for the burrows in any one ward were all interconnected and the rodents themselves were almost innumerable. Like all other decent citizens of nature's society, this animal took only what he needed, and the prairie dogs made up this slight loss by their incredible fecundity.

The Badger was, and still is, an entirely different factor in the prairieland economy. He is omnivorous, eating almost anything vegetable or animal that is digestible. He is also the champion digger for his size, and his method of gaining a living has always been to go at the problem bald-headed—and a badger can make an astonishingly large hole even in hard ground in an astonishingly short time. When he wants prairie dogs he goes after them directly, just digging into the ground, creating turmoil this way and that, trapping whole families in the collapsed earth, and devouring them as he uncovers them.

The American Badger is a most remarkable beast. It is low-slung, naturally obese, considerably flattened, and immensely powerful. There are documented records of these animals raising incredible weights by forcing their wedge-shaped bodies under them. They are still rather common animals, and it seems they have extended their range since the introduction of farming on this continent on a large scale. They are now in the Parkland Belt and even in the woodlands; they are all over the Northern Scrub Belt and are also found in the deserts. The reason for this may be that they are almost physically indestructible.

"Tumbleweeds" include various plants that break off at ground level and are rolled about by the wind, scattering their seeds. Among such are Tumbling Pigweed, Winged Pigweed, Bugseed, Tumbling Mustard, and Witchgrass.

Perhaps the most efficient controller of the prairie dogs—and it seems that these happy little creatures have long been the butt for all manner of predation—is the Prairie Falcon (known to ornithologists as *Falco mexicanus*), which used to live in great numbers all over this region. It is very like the Peregrine Falcon but larger and paler in color. These birds are common to the whole Southwest and are not ever seen east of the Mississippi. You may identify them in flight by dark patches where the wings join the body. They are not nearly so neat in appearance as most other falcons, notably their nearest relative, the Peregrine. They have from time immemorial specialized in hunting prairie dogs. The only strange thing is that the prairie dogs seem never to have learned that these sharp-eyed, swift, and efficient predators are aloft and consider prairie dog their standard diet. Prairie dogs are extremely alert horizontally and never miss even the slightest irregularity anywhere around them, but they simply fail to look up. They stare fixedly at your feet and vibrate their tails in terror as you approach, but they never think of looking up to see your gloved hand descending upon them. Thus it is that the prairie falcons come roaring down with wings almost closed like nose cones released from space rockets, extend

Bison of a kind that once preserved the prairies by "mowing" its grass from Alberta to Texas and from Illinois to Montana. Facing page: Portrait of a bull bison.

their taloned feet, and clobber the little rodents as they bumble about chewing grass stems.

There are other parties to the construction and maintenance of the prairies. Perhaps most notable among these are the gallinaceous birds—the Prairie Chicken, and the Sharp-tailed Grouse, that preposterous strutter. These game birds once lived in great numbers, each in its own appointed and rather specialized place, on the endless plains of the Prairie Belt. They had their own stamping grounds, and they, in turn, were the basis of still another natural economy. Their multitudes maintained the coyotes and the skunks.

PRAIRIE OX AND PRONGHORN "ANTELOPE"

As we have said, the prairies were originally dependent upon two animals—the little Prairie Dog and the mighty Bison. The latter is a large ox, one of a group of similar beasts that once roamed much of the northern hemisphere. There was, until recently, a very large species in Alaska that had enormous spreading horns; and there are still a handful of living individ-

uals of a European species known as the Wisent, now all in confinement. Bison once roamed from the spruce forests of the Canadian Lakes District to central Mexico and from the Rockies to the eastern seaboard. There is now evidence that they even inhabited the prairies of the Pacific coastal lowlands. Of the several species once extant, only two remain today, the Woodland Bison of the Great Slave Lake area which we have already mentioned, and the Plains Bison or "buffalo." As everybody knows, this animal was living by the millions all over the central part of the continent when the white man first arrived, but by the beginning of this century they were headed for, and once were very near to, total extinction. However, a group of public-spirited citizens banded together into a society for their protection, and as a result the remnants were gathered together and set out in suitable reservations, and their breeding was carefully watched. They have now made a rather fine recovery, but they will never regain their past glory simply because their country—principally the Great Prairies—has gone forever.

The Bison herds used once to drift all over the prairielands. They often traveled in almost countless lines, single file, that reached from horizon to horizon; and the trails their great hoofs

The Pronghorn or American Antelope is a unique animal with hollow horns which it sheds annually. Found all over the prairies, it is a left-over from preglacial times.

wore into the hard surface soil in many cases laid out the original roads followed by the white invaders as they straggled westward. Bison needed water, and for this they would dig with their front hoofs, making shallow, bowl-shaped and roughly circular depressions, called appropriately "buffalo wallows." (However, many of these depressions visible today, though attributed to the activities of the buffalo, apparently were really caused by wind action in natural depressions sometimes started by prairie dogs.) The Bison faced a rather more rugged and irksome existence than one might suppose, because the prairies are for the greater part of the year rather "difficult" and at other times can be really distressing.

In winter they are very cold and wind-swept and have a lot of snowfall through which every living thing has to dig for whatever dried grasses may remain from the scorching summers and autumns. The spring brings unusually low temperatures and often widespread floods before the grass greens again. Early summer means a brief respite, but then the atmosphere becomes troublesome; for it is on the prairies of the world that one really comes face to face with "weather" in many of its most violent aspects. At the end of summer, drought is almost invariably the rule. Then comes fire—under natural conditions started by light-

ning—that roars unchecked over mile after mile, consuming everything that has already been dried to tinder by the sun.

But so swiftly did the winds drive these violent fires along that their destructiveness was actually diminished, and animals that could duck into holes were almost immune from them. The fires just rolled over the thin ground cover and left it smoldering; sometimes it simply did not have time to burn at all. Also, as any prairie farmer knows, the wind can even be too strong, and then it simply blows the fire out as we blow out a candle flame. Nonetheless, fire was perhaps the worst enemy of the bigger animals, for they often could not fly fast enough before it and they could not withstand suffocation if it caught up with them. Yet, although often singed, they were seldom, it seems, actually burned to death. The jack rabbits and pronghorns could usually get away from it, since both were exceedingly swift animals with great staying powers. As a matter of fact, they did better than many of the birds, which tended to fly a short distance ahead of the flame front and then land and forget the problem till the heat hit them again. But even the swiftest animals seem not to have been able to get away from the torrential floods resulting from the violent electric storms and cloudbursts of late summer. Whole herds became overwhelmed and went bumping away into the bottomlands, often to be sunk in silts and deltas and fossilized like the extinct creatures of long ago.

The Pronghorn "Antelope" is a mysterious left-over from a bygone age. It stands today all by itself among the other ungulates or hoofed animals. It has rather gawky-looking upright horns that are hollow, grow on a bony core, and are shed but have a fork. This presents the question of how a horn that divides like a Y is shed. The process is most unusual. Each year a fully furred skin starts to grow up from the base of the bony core of the horn but *inside* the old horny covering. This finally reaches the tip of both the main and the branch tine, and as it grows, it bursts the old horn so that it splits and drops off. Another odd feature of the Pronghorn is the hair of its rump. This is long, stiff, and glistening white at all times, and can be raised or fluffed out by the animal at will by means of muscles under the skin. Pronghorns went into a serious decline along with the Bison, but today they have made a magnificent comeback and may be seen grazing placidly along the verges of main roads all over the prairielands.

The great Prairie Belt of this continent was a land of unique beauty before it was blanketed by the works of man. There are still pockets where, if one orientates oneself carefully, one may look out upon a vista of softly undulating hummocks and hillocks, all sere brown and featureless but laid out almost geometrically in perfect herringbone pattern. At first there appears to be nothing but dead grass on this land, but if you sit and wait you will note many small birds of exactly the same color as the drab landscape. Next a slight discoloration may suddenly move, and you find that a pronghorn was standing there all the time. And you get greater surprises. Of all things unimaginable in such a stark land, an enormous porcupine may come trundling along looking like a vast hairy mop and with no place to go.

But above all it is to the sky that one looks when out on the true prairie. Weather is perhaps the single most important factor in the life of man. Everybody, even the most troglodytic city dweller, looks at the sky the first thing every morning. And although the "sky" is similar everywhere around this planet, it looks completely different in different places. On the prairies it is forever a glowering and powerful presence, stretched taut above one like a great tent, in front of which sail majestically the clouds—all kinds of clouds: in serried ranks; in puffy formations; alone in tragic isolation; or in great, awe-inspiring masses. Over prairies there may be a great dark blanket, black as rolled steel to one side, brilliant sunshine to another, and a vast latticework of white rectangles covering the firmament in another, with vivid shafts of hard yellow sun rays descending to earth between them. You may drive along in half-darkness at midday watching a thin blue line ahead and be inundated with hailstones almost the size of golf balls in a sudden burst for half an hour, and then abruptly come out into soft sunlight under a cloudless sky; or you may be sitting stripped to the waist in blazing heat, see something like the hand of a man on the horizon, and in a few minutes be running for shelter in a downpour of tropical type but of Arctic temperature. The "weather" on the prairies is violent and sudden, and it is always with you.

BURNED BADLANDS

The great Prairie Belt is divided by some (including students of biology, of vegetation, and even of land form) into three separate subbelts. These are: first, to the west, on higher elevations near the mountain barrier, what are called "steppes"; second, the true grass prairies on the intermediate levels, covered with loess and sandy soils; and third, the alternating upland plateau grasslands and vegetated bottomlands. The difference between the first two cannot today be seen, even if it ever existed; that between the second and third is merely empirical. The point to remember is that this whole vast area consists of that which lies between the parklands and the temperate forests on the one hand and the scrublands, chaparrals, and Hot Deserts on the other. Its parts are all much of a oneness, whatever you choose to call them; their essential feature is grass.

Vast and monotonous as they are, they are not, however, altogether featureless. The most interesting oddity in them is what are called badlands. These are actually the heads of the incised river systems where the "bottoms" are too arid to be fully vegetated, and which thus form dry chasms in the otherwise more or less level plateau. The most interesting and fabulous are those of North Dakota (the Theodore Roosevelt National Memorial Park) and South Dakota (the White River Badlands). It so happens that the strata which make up these lands are, on the surface, composed of clays and other not-as-yet-compacted material which is very soft and easily washed away by water. They also contain, or once contained, interlarded beds of lignite or soft coal. This coal was deposited in inland lakes and swamps about 55 million years ago; and, after being covered up, squeezed, dried out, and partly petrified, in many cases it caught fire due to natural causes. Being highly inflammable and permeated with combustible gases, it simply smoldered away for centuries or millennia. Some of these coal beds are still burning today. The result is that the strata above collapse as the gases leak away and the layers of clay or other material immediately above are baked to the color of reddish clinkers with the firmness and general consistency of pottery. This material (erroneously called *scoria*), being harder than the other strata and reddish rather than their soft blues, grays, and greens, stands out most prominently today when the land is guttered by erosion. It very often forms the caps of buttes and the headstones on the fantastic pillars that dot the land.

The White River Badlands are surely one of the most wonderful and mysterious sights on earth. Unlike the Grand Canyon and other overwhelming topographical features, they are rather intimate. What is more, they are one-sided, as it were, in that they are formed all along a line where the land drops suddenly down from one level to another about two hundred feet below. Approached from the upper level, the badlands are invisible; seen from the lower level—and it is perfectly level—they stand up like a continuous wall. On a map, the lip of the upper plateau describes a vast fern-leaf pattern as the gullies of erosion divide, subdivide, and sub-subdivide again and again as they eat backward into the tableland. The strata here are horizontal, and as a result the whole place is almost geometrical in design. Yet the resultant formations are beyond the wildest imagining.

I once reached the lip of this vast, incredible area just at sundown under a clear sky. Looking over the edge, I was nearly blinded by the roiling masses of scintillating colors caused by the orange rays of the setting sun splashed over the many subtle pastel shades of the mud and clay walls. Then came a full moon soaring over one of the most outrageously-shaped buttes. For hours I meandered on, right through the vast one-sided chasm, in and out between isolated peaks and buttes, back and forth among the inky shadows, while the tops of the natural walls changed from yellow to orange to gold to flame to red to pink to amber and ultimately to purple, and on into the colorless spectrum of the light of the moon. This land is not beautiful: it is something that does not seem to belong on this planet.

159

Land
of the Bayous

The Delta of the Mississippi

There are areas on this earth that take on a most vivid character but only in certain circumstances, or literally *under* certain circumstances, for it is the atmospheric condition of the sky above them that brings out their wonder. Some of these are like the proverbial eyes of a toad—little islands of exquisite beauty surrounded by comparative drabness if not downright ugliness. I came across one of these in the area known as the Mississippi delta—and by this term I mean the true delta of the Mississippi as defined in the map legend, not the upriver bottomlands which local residents call "the Delta."

We came to this place unexpectedly while boating down a bayou which looked much like any other muddy creek, inlet, or river crossing a marsh. We had turned into a small side slough bounded by levees about six feet high covered with palmettos, willows, and other woody shrubbery. There were also some oaks standing to one side, but around the rest of the shore were only a few low bushes and clumps of tough grass. We climbed the bank and saw beyond it a seemingly endless marsh going off to the horizon. In the foreground at the bottom of an abrupt clayey slope was bare mud, in part covered by water and in part by short sedges. Beyond this was a carpet of bright green stems waving in the wind and dotted with egrets of pristine whiteness. There happened to be a small ginger-colored raccoon messing about in this mud when we appeared. He immediately went galloping off and disappeared into a solitary cypress tree festooned to its root with an enormous load of Spanish Moss.

The bank we stood on was a natural levee. The river was behind us, while to our left grew the scattered oaks. To the right the ground dipped slightly into a wood, the crown foliage of whose trees was a beautiful, soft blue-green but festooned with waving Spanish Moss. The edge of the wood was concealed behind a rampart of palmetto palms growing to a height of about ten feet. We wandered down the bank to this wood, which formed a fairly narrow strip between the marshes and the river.

That day the sky was cloudless and of a pellucid pastel blue. This was reflected from the surface of the dark brown waters of the river as a rather violent deep azure with an almost electric quality. The sunlight was of an intensity seldom seen except

The delta of the Mississippi is clothed in marshes and prairies intersected by a network of bayous, and here and there raised levees and hummocks. Inland are cypress forests.

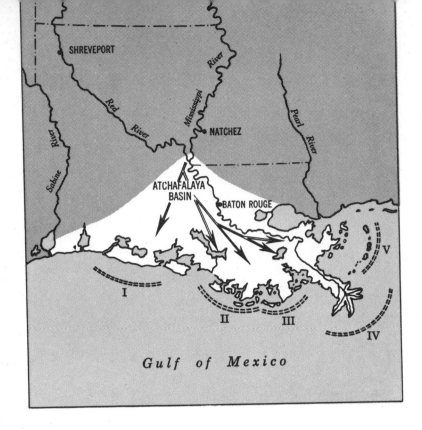

Gulf of Mexico

The extensive open marshes bordering the coast are saline. This small area, only 18,000 square miles in extent, is thus a natural province. It forms a triangle 300 miles wide at the base on the coast, about 100 miles deep at the apex, with northwestern and northeastern sides of some 150 miles in length. To the west it ends abruptly at the estuary of the Sabine River, beyond which an entirely different kind of coastal prairie begins. To the east it runs into the sea in the form of a 100-mile-long peninsula lying almost parallel to the coast and ending in a very strange topographical feature—a bird-foot-shaped minor peninsula through the "leg" and "toes" of which the Mississippi finds its way to the sea. North and east of this peninsula the coast breaks up into hundreds of islands. The "leg" is 50 miles long, and one of the "toes" is 21 miles long; it is estimated the entire structure is growing at the rate of between 300 and 600 yards per year.

The whole of this delta is sinking fairly rapidly due to what is called isostatic adjustment, which means that the weight of material deposited upon it is causing the underlying strata to be compressed and also to sag. Thus, while the delta keeps growing seaward, its main body is going down and also bending the adjacent true coast line to the north downward. This is causing the sea to flood in between the two on either side. As the greatest deposits are on the east, the sag is greatest on that side, and the sea has already flooded one hundred miles back west, between the delta and the main coast.

The whole delta is composed of old beaches and the filled-in lagoons that once lay behind them. The main river channel originally flowed southwest, but it has made four turns and now points due east (see arrows on map). The coast is thus a series of old river mouths, the position of which is identified by offshore arcs of shallows (see numbers I to V on map). The major current is the clockwise whorl of the Gulf, which pushes the whole delta to the east, but there are wind-fostered, inshore, countercurrents which cause beach material to move to the west. Offshore reefs are caused by shell banks embedded in silt.

The whole delta is a maze of lakes, rivers, canals, and sloughs, locally called bayous.

The delta of the Mississippi forms a natural ecological unit with very precise boundaries. (This is not the area that Mississippi valley folk call "the Delta," by which they mean the bottomlands between the middle Mississippi and the Yazoo rivers.) In some respects it is a southward extension of the bottomlands of the Mississippi valley, with which it is connected on the north via the narrow Atchafalaya Basin (between Natchez and Baton Rouge). Whereas vegetation tends to grow in a parklike manner on the limited drier areas in that basin, it does not do so in the delta itself. In fact, the latter lies south of and outside the Park Belt and is thus within the Prairie Belt; and, as the land has dried out on the inland side, open grassfields have come into existence there. The verges of waterways are lined with gallery forest, and the extensive swamps are for the most part covered with a closed-canopy swamp forest.

when it penetrates an almost saturated atmosphere. The exceedingly clean trees—for there was not one bit of dead branch or trash anywhere to be seen—stood like cutouts with dark trunks and billowing foliage above, while waving satin-gray moss formed a succession of draperies everywhere. Beneath, in unexpected but perfect contrast, the ground was carpeted with foot-high, almost unbelievably green grass. Nor was this all; for, growing in the grass, as if placed by the calculated hand of man, was a sort of subforest of palmettos of quite another shade of green and also all apparently without so much as a dead leaf. Through all this the yellow sunlight poured in golden shafts. Even more impressive was the silence. Not even the moss sighed in the gentle wind; it just waved, and the shafts of sunlight counterwaved.

In addition to the raccoon that we had surprised grubbing for his breakfast, less than ten minutes later we almost caught an animal with the delightful scientific name of *Myopotamus coypu* (popular name, the Coypu), whose presence will be explained later. We had also extracted an opossum from the base of a tree and had roused a family party of deer. A flooded part of the marsh was dotted at almost regular intervals with endless, small,

low mounds of nature's debris, and, although it was such brilliant daylight, there were comings and goings among these, as evinced by moving V's in the still waters. They were made by a vast colony of the muskrats for which this whole province is famous and from which furriers get the bulk of their raw material. Later in the day we disturbed a pair of otters.

There were wading birds standing about everywhere, including large numbers of great blue herons. It was most enlightening here to be able to compare all the members of the heron family at one time, for they were all there, even the great white, which only in recent years has visited this locality from its formerly very restricted territory in southern Florida. What is more, a highly experienced bird-watcher who had brought us specifically to see these herons was finally able to convince us that both the white phase of the Reddish Egret and the white immature of the Little Blue Heron (the adult of which is to my eyes quite black) were also present.

Even more interesting to me at the time was the extraordinary number of very small birds that twittered and flitted about between the palmettos and oaks and crept through the moss that hung from the latter. That some were warblers I could see, but

I was never so glad to have an expert along; while he was himself quite excited because he could identify some types that should not have been there at that time of year, but away north at their breeding grounds. He told me that some of these species stay in this, the far south, all spring and summer and may even nest there; he believes that they have always done so and have been spotted only in recent years as a result of the more careful surveys of the smaller and more specialized natural habitats in this province by local enthusiasts. This place was very isolated because it was the only stretch of wooded levee to be seen (from water level) within the bounds of the horizon, and it formed a meandering ridge only about two miles long.

Levees are natural banks constructed like retaining walls and running continuously along both sides of a river. They are caused by the river dropping its debris and silt in times of flood, and doing so most of all wherever its waters are slowed down. This is naturally among roots, tree trunks, and other obstructions that line its banks. This in turn prompts a sturdier growth of such obstructions; and so the process goes on until a quite high wall or levee is built up. Now, levees are places of refuge for all manner of animals, even those that can well survive in water or even live in it, for most of their time, like otters; and they also offer the only living quarters for purely terrestrial animals, notably birds. Levees are also favorite gathering grounds for reptiles and amphibians, and this place was outstanding especially for snakes.

Most people would feel that this would altogether set at nought the beauties of the place, especially since the majority of the snakes were cottonmouth moccasins, probably the second-deadliest of our indigenous snakes. Yet this animal, for all its unpleasant potentialities and its rather ugly appearance—it is a dirty blackish olive in color, unrelieved by the beautiful markings of the rattlers—is a perfectly decent citizen of nature that happens to get its living by striking its food, both on land and in the water, with poison-injecting fangs. Its normal food is mostly fish, but it takes also frogs and the giant Siren, a huge, slimy, eel-like amphibian of the salamander group that grows to three feet in length and has only one pair of tiny legs just behind the head. This creature lives in debris-filled water, and it will grab small rodents including even muskrats. Cottonmouths are exceedingly common all over the delta, and in temporarily or even permanently flooded areas every clump of grass showing above water appears to house one. Their distribution coincides almost exactly with that of the coastal fringe provinces from southern Virginia to south Florida, up the Mississippi valley to Illinois, southwest to the western edge of the East Chaparral, and up the Rio Grande valley to the Pecos River. Their young look quite different from the adults, and are almost indistinguishable from copperheads; and like the young of that animal also, the cottonmouths have bright yellow ends to their tails. These two snakes are, moreover, of the same genus, known as *Agkistrodon,* meaning "hook-tooth."

The Coypu—its fur is called "nutria"— is a South American aquatic porcupine that was introduced to North America forty years ago and is now widespread.

In addition to the moccasins, which we gave up counting, we encountered several water snakes known locally as Water Pilots; these may grow to five feet in length. They were all in small muddy pools in bright sunlight. They are the fastest swimmers among our snakes. Then there were numbers of the ceramic-looking green tree snakes twined around palmetto stems and looped over, just lying about on, or gliding through the Spanish moss. Looking even more like porcelain were thousands of little green tree frogs stuck onto things everywhere; and, to complete the color picture, in the shafts of sunlight the leaves were dotted with the delicate little anoles or fence lizards, all exhibiting their brightest green livery. The whole place was also alive with very tropical-looking butterflies, mostly various swallowtails, and all manner of fascinatingly constructed cocoons and egg masses of insects were attached to the Spanish moss.

HOW TO BUILD A DELTA

This place is situated at a most strategic spot in the great delta of the Mississippi River, close to the present main exit of that river, and just south of the junction line between the coastal marshes and the older deltaic swamplands. It lies in the middle of the eastern quarter of the delta and is an ideal place for observing most of the remarkable features of this extraordinary province; and it is still unspoiled.

Deltas are very particular things. Imagine a great river like the Mississippi for tens or hundreds of thousands of years busily gnawing away at the edges of a great basin of land up to the very tips of its every tributary, and hauling all the loose material downstream. Where its flow is swift enough, it will move boulders; where slower, mere silt; and the constant pressure from behind keeps it moving along fast enough to do the latter till it reaches the edge of the continent. Here it may encounter one of several conditions. It could find the bottom of the sea tumbling over a gigantic submarine escarpment with oceanic currents roaring by. In this case its silt would be whipped away. If, on the other hand, it hits a shelving, shallow coastal sea, especially one without much tide, its waters will push out and come to a slow stop and its silt will be spread far and wide. If this happens, the sea thereabouts rapidly begins to fill up. This causes the river to back up and drop its silt more quickly until, one would imagine, it had completely dammed itself and started a great inland lake. But it doesn't proceed that way.

First, the ponding of the river, or rather its tendency to back up, causes it to push harder and so cut channels through the obstruction ahead. Second, the surface layers of the crust of the earth under this mass get squeezed and compacted and then begin to sag, so that each layer forms a great bowl. This relieves the tension temporarily and permits the river to win the next round by piling ever more of its silt on top. Actually, both processes are going on simultaneously; but there are great swings, in time, controlled by several factors. The sea level may change, the whole crust of the earth may rise or fall due to crustal movements, and the rainfall in the river's drainage basin may vary so that more or less silt is available and the speed of the river is increased or reduced. That such variations have taken place during the formation of this delta may be seen from a glance at the map.

Facing page: The bayous are mostly muddy, but among the marshes are limpid waters crowded with fish, snails, and other small fry that form the food of wading birds.

There have been four major phases and one subsequent minor—or unsuccessful—phase in its formation. These you can identify by plotting the direction of flow of successive lengths of the river, starting from the "narrows" about its junction with the Red River, as shown by the arrows on the map in this chapter. The Mississippi originally "wanted" to go straight out to sea, which was somewhat west of south, and this it did for a time; but, although the sea was shallow and had only a very small tide, it also had a considerable current that whirled clockwise around the almost circular coast of the Gulf of Mexico (and now gives rise to the Gulf Stream to the east). This shifted the mouth of the Mississippi over to the east, grubbing away at its delta on the west side and redepositing the material on its east side. Matters continued fairly static until a period of less rainfall occurred to the north; then the river lost out to the sea and its mouth got pushed off to the east. Next the river regained the

The Snowy Egret, really a small heron, is again one of the commonest birds around the Gulf-coast lands. It has bright yellow feet and is often called "Golden Slippers."

Above: The Reddish Egret. Right: A Great Blue Heron, our second-largest wading bird. It nests from Quebec to Florida but most of its numbers winter in the South. Center below: Typical of the vast number of wading birds that live in the delta or pass through it on migration are this gallinule, coot, Louisiana Heron, and Snowy Egret.

upper hand and burst out with a new tongue of land (Arc II on map). This happened four times, but then the river encountered some assistance, as it were, from the land in its persistent battle with the sea, for it had pushed so far out that it had begun to form a "hook" and thereby created a slight whirligig or counter-current to its left side. This enabled it to make such headway that it did virtually dam itself up (Arc V on the map) and, having thus covered its left flank, it burst out at its old mouth (Arc IV), where it is today, penetrating into "enemy territory."

A Louisiana survey has calculated that the Mississippi carries one million tons of sediment to the sea every day of the year. In a year, this is equivalent to a block of land one square mile in area and three hundred feet high. During the eleven thousand years since the last "retreat" of the ice up north, it has there-fore dumped sediment to a depth of two hundred feet over the entire eighteen thousand square miles of its delta: yet that delta is still only just above sea level! Where has it gone? Down below, to form a great inverted dome in the earth's crust, creating thereby complex pressures and tensions that affect a wide area around; for you cannot push a solid into another solid without something giving way. It is a strange thing that deltas, which appear to be the lowest and softest places on earth, really form some of the hardest "nuts" in its crust. When a whole subcontinent sinks, as northern Australia has done, among the last things to go down are the deltas, as is seen in the Aru Islands in the Arafura Sea, which are only the old delta of a vast river that once ran north off that land.

DOMES OF SALT AND SULPHUR

The amount of sediment actually accumulated in the Mississippi delta is not known, but geologists state that it is more than thirty thousand feet in depth. At the present rate of deposit, this represents six and a half million years, which takes us back to about the beginning of the so-called Pliocene era, the stage

before the Pleistocene or "ice age." It could all therefore be of comparatively recent origin, geologically speaking; and there is considerable reason for supposing that it is because the delta as well as all of central North America was under the sea prior to the Pliocene and perhaps even for a time during the subsequent Pleistocene. Thirty thousand feet is nearly six miles, and you cannot, as I have said, push rocks down six miles in the middle of a 250-mile strip without something giving way; and something has. It is the surrounding surface rocks, and they are being pulled down, too, so that the sea is flooding in around the edges of the delta and could turn it into a great inshore island.

Possibly because of these tremendous pressures, there are, dotted about the delta and mostly along the line dividing its more modern coastal marshlands from its older deltaic swamplands, a number of mysterious, large, circular domes. Several of these, and notably Avery Island, are composed of solid rock salt apparently squeezed up (in that case from a depth of more than fourteen thousand feet) like paste out of a tube and then spread out on top of the sediment. This Avery Island is today owned by a private corporation which maintains a wonderful bird sanctuary and a magnificent botanical garden there, in addition to the oldest salt mine in America and a factory producing the famous "Tabasco Sauce" from oil, vinegar, salt, and peppers grown on the dome. Other domes are formed of pure sulphur; and from almost all of these domes oil also gushes from the depths. There are oil domes both near the surface and deep down. The whole strange phenomenon is caused by the incalculable weight or pressure, which at depth is equivalent to great heat, so that it distills or squeezes these soluble substances out of the rocks in which they were entrapped; and these break through to the surface when any crustal movement gives them an extra pinch. The whole delta is like a vast chemical plant initiated by the Mississippi.

YOUNG MAN RIVER

This river is still often referred to as "the biggest river in the world," and such statements may even be found in schoolbooks. It frankly is not so in any respect. First, it is a bit shorter than the Amazon and considerably shorter than the Nile, the Nile

Above left: The American or Common Egret. Below: Otters at play.

being 4160 miles long, the Amazon 3900, and the Mississippi 3800. In volume of water that it carries to the sea it is quite paltry, coming thirteenth on the list, after the Yangtze, Congo, Amur, Yellow, Lena, Mekong, Niger, Mackenzie, Ob, Yenesei, Volga, and the Parana-Plata, and just equaling the Nile. In total drainage area it comes third to the Congo and the Amazon; while in number of tributaries it is greatly surpassed by many tropical rivers. In actual size it is small in comparison to dozens of other rivers, its width and depth, where it is finally concentrated before it debouches onto its delta, being a little less than a mile across (4500 feet) with a navigable channel 300 feet wide. The depth at this point (Cairo on the Mississippi) is only 9 feet! The Amazon at a comparable point is over 50 miles wide and over 120 feet deep.

The matter of confluents or tributaries and of effluents or "mouths" is rather widely misapprehended, and the subject of bayous is downright muddling. Confluents flow into rivers and effluents out of them, but bayous need not flow at all and do not have to be connected to a river. The term "bayou" appears originally to have been applied by the French to old wiggles in the main river that had got lopped off and left aside as C- or S-shaped lakes, called by geologists cutoff lakes. By extension, the name was applied also to the endless meandering little lakes, and then to riverlets, creeks, and natural channels often called "canals," and even to the endless sloughs that dissect this delta. Today the matter is further complicated by a tremendous network of man-made canals, drainage ditches, and channels for oil operations, so that the whole is a latticework of waterways.

THE BATTLE OF THE WATERS

The battle of the waters along this coast has been closely studied and may be readily observed in an area (facing Arc I on the map) in the west of the delta now known as the Rockefeller Wildlife Refuge and Game Preserve. Here almost every type of littoral, coastal, and deltaic structure and vegetation may be seen, ranging from open sea to inland lakes. It consists of 82,000 acres of marshland with a coast line of a little over twenty-six miles. The only firm ground in the whole region is the beach itself and a few hundred feet or yards back of this, and two small strips inland where old beaches cross the area. The marshes are of three distinct kinds running in parallel belts. The farthest inland is a fresh-water marsh of tall grasses growing in about a foot of water. The middle one is brackish with shorter grasses, which sometimes dries off for a period in the winter but which is really a mat of roots floating on an ocean of liquid mud. The third belt, nearest the sea, is saline. The whole is cut by half a dozen channels which let the fresh water out at low tide and bring salt water in at high. Landward of all this is a string of shallow lakes, and behind them again we enter the true deltaic prairies, which envelop occasional old islands that might be called hummocks and meandering bits of old levees stranded amid the sea of grass. This continues inland until the cypress swamps and the slightly higher lands are reached, and these then continue inland to the delta. Thus we have first coast, then marshlands, then prairies, then the old delta.

The beach is composed of sand mixed with a great deal of broken shells and some silt, the coarser material being neatly arranged on the upper beach. There are long stretches where the sort of plum pudding of shells known as *coquina* is found—bits of shells and whole shells, sand, and some small limy concretions bound together with calcium carbonate. Since most of the winds blow from the east or southeast, contrary to and athwart the main deep-sea offshore current, there is a steady inshore countercurrent that pushes all this material to the west.

The marshlands, over which the surface of the water table coincides with the surface of the land, are huge, open, soggy areas covered with grass and everywhere cut into by little incipient lakes and meandering channels. It is also crossed by old beaches called "beach-ridges" or *cheniers,* which may actually rise over ten feet above the otherwise flat surface, and are leftovers from periods when the sea suddenly retreated. The step up to or onto the prairie is very clear, the short marsh grasses suddenly giving way to the much taller prairie grasses. This latter is a slightly undulating flat plain sloping very gently—only about two feet per mile—toward the coast. Throughout it stand concentrations of trees alongside streams or where streams formerly were. This is the newest or youngest and most seaward-lying of four distinct belts that snake across the whole delta, each of which marks one of the major changes in land level and/or rainfall in the Pleistocene period that we mentioned above. At first, this whole land looks flat and much the same, but when one takes even a little time to look at it, one may see a working model of many of the great geological processes that have built our earth.

These vast marshlands are, throughout the whole province, a home for a wonderful wildlife for the most part adapted to living on mud. Man has disturbed it not a little with his diggings and ditchings and burnings, and also by extensive trapping which was once quite uncontrolled. He has also made an even more horrible mess of its waters, sometimes by making them look too clean! Industry is now pushing into this whole area and pollution is rampant, but there is still a great deal of the land and of its wildlife to be seen.

The pre-eminent creature of these prairies and marshlands is the rodent called the Muskrat—or more properly the Musquash,

The Osprey (Pandion haliaetus) is a bird of prey about midway in size between the eagles and the larger hawks. A fish-eater, it descends on its prey vertically with extended legs and talons. It winters around the Gulf.

one of its original Amerindian names, for it is not a rat in the pure sense but a large vole, belonging to the Cricetid as opposed to the Old World Murid group of the rodents. It is to be found almost all over this continent in suitable localities, but nowhere is it so abundant as in this province. It is a large rat-shaped creature with very small ears, enormous webbed hind feet, and a naked, scaly tail that is compressed from side to side. In over-all length it may grow to two feet. Its skin is completely water-proof and bears a thick, soft underfur and a long, glistening overcoat of firmer hairs. It is of various rich shades of brown, dark along the midback, lighter to reddish on the flanks, and much lighter below, even to having a white throat in some races. It gives off a rather pleasant musky, aromatic odor; but it is not what one might call a friendly beast, either to man or its own kind, and it can give a most destructive bite. It constructs feeding dumps or lodges on open water or among grasses, to which it hauls vegetation to be eaten. These are individually owned projects.

Muskrats either build lodges in the open or undertake large constructions in banks for winter use, wherein up to a dozen individuals may reside and in out-chambers of which the young are produced. The lodges are made of countless little oblong rolls of vegetable fibers, grass stems, and so forth, all neatly rolled by the animals. Muskrats have several litters of up to nine or ten young per season after only a thirty-day gestation period, and the young are weaned in a month.

Half a century ago a man in Oregon brought to this country from the La Plata area of South America another animal that looks superficially like a muskrat multiplied in bulk by about ten. Actually it is a member of an entirely different group of the rodents—that of the porcupines, as opposed to that of either the rats or the squirrels, to which latter a third animal of similar habits, the Beaver, belongs. Its name is the Coypu, that *Myopotamus coypu* mentioned earlier, the fur of which is known as nutria. This animal did very well in the northwest but promptly "escaped" and somehow managed to get great distances over the continent, every now and then cropping up in a new locality—much to the surprise of local folk who either had never seen such a "rat," or mistook it for a beaver, or thought that their local muskrats had suddenly taken to breeding giants. At first there was considerable agitation as to whether this introduced animal was going to oust some members of the indigenous fauna, but it seems that the creature has settled down comfortably in a natural niche that was actually empty; and this may well have been that left by the then fast-vanishing Beaver. The Coypu did not disturb the muskrats but lived alongside them, keeping in its own little ecological zone, feeding on coarser vegetation, and breeding happily. This animal has been so successfully introduced to the Mississippi Delta that there is some apprehension there as to the future of fur-trapping and even the balance of the natural economy.

EMPTY SHELLS

As you drive about this delta or boat about its rivers and bayous, you will hardly ever be out of sight of either great piles of white stuff or of boats laden with it. These are shells—hundreds of millions of tons of the empty "houses" of bivalve shellfish. The roads are made of them, they litter and permeate the soil of the fields, they are piled up everywhere by both man and nature; they come pouring out of vast factories where their living contents, mostly in the form of oysters, are canned; and they come by the endless truckload from the oyster counters of New

Orleans and every other town, hamlet, and homestead. They are of two principal kinds, which may be loosely called oysters and clams, both of which are bivalves or two-shelled mollusks.

The clams are of numerous species and are found from the deeper waters of the ocean to the high-tide mark, as well as in the salt and brackish lakes, and even in some fresh-water lakes and rivers. They are all of nondescript outline, either almost round or almost rectangular or oblong; they are all rather thick and are white, but are usually covered externally with a thin brownish skin of chitinous material related to the material of our fingernails. During life they are all busily engaged in

Muskrats are semiaquatic voles, unique to this continent; their pelts form the basis of the modern fur trade. They are rather ingenious, digging extensive tunnels, draining ponds, and constructing lodges.

extracting calcium carbonate out of the waters and converting it into their shells. Then they die, and all this material goes into the sediments at the bottom of the water, since their "dead" shells descend thereinto. This has a tremendous influence on the kinds of rocks that are eventually made out of these sediments.

Along the coast the oysters predominate, as they also do in many salt-water lagoons and ponds. Oysters grow all together, the young settling on the old and on dead shells and growing there until, under normal conditions, they usually form vast reefs. Others happen to fasten to small inanimate things when very young and grow isolated and ready for the table, as one might say. Today man has practically taken over the life of the oyster of this coast and has developed an enormous industry therefrom, but he is sensibly putting the shells back where nature intended them to end up. He is thereby encouraging little oysters and also building the land in a manner commensurate with the current geological trend.

The life of the oysters is by no means banal, and their part in our history is almost glamorous. They have been eaten, and in the vastest quantities, by all coast-dwelling peoples wherever they have been found since palaeolithic times. Miniature mountains formed of their shells stretch for miles in Denmark and other countries where our stone-age ancestors pitched them out

of their back doors for centuries on end. Roman emperors and Aztec emperors had them rushed to their tables, packed in snow, by relays of runners on horseback or on foot. The Romans placed their major settlements in England by the best oyster beds, and boasted of the fact.

The oyster itself usually begins life as a male but then changes to a female and usually back again, sometimes several times. These bivalves breed, in this area, from April to October, during which time they exude a milky fluid. This is either the milt of the male or the countless millions of minute eggs of the female, one of which can give rise at one time to up to sixty million eggs. Both milt and eggs are merely let out into the sea, where the sperms find the ova. After fertilization the usual procedure of cell division goes on until in only a few hours there is formed a minute spherical body covered with even minuter hairlike processes called cilia. These thrash about fairly systematically and keep the little thing afloat so that it is moved away by currents. Eventually it starts to grow two tiny shells; and when these get heavy enough, they cause the animal to sink to the bottom, where it immediately attaches itself to some firm object for life. This stage is called "spat," and by that time the oyster is pretty well organized internally for pumping water through itself both for food and for oxygen; but it is very sensitive to fine silt in the water and must be raised off the bottom. This is the principal reason for returning the empty shells from our tables to the sea—so that the little spat can perch up in clean water. The cilia have by now retreated into the body of the animal, but they continue to thrash, so driving a constant stream of water into the gut and around the gills—at the rate of about fifty gallons a day for an average Bluepoint, incidentally!

The animal itself is enclosed in a mantle, and it is the edge of this that secretes the shell by a most complicated process, part internal through the blood stream and part external by a sort of "electrolysis" of the water in which many salts are dissolved. The shell grows from the inside, layer upon layer, and if some particle of grit or irresolute small creature gets under the mantle and causes irritation, the oyster starts to build a little shell round it to smooth off its rough edges. Thus are pearls born. The oyster, I fear me, is not necessarily a very clean feeder; in fact, it can be an exceedingly filthy one from our point of view. Nevertheless we almost all eat it. Why this should be so is obvious, for it undoubtedly has a very pleasing taste, full of saltiness. Oysters are ready for the table in about two years, but they seem to be able to live to a very great age.

The oysters and the clams have, as a matter of fact, played almost as great a part in the formation of this delta as the river itself, and they are a somewhat prominent feature of its existence today. They will continue to be so in the future unless man once again plays havoc with ecology. So far, for once, he is doing the right thing in cooperation with nature, but still the oysters are diminishing drastically. This is partly due to pollution, mostly by oil which, though it has not been proved to kill them, gives them a taste that is just not acceptable to humans. Man has lived with the oyster for endless millennia; and perhaps he can still come to a mutually satisfactory accommodation here too, despite his need for petroleum.

171

Flatwoods
and Everglades

Peninsular Florida

13   The peninsula of Florida, although today the principal human playground on this continent, grows a very large part of the citrus crop and includes huge farmed areas, valuable mines, and timberlands. It is also, though few people seem to realize the fact, one of the foremost cattle-raising states. But it still contains extensive wild areas. Despite the fact that a hump a hundred feet above sea level is regarded here as a mountain, it is a most varied land, and it remains a paradise for the naturalist in whatever department he may be most interested. The peninsula itself may be divided into three parts—a northern that is clothed in the open pine forests typical of the great Southern Pine Belt; a central that is basically grassland and represents the easterly extension of the Prairie Belt; and a southern, covered mostly by swamps, that represents a tag end of the Northern Scrub Belt.

The peninsula has an underlying backbone composed of limestone, which reaches the surface in a boomerang-shaped ridge starting in the panhandle of the state and curving down through the middle of the northern or upper third of the peninsula. This formation, which has some fascinating features, as we shall see, then subsides under the more recent deposits that form the main

Of the two species of true alligators, this one is found in the Gulf states and the other in the Yangtze River. Right: Some plants of subtropical appearance, such as these broad-leafed Thalia, grow in the vast Florida cypress swamps.

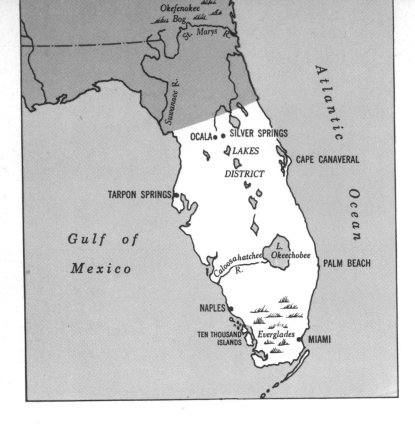

Peninsular Florida is really an island, being separated from the Southern Pine parklands by the St. Marys River, the Okefenokee Bog, and the Suwannee River and swamps. Geologically it is a new land, having been formed around a string of low islands and reefs during Pleistocene times by the materials washed off the eastern Appalachian piedmont and moved down the coast by inshore marine countercurrents. It now forms a low-domed ridge, never rising over 350 feet above sea level.

This peninsula is divided into a number of north-to-south strips—six in number in the north, three in the extreme south— each different and each subdivided into sections from East to West. Along the whole Atlantic coast there is a fringe of sand dunes and beaches; inland from these lie, in the north, a long belt of swamps about the St. Johns River; and south of this, a low plain dotted with pines, called "flatwoods." The next strip west constitutes the spine of the peninsula; it starts in the north in the form of low, subdued hills formed by the ancient islands and reefs, but then gives way throughout the central area to low, rolling country dotted with innumerable lakes and culminating in big Lake Okeechobee. South of this the country changes to the so-called "Everglades," which are vast open saw grass marshes dotted with low islands, locally called "hammocks" but elsewhere "hummocks." These do not reach the coast at any point.

To the west of this central spine lies another long strip of flatwoods, but in the north this contains a unique stretch known as the limestone sinkhole belt that turns northwest, crosses the Suwannee River, and continues on into the Florida panhandle. To the south of the Caloosahatchee River, which drains west out of Lake Okeechobee, the flatwoods devolve into a huge swamp known as the Big Cypress. Finally, along the Gulf or west coast, is a fringe of swampland broken by mud flats, reed-filled estuaries, and sand beaches, and cut by three major swamps—the lower Suwannee, the Hillsborough River Flats, and the edge of Big Cypress. The southern extremity of this area, south of Big Cypress, is a mangrove swamp fringed by mangrove-covered islands named the Ten Thousand Isles. This curls round the southern tip of Florida to meet the Atlantic sand beaches, which then extend for a hundred miles southwest in the form of a long string of small cays.

This peninsula may be divided on phytogeographical grounds into three belts running from west to east. The northern is part of the Parklands Belt; the central a continuation of the Prairies; and the southern an outlier of the Northern Scrub Belt. The last is often referred to as being "subtropical," but it lies north of the Tropic of Cancer, which is today regarded as the northern limit of the subtropics.

body of the country, but goes right on into the Caribbean and appears at the surface again in the Greater Antilles. The rest of the province has been built up around this ridge in easy stages during what geologists call the Pleistocene or "glacial" and the Holocene or "postglacial" periods, covering a time period of only a million years. The limestones of the ridge were laid down in a warm sea much earlier than this.

They have all the usual characteristics of limestones, one of which is that they may be dissolved by the carbonic acid contained in rain water. This surface water, soaking down into these strata, tends first to form little runnels along the natural cracks in the rocks, then to expand these into channels and finally into a network of caves. These in turn continue to enlarge, and if they are near enough to the surface of the land, their roofs sometimes collapse, resulting in what are called sinkholes.

The astonishing thing about such sinkholes in Florida is that the water may flow up out of them rather than down into them. Silver Springs, near Ocala, is an interesting example. This is a large "boil," and its point of water outflow is about seventy feet below the land surface. There is a considerable cave here, and from the floor of this the fossilized and semifossilized bones of several animals have been taken by skin divers; these include bones of mastodons and of another elephantine creature. It is a beautiful place, its waters especially so.

But I know of another "boil" with numerous clear effluents that is not too far away from this place and is even more beautiful, being so far altogether untouched by commercialism or other human activities. It also centers around a large spring but one not so deep, and it has three main exits. Its water too is absolutely clear and filled with little nondescript fish, many large gars and alligators, several varieties of water tortoises, and other clear-water creatures. It is surrounded by swampy-looking but firm land grown with cypresses, pines, and oaks, all festooned with Spanish Moss. There is much natural grass along its verges, and its waters are filled with waving, dark green, aquatic plants, while acres of water lilies and other vegetable things float upon its surface. To swim in this water below the surface is to enter a land of complete perfection and considerable mystery. The bottom is pure white sand; and, using a pair of goggles only, you will here find yourself in the most intimate contact with all

Above: The West Indian flamingo may once have nested in Florida, but it now appears there only in captivity. In low water they scoop up mud with their bills backward and upside down. Below: The Purple Gallinule (Porphyrula martinica), one of the most colorful and "impertinent" of birds, walks about on lily pads in swamps.

174

manner of aquatic creatures. The smaller fish come right up to your nose and peer at you. The gars, some of which are alarmingly large, tend just to move aside but always cautiously, and then move in your direction of travel without any apparent effort. They glide along beside you at a discreet distance until your breath gives out.

The alligators are the most fascinating of all, since they seem to be totally indifferent to one. Most of them that I have met underwater have been either just lying on the bottom or walking along it with a kind of measured pace. At first the larger ones startled me, but it seems that they are so sated with their natural foods that they will not bother to grab for any larger, colorless object that comes by. The more dangerous things—and these include hungry or alarmed alligator snapping turtles—lurk in muddy, vegetation-obscured, or other darker places. Wading about in this you may get "chopped," as the local people put it.

Here is a world apart, a wonder world under water that is altogether unique. You can go swimming in the Okefenokee, the Suwannee, and any place else in Florida if the weather has been fine for a period and if the water is low and has had time to deposit its turgid silt and to clean itself. There is tremendous scope here for the skin divers, since vast accumulations of Amerindian dejecta, like pots and stone tools, are assembled in the bottom of these waters, not to speak of more ancient fossils.

The limestone ridge coincides with the position of the first islands that formed during the initial retreat of the ice. At this time, all the rest of the area was covered by a sea which has been appropriately called the Okefenokee Sea, but these islands may have survived from the earlier land mass that existed prior to the "ice age."

CACTUSES THAT PADDLE

Some authorities regard all of peninsular Florida down to the region of Lake Okeechobee as a mere southward extension of the great Southern Pine Belt, and the portion south of that point as a distinct province which is usually described as "subtropical." However, others have wisely, though somewhat hesitantly, pointed out that there is really little marked difference between central Florida and southern Florida, and have suggested that the two should be combined. With this I disagreé, for central Florida has not only a great deal of natural open grassland but much artificial pasture that supports tremendous herds of cattle typical of the prairie, while botanists have long puzzled over the occurrence of prickly pear and other cactuses and western scrub and desert-type plants in southern Florida, where they grow happily in saturated as opposed to desiccated soils. This presents no mystery, for southern Florida is but an eastern outlier of the Northern Scrub Zone. The triangle south of the Caloosahatchee River, Lake Okeechobee, and Juno Beach is another matter. This is a complex that starts on the Gulf with a wide belt of mangroves and mangrove-covered islands; then plunges into the Big Cypress Swamp; then out onto the seemingly never-ending area of open waving saw grass, or "everglades"; and finally dips slightly to the Atlantic coast.

Today, central Florida presents rather a dreary picture to the

Right: Cypress swamps have a glassy beauty in winter when the trees have lost their pale leaves; but the waters are still full of small life. Far right: The famous Everglades are not glades but expanses of saw grass dotted with "islands" or hummocks on which palms and large bushes grow.

176

naturalist. The citrus groves with their neat lines of dark, shiny, green-leafed trees and the immaculate bare lanes between them go on for mile after mile over the gently rolling downs. Every now and then small lakes or ponds appear with some ducks paddling about and a few reeds growing around. Then come more miles of closely cropped prairies with complacent domestic cattle standing about. But there are delightful hidden spots to be found just beyond the citrus groves.

In Osceola County (which is over 150 miles south of the national park of the same name) and in Okeechobee, Highlands, De Soto, and even parts of Charlotte and St. Lucie counties, stretch literally hundreds of square miles of more or less unspoiled country. I found a little lake once in northern Okeechobee County that did not appear on any of the maps I was carrying, though it was considerably larger than many shown even on road maps and it was not too far from a road of a sort which was marked thereon. I happened to come upon this place in early evening when I was, I now believe, lost. It was completely hidden among low, gentle rises covered with a paltry shrubbery about three feet tall and composed of nondescript herbs, some stunted, vaguely woody things, and some desiccated grasses.

This lake was S-shaped, and all along one side and round one end it was fringed by willows, of all unexpected things. The other verge was a fairly wide margin of rushes and water grasses. There was an island in the middle at one end, and I started to wade to this and finally attained it by swimming a bit. This island proved to be an ancient "hummock" with its typical dense growth of small-leafed evergreens, but it was completely hollow inside. This I found out by mistake; and, on crawling into it, I was assailed by a most solid odor, and a vast number of disturbed things went barging off through the almost complete darkness into the water of the lake beyond with a tremendous splashing. Once inside, I could stand up and walk about, on hard-packed earth and feathers. I would not like to estimate the number of water birds that lived there. Gaining the other side, I peered cautiously out at ground level (which was virtually at water level) and then, having lugged my field glasses along, I was permitted the best bit of water-bird watching ever.

Besides coot, Florida gallinules, little blue, great white, and great blue herons, a couple of egrets that I think were the self-introduced West African cattle egret, what I could swear was that diminutive attraction named the least bittern, and two sub-adult herring gulls, the following ducks, as far as I could later determine from my somewhat sodden notes, appeared: black, pintail, blue-winged teal, baldpate by the dozens, a shoveler, lesser scaup, a lot of what I assume were buffleheads always off by themselves and very active, and a host of very small, apparently coal-black, diving types that stayed far away and defeated even my high-powered binoculars. I have never been much of a duck enthusiast, but I admit being enthralled by the sight of all these apparently happy and busy cohorts feeding, cleaning themselves, or just mucking about on the placid waters in the slanting rays of the evening sun. And yet all around for miles were dull, open prairies.

There is a lot that could be said about central Florida, with its multitudinous lakes, its seemingly interminable flatwoods and clean-looking pines, and its ground palmetto and grass. And it would be possible to wax quite enthusiastic about the succession

A large part of the Everglades is flooded during the summer, but in winter the waters contract into channels and all the aquatic life goes with them.

of different types of growth one sees in passing down the west side near the coast, through the various patches of pine, cypress, open wet pastures enclosed in thick oak stands rather like parts of Africa, thinly flooded fields, masses of tall cabbage palms, open salty or sweetwater marshes, and other assorted *oikoi,* or "houses." Today, unfortunately, the coastal strip from Tarpon Springs south almost to Naples—an important ecological turnover point—is, frankly, a sorry mess, due not only to normal human litter but to an inordinate amount of roadside advertising and similar horrors.

The Atlantic coast is worse and is virtually a continuous strip development, though here some as yet quite unspoiled parts on the seaside and some fascinating wild dune country to the landward still exist. Also, there is a place between Cape Canaveral and Palm Beach where, to a botanist, the most ridiculous state of affairs may be seen. This is modern, blown, beach sand rolling away in regular dune formations under a pure stand of pines, covering not only the soil but everything vegetative in sight. The offshore sandspits, sand beaches, and dunes continue all the way down to the tip of Florida and out onto the cays. The eastern flatwoods march along behind them inland all the way down to Miami, where they become lost in that great modern city complex. South of that begins the Miami Rockridge, a somewhat different ecological bit.

The Caloosahatchee River and its originator, great Lake Okeechobee, form the real base of the central area. This lake is a rather frightening expanse that for some unknown reason looks flatter than any other piece of water I have ever seen. Perhaps it is that the surrounding country is so flat; yet again, it may be the quality of the sky over it, which—like the shallow "whitewaters" of the Caribbean—does actually reflect its placid colorlessness in most lights. This body of water teems with fish.

SAW GRASS AND GAMBOOZIES

So we come finally to the bottom end of the peninsula and to a land that for some reason is exciting to scientists and tourists alike. It is a rather dreary-looking bit of country, heavily infested with mosquitoes and, over wide areas, smelling almost as badly as a wood-pulp factory. As a bit of North America and particularly of the United States, it is both unique and very odd, and it has a subtle charm. Now that the most interesting parts of it have been taken over by the United States Department of the Interior as a national park, its true fascination is coming to light.

On both the Gulf and Atlantic sides there are within this subprovince about three hundred square miles of "flatwoods"—in two sections, the larger one on the east, the smaller on the west. Everglades start from the bottom edge of the Okeechobee and fill the center of the triangular tip of the peninsula. To the east of them lies only the narrow Atlantic coastal fringe, but to the west, on the Gulf side, is, first, the famous Big Cypress Swamp area and then, south of that, the Ten Thousand Islands and associated coast clothed in mangroves. This runs down to and around the extreme tip of the country. This subdivision is fairly simple, but the everglades themselves are not.

Imagine an evening of soft sunlight with a sky getting set to turn every range of yellow, orange, flame, and red—without a cloud, and without wind. Imagine also that you are squatting on a pile of slightly damp rubbish beside a small meandering channel entirely filled with lily fronds except for one stretch of open water which is jet-black. The trees around you are not over twenty feet tall and mildly uninteresting—just green. The pond, slough, or "waterway" you are observing is absolutely still and seems to have no current, yet it is full of life, as presently appears. Most of it is covered with floating vegetables, mainly lilies, and upon these you may soon note an almost violently colored bird of gawky outline, tramping about, looking, and occasionally pecking. This creature is of a most magnificent color; a mixture of iridescent blues, purples, and deep greens, with a sharply contrasting bill of vivid flame tipped with yellow and a forehead mask of pure white. This little bird is the Purple Gallinule. It is devised to walk about on lily pads.

Then the water gives a mild "blup," and if you stand up quietly and look down, you will see a large alligator "wobbling" along just below the surface surrounded by a mass of large gars and bass—the one a very ancient type of fish, and the other a most important factor in the natural economy of this whole area. Why the reptile does not snap at the fish or the fish go away from their natural enemy is inexplicable, but they all live in these waters imperturbably and presumably contentedly. So also do the water tortoises—locally called "turtles"—and countless smaller fish called *Gambusia,* and fresh-water bream. Also below the water is an abundance of water snails, fresh-water clams, mussels, and other small food. As the sun drops lower, the birds begin to arrive—wood ibis, herons of several kinds, and all manner of ducks. They come soaring overhead, often just skimming the low treetops, and usually landing either in the water or on their appointed roosting trees with a considerable emphasis and uproar. All manner of unseen ones make noises at you out of the dense, tangled vegetation that grows knee-deep in the inky waters. This is an unforgettable place.

During the summer the everglades are alive with animals, but in winter they are a dead land and all the animals are concentrated in the water channels, where they are then so packed together that the fish may nuzzle the alligators, as we have seen.

All manner of birds, like cormorants, come at this time of year to fish; in summer they go away to the coast. Sometimes the water gets so low that the oxygen is not sufficient for the crowded fish, and they die off by the ton; and it may get so low that the big alligators drive all the lesser ones out into the everglades, where they have to make wallows for themselves by rocking back and forth to get down into the water table.

There is a strange life cycle in this land that begins with mosquitoes. When the summer rains begin, the water rises quickly and starts to flood out onto the glades. This causes the eggs of the mosquitoes, which have been lying dormant all winter, to hatch. Then the little fish named the "gamboozie" come to feed on the seething masses of larvae. Then the bream move out in pursuit of the gamboozie, and next, the bass after the bream. Then, the gars go after the bass, and finally the alligators move out after the gars. In the fall everybody reverses himself and —led by the gamboozie, who either get caught in small holes in the rapidly drying saw grass or scuttle for their tiny winter food in the perpetual water channels—they all stream back again. In the national park there are only a thousand acres of winter water compared to nearly a million acres of saw grass, so the concentration of life in the former is terrific.

"HAMMOCKS" AND PHOENIX TREES

The everglades have a dry winter season and a wet summer season. The whole area—fifteen thousand square miles in extent, of which three thousand are contained in Everglades National Park—is quite flat and just about at sea level. Some ridges along its eastern edge are of the great height of twelve feet, and some of the hummocks reach an altitude of six feet. It is really divided

The American Alligator is not aggressive, and even old bulls will move away from people unless molested. They make fearful noises in the swamps in the mating season.

horizontally into three strata, which show up in one vast checkerboard pattern. These strata are: first, a layer of fresh water, which appears on the surface in the form of endless channels, pools, and meandering little lagoons that never dry up; then the glades themselves, which are great open areas covered with saw grass, wet in summer but dry in winter; and finally the hummocks, which are never flooded and are covered with a dense growth of evergreens and other trees and shrubs sometimes standing forty feet tall and consisting here of some subtropical West Indian forms, some indigenous species, and other more typically northern kinds. The more tropical growths are able to survive here because the occasional frosts do not penetrate the saturated atmosphere of these hummocks.

Two other types of vegetative topography are also to be seen here. First, there are the large pine stands that occur sporadically in the northern half of the area. These are really very large hummocks and were brought about, or at least kept pure, by natural fires. In the early days of settlement these fires, set off by lightning, used to rage right across the peninsula from the region of Miami to Tampa and sometimes were recorded as having a two-hundred-mile front. They were naturally deplored as being destructive, and immense sums were spent on fire protection and fire-fighting machinery. But then it was discovered that the pine trees were beginning to shrivel and dry and that no seedlings were produced, whereas in the glade areas the grass began to disappear under a solid growth of willows. Investigation showed that fire was an essential feature of nature in this country, and that almost solely due to it, both the pinelands and the everglades may be attributed. The pine trees have exceedingly thick and almost completely fire-resistant barks and their branches start high up; their cones are very hard and tight; and young seedlings are very sensitive and easily choked by herbage. Saw grass at the same time is not what is called a climax growth (a sort of end product of all the checks and balances of nature) but an unstable intermediate stage that will strangle itself if not periodically fired, while such hardy and woody things as willows will take root amongst it and soon oust it. Thus it was found that fire was needed to clear out the herbs and brush beneath the pines, to split the cones by heat, so scattering the seeds and giving them a chance to get started before the choking herbs returned. It was also needed to burn out the fragile willows and other low growth while leaving the roots of the saw grass untouched in the water strata.

The other oddity of the everglades is the domed hummocks, as opposed to the normal, flat-topped, evergreen ones. These are cypress stands and are actually water-filled hollows, not domes of firmer land. Cypress likes water and grows taller the deeper it is, so that the biggest trees are in the middle and the smaller ones at the outside; hence the domed profile.

GUMBO SOUP AND BEAN POISON

When you get about three-fourths of the way toward the tip of the peninsula from the Okeechobee, you begin to notice something else on the great glades. Here, in addition to the flat and domed hummocks, you will see tiny, isolated shrubs of a neat, rather shiny appearance beginning to appear among the grass. At first they are just dark dots, but as you go south they rise up out of the grass until they appear to be marching about on numerous stiltlike legs. Finally they get thicker and thicker and begin to clump together and ultimately close up completely to form a true closed-canopy forest. These are the red mangroves, the least sea-loving of the three kinds found here. They actually

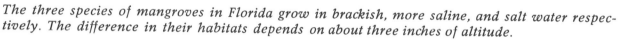

The three species of mangroves in Florida grow in brackish, more saline, and salt water respectively. The difference in their habitats depends on about three inches of altitude.

form the southern barrier of the saw grass, but they straddle a most interesting transition zone where the water alternates between fresh for half the year and salt for the other half, and where a certain kind of palm *(Paurotis)* alone is found or can thrive. Beyond the red mangroves comes a belt of the so-called black mangroves, and then finally the white mangroves. These trees march out into the shallow, muddy sea waters and cover all the offshore islands and some of the cays. The amazing thing is that the distribution of the three species is determined by differences of as little as four inches in the land level, for all of them can grow in saline waters.

Down at the southern tip of the United States, out on the sea side of the mainland mangrove-stands, there are two quite distinct and unique minor vegetational belts, caused respectively by perpetual salt spray, and by occasional *huracanes* (the old Spanish spelling of the Arawak name for these winds). The salt-spray marshes are open areas covered with short, succulent plants and various herbs, often with small bright flowers like the sea daisy, and with some Sabal Palmetto. Behind this may be seen from the seashore itself a rampart of most odd appearance. This is a tangled mass of dead and starkly silver-gray, gnarled and twisted trunks intermingled with masses of billowing bright green. These are the buttonwood trees that always persist in growing right into the face of prevailing salt-filled ocean winds but which always succumb to every hurricane that comes along (about every forty years in each small locality) and to being blown landward in a tangled mass by winds and waves. Most of the big ones are thus killed, but the small ones and the seeds survive and go right back to work, growing seaward again. Under the buttonwoods are some hardy grasses that like saline soil and the cactuses that so puzzle everybody. Here, however, we are in the Northern Scrub Zone, so that only the slightest elevation of this land would exterminate the mangroves and bring in not northern growth or even saw grass but chaparral.

But even here the hummocks continue, for they are but ancient islands and the first pieces of land to have come up out of the sea. They have a different plant growth. Inland, there used to be quite a lot of a species of mahogany, but it has been now mostly cut out, and the Park naturalists think that it is dying out in any case because of changes in the land surface and possibly the climate. On the more southern hummocks grow the small soapberry trees, the leaves of which when crushed actually form a thick lather; the gumbo-limbo, with a copper-colored bark from which the essential ingredient of the original "gumbo" soup was made; many strangler figs; and some old Caribbean favorites like cocoplum and pigeon plum. Also flourishing is the really deadly Cherokee-bean tree, with sparse, ordinary-looking leaves, red flowers, and beanlike fruits that are a violent neurotoxin. In fact, one should not even brush against or place a hand upon the trunk of this tree. This is not by any means the only dangerous plant in the area, as we may see when we turn to another just as deadly—the mangrove.

VEGETABLE MANTRAP

Mangroves cover untold millions of square miles all over the lower and flatter coasts of the tropics and subtropics wherever continental alluvial silt exists. They do not do well on sandy or other oceanic and sea-deposited coasts. While the mangroves of

This impressive sight is the configuration of the bottom of shallow seas covered by water almost as clear as the air.

182

southern Florida are quite impressive in parts, such as south of Everglades City to Lostman's Creek, they are paltry little things compared to the growths of the equatorial regions or even of the subtropics, where they may grow to over sixty feet in height and have massed, impenetrable aerial roots springing from their large trunks as much as ten feet above ground. To be lost in a mangrove swamp, with or without a machete, is probably the most lethal accident that could befall anybody.

Mangrove stands that are apparently lifeless are not so, though they seem in a way to "filter" animals so that only one type of each large group is found in them. There is usually a small carnivorous mammal, in this case the raccoon; there are only a few birds, and these almost exclusively along creeks; invariably a crab; and then there are mosquitoes and, what is worse, the sandflies.

In Florida, if you get lost in the mangroves or your plane is downed among them, you will be supremely unlucky if you do not have at least two handkerchiefs, many safety pins, and preferably a spare shirt. The first thing you should do is make a face mask out of one handkerchief and a tuck-in neck mask with the other, then replace your headgear if you have any. Next, roll down your sleeves and button them tight; then tuck your pants into your boots, and button up your collar or pin all these things tightly. If you have a spare shirt, put it on, because by wiggling a little all the time you can break off the mosquitoes' proboscis between the two meshes. If you are a woman wearing a skirt, you had best divest yourself of underclothes and use them as wrappings for your legs, tear up anything else you can spare to make thongs to bind these and to make some arm coverings and a head mask. Try generally to make a continuous covering all over yourself, since you can be blinded or otherwise quite incapacitated in a surprisingly short time by mosquito bites. The average person simply does not know what a hundred square miles of hungry mosquitoes can do to a human being. Do not take mangroves lightly; they are deadly.

KEY DEER AND SEA COWS

Beyond the tip of the mainland lie the so-called "keys" or cays. These form an immensely long, curving belt of sandy, wooded, and coraline islands fingering out into the Gulf. On some of these are the little stunted variety of deer that are now at long last quite famous, and that some people have made great efforts to protect. Cays still exist that are not spoiled, and they smack of the Caribbean though they are not equivalent to the true cays of the West Indies, which lie to the equatorial side of the desert belt. There is coral—unlike Bermuda, where it is absent—but it is a sort of outwash of the great Gulf whirligig, and if the Gulf Stream were cut off, it would probably all disappear.

Both on the cays and along the whole west or Gulf coast, from Cape Sable to the Suwannee River, may still be found in limited numbers the Manatee or Sea Cow, those placid, munching, marine and estuarine mammals related to the elephants. They grow to about ten feet (the record is thirteen feet four inches) in length. They have two small foreflippers on their inturned wrists and walk along the bottom, and they have great, circular, paddle-shaped, horizontal tails. But for all their placid appearance they can get about at some speed, make unexpectedly sharp turns, and deliver thundering blows in all directions with

An ash "slough" or slew, a type of swamp found in Florida. Cypress trees flourish in it.

their tails: I know, because I have ridden them in shallow water, holding on by sticking my fingers into the soft holes in front of the foreflippers. It is a great experience and rather pleasant, for you just go rushing along, and after a time the curious beasts seem not to bother about their "Old Man of the Sea" and really seem to enjoy the antic. They have extraordinary mouths with great clumping, side-moving, bulbous lips covered with bristles, and tiny eyes surrounded by wrinkles. They feed on such vegetable matter as sea grasses and what are called locally "water lettuces," some of which are violently poisonous to us, as I can personally attest.

There is a persistent legend that the manatees are the origin of the mermaid tradition because they do have a habit of standing straight up in the water and observing you, and have breasts up almost in their armpits, not too far removed from the position of our own. However, they never hold their babies to their chests with their flippers, as is often alleged.

VANISHED SEAS AND FOSSIL BEACHES

The whole historical basis of peninsular Florida is still manifest to the geologist in its present land surface and to the botanist in its vegetative cover. There were four major stages in its formation, during which seas named the Okefenokee, Wicomico, Pamlico, and Silver Bluff more or less covered it, bathed its numerous islands (or hummocks), or surrounded what is its present shore line. Although the Gulf Stream swirls northward up its east coast, inshore-counter currents made up mostly of great eddies are also found starting from just below Cape Hatteras. These act like the brushes of a carpet-sweeper, swirling the beach material and steadily driving it southward. The whole of Florida has actually come off the Appalachians and, for over a million years, has been slowly grubbed off the Georgia coast by these eddies, then filtered and sorted, and redeposited, first into a string of islands, then between these and extending them to the south, and finally turning west till we get the great hook of present-day Florida.

The actions and modes of deposition of this material form a fascinating story; and by following these old coast lines via the parallel dune formations, geologists have been able to reconstruct the stages in the formation of Florida. Along the way, the vegetation has come about in a rather unique manner. This, apart from that of the open prairies, the flatwoods, and the typical hummocks, is divided between two types of mixed growth called the Sandhill (composed mostly of long-leaf pine and turkey oaks) and the Sandpine "Scrub." Of the last there are three subtypes: those found on old dunes, those on old and new beaches and offshore bars, and those on the so-called hilltops, which are mostly the original islands of the Okefenokee Sea period. These are flat-topped and between 125 and 140 feet above sea level today, and are usually surrounded by areas of Sandhill vegetation or by flatwoods. These ancient islands have managed to retain their individuality as well as to preserve their special types of vegetation, and each forms a unique ecological niche. The Okefenokee beach level is now at about 150 feet, that of the old Wicomico Sea at 100 feet, of the Pamlico at 25 to 30 feet, and of the Silver Bluff Sea, which existed after the last great ice advance, only 8 to 10 feet up.

Peninsular Florida is one of the most interesting and instructive provinces on our continent. So much has gone on there so recently, and so much is still taking place there under our very eyes, that we can here get many of the basic lessons in ecology which in other places are hidden by age.

Land of
the Mesquite

The East Chaparrals of the North and South Scrub Belts, and the Deserts of the Rio Grande

About the mouth and lower reaches of the Rio Grande, on both the Mexican and American sides of the border, lies a beautiful land of somewhat varied appearance that is a veritable paradise for the naturalist. This forms a triangle, fronting on the Gulf coast and running inland to an apex about Eagle Pass. This province lies between the great Prairie Belt on the north and the subtropical savannahs on the south and thus is composed of both the Northern and the Southern Scrub Belts and the Hot Desert. However, due to the proximity of the warm waters of the Gulf and the mild moist winds that move up the coast with the circulation of those waters, it is clothed in a much more luxuriant growth of plants than it would otherwise be (and it does not look anything like those scrub belts farther inland), whereas the desert is here compressed to a mere line of somewhat greater aridity.

If we enter this province by land from the northeast across the black prairies and oak belt, we come upon it suddenly at the San Antonio River. Here the grass cover of the whole land breaks up into patches and becomes scarce or nonexistent. The massed oaks and Spanish Moss disappear, and in their place stand delicately green, feathery-foliaged trees with dark trunks and a general appearance of great cleanliness. We have entered an entirely new country.

The name of this tree, known as the Mesquit or Mesquite, is derived from the Spanish *mezquite,* which in turn was a transliteration of the Amerindian Nahuatl *mezquitl.* It is a North American plant belonging to the mimosa group of the pea or leguminose family, which contains beside peas, beans, clovers, vetches, alfalfa, lupines, and peanuts, many herbaceous flowering plants, shrubs, and trees, and among the last the acacias. The Mesquite *(Prosopis juliflora)* has feathery leaves, twigs armed with sharp spines, and white spike-shaped inflorescences that turn yellow. It bears pods about five inches long, containing beans with a high sugar content. It also has a very fine, dense wood much used in cabinet work today but in bygone times as fuel; its beans are quite nutritious and are eaten regularly by men and many animals, and its flowers are a good source of nectar and pollen for bees. There are forty species of mesquites, ranging all over the North and South Scrub and the desert belts. Their mightiness stems from one of their particular aptitudes and from a special feature of their physiology.

Mesquites are essentially dry-area plants and can grow in advanced desert conditions, but they are apparently originally indigenous to the outer scrublands. They are extremely hardy and rather fast-growing at first, and they can rapidly crowd out other trees by grabbing the available soil moisture and dispensing a fairly deep shade, all of which fosters their spread throughout the chaparrals and the scrublands generally. However, it also has made it possible for them to spread in other directions; and within the past three centuries they have done so to such an extent in one direction, namely, onto the prairies, that not only forestry men but stock-raisers and agriculturists are becoming seriously alarmed.

Mesquite, it is believed, was once confined to the scrub and desert belts and is apparently indigenous to this province, commonly called the East Chaparral area. Today, it has spread not only up and over the Balcones Escarpment (see map) but across the Edwards Plateau on the east side to link up with the parklands and thence north to Kansas; and it is still going. To the west, Mesquite has long since topped and crossed the Stockton Plateau and spread up the Pecos valley; but there its presence is not so alarming since so far it is confined to the strip of scrubland that goes that way. In the east it is considered a menace because it is rapidly encroaching on the prairies, and once it does so *en masse* it destroys the grazing and is difficult and costly to eradicate. Some seventy-one million acres are already so affected in Texas and Oklahoma alone. It seems that Mesquite was originally kept off the grasslands by the indigenous fauna, but since the latter has been virtually eliminated—especially the bison herds and the prairie dogs—substituted cattle have been no match for it. Also it acts as a firebreak, and natural grass fires seem to have been one of the essential features in the maintenance of the prairies as grazing lands for animals.

The Mesquite is the dominant plant of the East Chaparral Province, especially north of the Rio Grande, but two other small bushlike trees run it a close second. These are the Huisaché (pronounced we-sa-cháy) or Sweet Acacia *(Acacia farnesiana),* and the Huajilla (pronounced wa-he-ya) or Cat's Claw *(Acacia greggii),* which is also often simply called the Chaparral. The Huisaché has beautiful, marble-sized, puffball-shaped yellow flowers, and its leaves are highly sensitive to touch. Some huisachés are profoundly spinous, others lack spines, but the cat's claws are like barbed-wire entanglements—hence their name. These are the principal trees of the North Scrub Belt in this province, at least on the coastal and inland plains north of the Rio Grande; but they are associated with a large number of other shrubs and herbs, all of which bear lovely flowers.

THE HIDDEN DESERT

Ignoring for the moment the coast on the one hand and the upper or western part of the triangle on the other, let us imagine ourselves traveling due south, first crossing the Rio Grande valley and then continuing across the plain, on Mexican soil, to the Ancient Mountains with the mighty Sierras standing behind them. The land is first low rolling country, almost a level plain cut by numerous west-to-east watercourses, each in its own small valley. These are filled with profuse plant growth and quite large trees. Many of these are quite deep and are called locally

Prickly-pear cactuses form a large group now found wild all over the United States and in many foreign countries, in some of which they have become a serious blight.

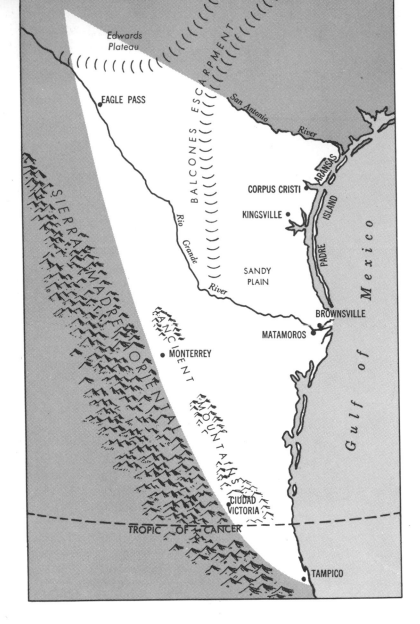

by the escarpment leading up to the Edwards Plateau, and on the south by a string of low and ancient mountain ranges that stand isolated on the plain and stretch from a point somewhat north of Monterrey to near Tampico. The western apex of the triangle is at Eagle Pass on the Rio Grande.

This province contains within its narrow compass in this area the whole of the North Scrub Belt, the true Desert Belt, and the whole of the South Scrub Belt, which in other parts of the world may each be over a thousand miles wide and which, combined, may in places cover over two thousand miles. All these belts are much compressed here, the Desert being all but squeezed out of existence, appearing only as isolated bare areas and, south of the Rio Grande in its lower reaches, being discernible only by an expert. The scrub belts are profusely vegetated with chaparrals of various kinds. These diminish in luxuriance as one goes west and gradually deteriorate into typical scrub growth at the western apex of the province. Actually, as shown on the map, the desert continues northwestward to the Big Bend of the Rio Grande and beyond that onto the Chihuahua Desert, up the Tularosa Valley, and north along the eastern face of the Sacramento Mountains, finally disappearing under the uplands of the South Montane Province.

South of the string of Ancient Mountains lies a low gutter some fifty miles in width which levels off to a flat, elevated plain to the southwest. This terminates abruptly at the feet of the enormously steep Sierra Occidental, which rises from its edge without so much as a foothill for miles. In fact, for a stretch of some two hundred miles west of Ciudad Victoria, this plain dips down into another slight gutter at their feet. This strip of territory, although supporting a flora looking much like that of the province here under discussion, is not of it, but lies in the great Savannah Belt of the tropics dealt with in Chapter 21. The territory between Eagle Pass and Big Bend is included in Chapter 15, along with the South Montane Province.

This province, known to phytogeographers as the East Chaparrals, may be divided into first a north and south part by the Rio Grande, and, secondarily, into a series of subbelts cutting across these and parallel to the coast. These are, counting inland from the Gulf of Mexico, a continuous offshore sand strip with dunes, an inland waterway filled with low islands, a swath of almost continuous marshes separated from the real coast by vegetated dunes, a low coastal plain cut by rivers and arroyos, and two wide platforms of slightly increasing altitude. The Rio Grande cuts through all these in a narrow flood plain.

This is a small but very distinct and important province. It lies on the west coast of the Gulf of Mexico between the mouth of the San Antonio River in Texas and the region of the port of Tampico in the state of Tamaulipas in Mexico. It forms an almost perfect triangle pointing west: 250 miles along its northern face, 500 miles along its southwestern, and just 400 along its eastern, on the coast. Down the middle of this lowland plain flows the Rio Grande River. It is bounded on the north

---

"arroyos," though the term is inaccurately applied to them, since most have a running stream in their bottoms all year round and some contain considerable rivers that are positively leaping with fish. In fact, I have never entered any river that was more piscinely alive than one that passes through this area. Its shimmering surface meandered between modest clay banks, it was brackish, and it was continuously plopping all over at about ten-foot intervals with leaping fish. When I entered its limpid waters, the hair on my legs and arms was attacked voraciously but weakly by countless catfish and other water creatures. These gulleys or "arroyos" are filled with vegetable growths ranging from lush herbs to towering examples of the upland bushes called "knockaway" or anacua trees (Eritia anacua), cedar-leafed elm, and vast ropes of wild grape (Vitis candicans). There are also veritable hawsers of poison ivy. All of this makes an almost

jungly mass that fills the gulley to its brim and attracts a large assemblage of birds.

The best place to see this country at its most typical is the Welder Wildlife Foundation Refuge, a privately initiated institution that lies just at the junction of the coastal and the Rio Grande plains in San Patricio County, Texas. This is composed of slightly rolling country of open grass with scattered stunted cactus, and many grouped bushes of all manner of forms but almost all bearing sharp spines—mesquite, huisaché, gum elastic, western hackberry, Mexican persimmon, brezil, and so forth. In the slight depressions of this land are many shallow lakes fringed with rushes and reeds and rank grasses, and upon them innumerable water birds float gently. On the drier upper areas there is that most enchanting of all native birds, the Road Runner, an impertinent kind of ground-living cuckoo.

This whole inland area in precolonial days must have been remarkable; it appears to have been kept in something like its early condition by means of fire, both naturally generated by lightning and artificially by the Amerindians. The Spaniards brought in longhorn cattle and horses, both of which went feral in droves and which for a period much altered the landscape, eating out the underbrush and permitting grass to take over. But these too, like the Amerinds, died away, and the natural flora began to take over again. Deer also multiplied and other more docile strains of cattle were introduced, and in the Welder area —now protected—a limited number of the latter are allowed to roam at will to keep down the underbrush and to permit some grass to survive. There is now estimated to be about one of the small Texas White-tailed Deer per eight acres hereabouts. Thus this bit of territory, it is believed, once again looks not too different from what it did before the European came to upset the biological balance (though it is thought that it was even then not a climax type) that is supposed to have prevailed under the Amerindians.

This northern half of the triangle (see map) is formed of three great steps—the Nueces Plain inland above the low Bordas Escarpment, the main coastal plain, and the coastal lowlands strip of marshes. The second devolves to the south into a large sand plain. The valley of the Rio Grande, from its mouth to the present town of Rio Grande, is rich alluvium and is now extensively cultivated, but west of this point it becomes very arid on both sides of the river. Here we have entered the Desert Belt which forms an expanding wedge to the east but is, as it were, plugged by the delta and the intensively cultivated lands of the river valley. When these lands are left fallow they develop a desert form of chaparral without any grasses, with many cactuses and a tangle of small-leafed, stunted bushes. Proceeding south from the river toward the Mexican Sierras, one encounters a very interesting development.

DESERT BARRIER

First, there is a wide reach of cultivated fields and then suddenly a narrow desert belt. On the main road south from Mata moros and Brownsville this belt is only about twenty miles wide and might well be missed by anybody except specialists, for it doesn't look very different from the scrublands to the north. The vegetation is, however, reduced to a few kinds of lowly bushes and clumps of hard-stemmed herbage, with many small cactuses. The ground is bare and stony, and almost all signs of wildlife disappear, at least during the day. By night a paltry fauna of small animals, mostly rodents, makes its appearance. But, despite the fairly abundant food supply that these offer to predators, everything else seems to shun this strip—even foxes, coyotes, skunks, and others that are abundant to both the north and the south. The true deserts form one of the major "breaks" in the distribution of plants and animals between the tropical and subtropical on the one side, and the temperate and boreal on the other. The animals—even the insects here, I am told— "know" this, and simply will not cross this barrier and do not even enter it to feed.

South of this sterile strip we enter an entirely new land again. At first sight this looks even more like the Northern Scrub Belt in its subforested or chaparral form. Flowering shrubs, many with broad leaves, mimosas and acacias, and the flowering cactuses begin again; but there is a difference. Most of the plants are even more spiny, and broad-leafed bushes, shrubs, and even small trees gather in greater profusion. The cactuses get bigger,

The Ghost Crab, adapted to the sandy shallows of the Gulf coast, resorts to the beach in search of food and can live for long periods out of water.

and one lot of herbs after another leaf and flower throughout the year and even in dry periods. The most notable bush is the Nakahuita with its covering of beautiful, four-petaled white flowers, while the undergrowth is given a pale bluish cast by the little Saniso bush. This continues with some variation until one climbs in among the flat-topped low mountains of the ancient coastal range. At this point somewhat intensive agriculture begins again along the modern highway; but if you walk or ride back a mile or so from the feet of these mountains, there is another break so sudden you can sometimes actually stand with one foot in one belt and the other in the next. The difference is between grass underfoot on the south side and no grass at all on the north side. It is a most surprising phenomenon and looks as if fire had eliminated the grass. Here the subtropical savannahs begin.

TWO HUNDRED MILES OF SAND

This province may thus be divided into northern and southern portions by the Rio Grande and the much compressed Desert Belt, but it is even more dramatically subdivided the other way —i.e. from east to west—into three parts—a coastal, a central which we have just visited, and an inland area which we will pass through on our way to the next province. The coastal strip is a land unto itself and most fascinating. It varies widely in both appearance and content, and has to be broken down into at least five strips all running parallel to the coast line. First, out to sea, lies a string of sandy islands covered with sea grape and other low, tangled, salt-loving vegetation. Second, about three to five miles offshore is a sandspit, not a mile wide, that stretches all the way from Galveston to Tampico with only occasional breaks opposite the mouths of the larger rivers and where some shipping channels cut through it. One stretch of this, Padre

189

Island, located off the Texas coast, is seventy miles long and is now connected with the mainland by a causeway and bridge at the southern end at the mouth of the Rio Grande so that cars can be driven its entire length along the beach. Third, inside this sandspit lies what is called the "Inland Waterway."

This is a shallow paradise for fish and fishing birds, and it is dotted and sometimes filled with low sand or salt-grass-covered islands between which meander narrow channels. To the landward side of this inland stretch of water comes the coast line proper. This, the fourth belt or strip, alternates between vast open grass-covered marshes and bights with many creeks, channels, and ponds, and stretches of sand beach rising to modest clifflike banks. These are old sand dunes. Some are covered with beautiful lush grass, whereas upon others stand continuous closed-canopy forests of evergreen oaks all leaning madly away from the sea and the wind. Their trunks are naked and very pale, and their lower limbs writhe like things possessed, while their dense, dark-green head foliage trails off landward like a semideflated air cushion. To landward of these marginal dunes lies the fifth coastal belt, which is the coastal plain, so called, known alternatively as the coastal prairies. These are not true prairies though in large part covered with very short grass. Upon them are many pools, ponds, and shallow lakes, and all about them meander dry chaparrals. Little groves of stunted gallery forest grow along the stream beds, and they are dotted with clumps of cactus, here mostly prickly pear, engulfed in herbs and thin-stemmed bushes and mesquite trees; there are also copses of stunted oaks and other trees. This country continues inland to the first low escarpment. Its soil is mostly sandy, with wedges of fine silt where rivers flow from the uplands.

The same arrangement extends along the Mexican coast south of the Rio Grande delta, which forms a large open area of marshes and mud flats bounded on the seaward side by sand dunes. However, the South Scrub vegetation lacks grass even immediately behind the coast, the leaning oaks are scarcer, and the chaparrals grow in massed formation right down to the dunes, which are covered with creeping salt-resistant succulents. Salt marshes continue and are just as extensive. On the offshore sandspit there are dune grasses, but the sea grapes and the buttonwoods have here moved in from the islands beyond and sometimes form dense low masses where many colonies of birds breed. Beneath these may be dark, dank, bare, black mud. At the southern end of this stretch of coast the evidence of past hurricanes often extends for miles inland in the form of ramparts of deadwood and other vegetable debris.

The sand dunes all along the offshore side of the sandspit are very remarkable in that they lie in an evenly spaced rank, in echelon, all having their long axis running from northwest to southeast. They average about thirty to fifty feet in height and are held together with bunches of coarse grass. On the inner or

Top left: The so-called Brown Pelican is, in its adult plumage, a satiny gray bird with vivid white and yellow markings. This species is maritime and is represented on both coasts.

Top right: An American Avocet, a highly colorful wader that is now common over a large part of the South and West. It has a curiously upturned beak.

Bottom: The Spoonbill appears in great flocks all around the Gulf coast. One of its chief nesting places is an island off the Texas shore.

190

landward side of the dunes this joins up to make a kind of meadow about half a mile wide, which in turn merges into a wide muddy beach that passes imperceptibly into the water of the lagoon. On the seaward side of the sandspit there is a continuous clear beach about a hundred feet wide and perfectly level. As you drive along it, however, you will come to regularly alternating stretches of flat wet sand and slight ridges of soft dry sand. Seen from the air, these give the whole coast a banded or striped appearance. The curious thing is that the dry strips or spits have no connection with the spacing of the sand dunes nor their orientation, but run directly at right angles to the water's edge at every point, so that they may point anywhere from northwest through east to south.

The beach itself is a rather clean one but for the shells of a number of mollusks and, twice a year, countless purplish blue gas-filled bladders of that remarkable coelenterate related to the jellyfishes and called the Portuguese Man-of-War (the reason for the name being that the sails of the exploratory fleets of that nation in the early days were often dyed bright blue-green). This creature is not just one but a colony of animals, of very varied shapes and sizes, each adapted for special purposes. The upper part is a gelatinous bladder filled with gas, which rides above the waves but which can be deflated so that the whole colony sinks below. Underneath this are numerous appendages, including whiplike structures that may trail as much as a hundred feet down into the water. These creatures do not just drift with the winds and the currents: they have been observed traveling steadily across both at a fair angle. In the appendages live one of the communal types of creature that make up the whole complex. These have barbed whips that can be shot out at prey, sting by penetration, and are for their size much more deadly than most if not all snakes. There may be thousands in one colony, so their concerted efforts can be deadly even to humans. Their poison persists after death and even when the creature is desiccated, so that one should be very cautious in handling those stranded bladders to which the shriveled remnants of the jelly-like appendages may be adhering.

EMPIRE OF THE BIRDS

If one sits quietly on the seaward beach of the great sandspit one will have friends. There is not much variety of wildlife but for herring gulls and the delightful laughing gulls—which do indeed give vent to just about the whole gamut of noises made by human beings when laughing. The former mostly stand or tramp about the upper beach; the latter flap about over the shallows inside the breakers. Then there are several species of terns that come spiking by on the wind, peering ever downward and occasionally plunging headlong into the surf. But, apart from these, the only ever-present denizens of the beaches are the tiny sanderlings, which rush endlessly and somewhat hysterically back and forth at the very edge of every incoming and outgoing surge of the spent waves on the wet sand. These are small, most aggressive birds, with dull brownish gray coloration above, light undersides, dark legs, and long beaks. Each maintains a private territory at the water's edge and works it ceaselessly and furiously, pecking at every tiny morsel the sea floods ashore—mostly a small, flattened kind of crustacean called sand hoppers. If one bird inadvertently runs into the territory of another it is immediately attacked and run off by the owner. These little birds run so fast they look like mechanical toys.

The inner or landward slopes of the dunes are almost completely sterile, but as you descend onto the mud flats and

approach the inner waterway, you enter a veritable empire of the birds. The island-studded and protected shallow waters all the way down this coast, and the marshes, vegetated dunes, wet prairies, ponds, and creeks of the true coast for as far as they extend inland, are crowded all year round with so many different kinds of birds in such enormous numbers that one becomes almost glutted with the sight of them. Nor are these all sea and wading birds, for the bushes, the sedges, the oak trees, and the ponds, copses, and mesquites inland, are also filled with the constant fluttering of millions of others. It has always surprised me that one should have to visit a flat and in many respects rather commonplace area of lowland in order to see massed armies of so many totally different groups of bird species assembled. This east coast of Texas is the only place on this continent where you can see such a variety of species. To corroborate this I may say that in the 1956 edition of a list of the birds seen on this coast (*Checklist of the Birds of the Central Texas Coast,* by Conger N. Hagar and Fred M. Packard) no less than 460 assuredly determined and 24 unconfirmed species had been identified. During a visit to Mrs. Hagar in 1959, I learned that her list of positively identified species is now well past the 500 mark.

There are two outstanding and interrelated aspects of this bird land, the first a general one and the other of an individual and almost personal nature. These are migration, and the bird known as the Whooping Crane.

THE PASSING OF THE GREAT

These great birds with a wing span of seven feet, glistening white except for jet-black wing tips and a red face, were never numerous (because each pair needs about a square mile to maintain itself and its young), but they were once widespread from the Arctic coast to central Mexico and from Utah to South Carolina. By 1920 their range had been drastically reduced due to the draining of marshes and the extension of agriculture, and the total number of the birds had fallen to less than fifty. The last nest was noted in Saskatchewan. Then began a campaign that does much credit to the human race as a whole. All manner of people banded together to try to save this bird from extinction. This was hardly the first attempt to save a species of wild animal (conservation was not altogether unknown even among the ancients) but it was almost the first, if not the very first time that the citizens of a nation combined officially to do such a thing and used all the resources of modern publicity to get it done.

The first thing that was done was to take a census of the remaining birds and confirm every possible detail of their habits and life cycle. The latter was found to entail their migration annually to the Arctic Circle in spring, starting about early May, and back again to southern temperate latitudes in the fall, arriving in late October—a distance of over two thousand miles. The surviving birds all apparently wintered on one peninsula in this province—the Aransas, in southeastern Texas. From here they flew almost straight north over Oklahoma, Kansas, Nebraska, South and North Dakota, and Saskatchewan to the region of the Great Slave Lake in the Mackenzie district of the Canadian Northwest Territories. As a result of this, "refuges" were set

The Gray Fox is very widely distributed today but seems to be primarily a parkland and scrub-belt species. It is a surprisingly good tree-climber.

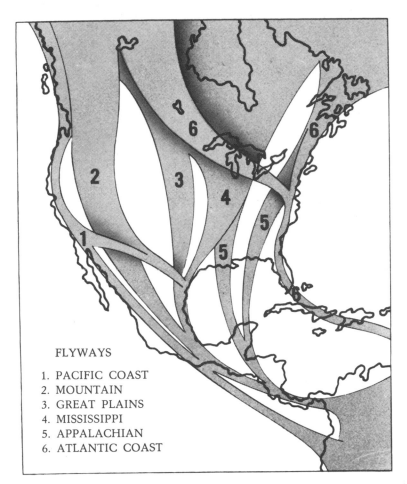

The Migratory Highways of the Birds. (Based on a map by Roger T. Peterson, National Audubon Society.)

FLYWAYS

1. PACIFIC COAST
2. MOUNTAIN
3. GREAT PLAINS
4. MISSISSIPPI
5. APPALACHIAN
6. ATLANTIC COAST

eleven thousand miles from one to the other. Its route is first across the North Atlantic, then all down the western coasts of Europe and Africa, and thence over the stormy void of the latitudes known as the "roaring forties" to the broken ice belt of the southern polar regions. Most amazing is that the young birds in their first year accomplish half of this virtually circum-global expedition without outside assistance. On the other hand, there are birds which migrate only from a wood where they spend the winter to a neighboring field for the summer and then back again. Nor are birds the only animals that migrate. Quite the contrary, for it has now been discovered that a very large number of all animals—ranging from worms to mammals—make seasonal shifts in their place of residence.

But birds are, of all migrators, the most superb and the animals which are most readily seen thus engaged. Yet, although many millions of them pass over the heads of most of us twice a year, one could die at a ripe old age without ever knowing that such a phenomenon took place. These great semiannual movements for the most part follow set and invariable patterns; and what is more, they proceed along regular airways like the best commercial plane services. These are appropriately called "flyways."

In North America there are six of these (see map). This is the over-all pattern, but it has now been discovered from close observation over some fifteen years in the area we are presently describing that there is a cross-continental side switch made by many western birds that turn left into the Rio Grande valley on their way south and so join the central stream. Thus we have here a semiannual mixing of species from the east, central, and western regions of the North American continent, which in great part explains the enormous variety of birds seen in this province. This fascinating aspect of nature is an integral part of the scene on the coast of the East Chaparral Province, for there is hardly a day in the year when one is not here reminded of the endless passing of birds from far extremities of the earth to the nearby arroyos or to the upper levels of the Mexican mountains. Never a day passes here but one encounters some new species of bird that simply was not there the day before—in a roadside ditch, on a telephone wire, on the beach, or in a bush behind the house—and they turn up in droves, not as lone harbingers or lost sentinels.

aside at Aransas, Texas, and in Wood Buffalo National Park in Canada, for their winter and summer safety respectively.

Meanwhile, however, the number of birds had sunk to a low of only about twenty and grave doubts were entertained as to whether all the effort was not too late. However, the great birds continued to wing their way north and south each year, luckily at such altitudes that they were for the most part out of range of the free-firing gunmen, let alone the sportsmen. Considerable propaganda also aided them by making country folk all along their migration route aware of their existence, their times of passing, and their plight. On the whole, man responded unusually well, so that very slowly the birds have made somewhat of a comeback. Moreover, in 1959 they were for the first time reported in eastern Montana, in Missouri, and in Illinois on their way north. Nothing could be more encouraging to all those who wish these birds to be saved from extinction.

THE PASSING OF THE LESSER

Migration is not a simple affair. Almost everybody has heard the expression, but very few except trained biologists know precisely what it means. The average person thinks of it as having something to do with birds flying back and forth in the spring or fall from north to south or vice versa. This notion has more than just a grain of truth, for true migration indeed means a regular seasonal movement of animals from one place to another. However, its range of variation in time, place, and extent is tremendous. For instance, there is a bird, the Arctic Tern, that spends a part of the year in the Arctic of the New World and another part in the Antarctic south of Africa, and the rest of the year flying the

THE RETIRING ONES

The mammals of the East Chaparral, like mammals everywhere, are much more conservative, and they are much less often seen, being for the most part nocturnal. There are the ubiquitous raccoons and opossums, innumerable mice and rats, coyotes, gray foxes, some otters, long-legged jack rabbits, and little cottontails. But there is also the Peccary, the piglike ungulate of tropical America that once, as we know by its bones found in caves, existed as far north as New York. This is a shy one indeed, venturing out into the open only at night. Then there are the sun-loving reptiles and the temperature-controlled frogs and other amphibians, the insects, and the perennial spiders and snails. All seem to appear and disappear with pronounced seasonal rhythm.

The most notable and commonly seen mammal is the armadillo of the so-called Nine-banded species *(Tatusia novemcincta)*. This always somehow seems to be a most unlikely citizen of the United States, but it has always been present in south and east Texas and has now spread east both on its own initiative and with human assistance, not only to, but over, the Mississippi;

and it has reached even Florida. It is a myopic, bumbling creature that wanders about by day and by night grubbing for insects and other morsels of animal food and ingesting with them a lot of earth, so that its droppings form little natural "marbles." It sleeps in large holes that it digs for itself, and it is so strong that if you catch one by the tail as it is disappearing down its hole, you cannot pull it out by brute strength lest its sturdy tail be torn from its compact little body. However, these primitive animals, once they realize that they are being approached, can take off at an incredible speed on a curving and zigzag course that can outdistance any man and that they can maintain blindly in the thickest ground cover. Incidentally, armadillos always have quadruplets and all the young are always of the same sex because they are all developed from a single fertilized egg. The two primary divisions of this egg, unlike those of other mammals, separate completely in the womb and begin new embryos.

ETHEREAL FLYCATCHER

Despite the immense numbers of birds to be seen everywhere, notably in the Aransas and Laguna Atascosa refuges, perhaps the most remarkable assemblages of all are on the delta of the Rio Grande. Here are seemingly horizonless expanses of wind-furrowed grass and bare mud. To approach the area there are only two roads and to stray from these is to become bogged down in mud to your ankles, knees, or waist. To seaward there are solid acres of both dry and wet sand, and dunes capped by tufts of grass, with firm beaches beyond them, while to landward are enchanting green pastures enclosed in tangles of spiny, pale green bushes, flowering cactuses, and even some palms, all loud with the ululations of numberless birds. In fact, many of the best bird singers here are kinds that seem, like the ubiquitous Boat-tailed Grackle, mostly only to croak, screech, or yell in other places. The intermediate belt that curves across the delta is a land of enchantment and much mystery.

The thing here that impresses one most of all is the vast numbers of the Scissor-tailed Flycatcher. They line the bushes, fences, and especially power lines by the thousands, always spaced out more or less equally. Every now and then one will flip up into the air, grab its unseen gnat, and alight again in its own place. These birds are of a beautiful general color that cannot be adequately described—a smooth, lustrous, grayish pink, flesh color. The beak is slender and the eyes small and bright; on the top of the head is a vivid vermilion tache, and it bears a pair of small marks of the same color on its "shoulders." The wings are dark brown in repose, and the tail, which is more than twice the length of the bird itself, consists primarily of two immense, somewhat twisted central feathers, pale rose in color, with spatulate black paddles at the end. The other pairs of tail feathers are of progressively shorter length and are also black-tipped. When the bird flips into the air these tail feathers make semigyroscopic motions that have to be seen to be understood. These birds have a certain ethereal quality about them that epitomizes this country with its wide-open skies and gay winds and its feathery mimosas. But neither the masses of grackles, strutting about like drunken guardsmen with bandaged knees,

A typical feature of the coast of this province is the laughter of these small black-headed gulls all day, often at night, and in all weathers.

nor the breezy flycatchers on their elevations are by any means the sole possessors of this delta land. They are confined to the landward side.

As one wades out onto the mud flats and marshes, all manner of other wondrous creatures spring into view. Here are great flotillas of White Pelicans, bobbing in unison just off the muddy shores and dipping below to the shallows for clams and other tidbits. These will take off in orderly formation only when you approach too close. In the sloughs and natural ditches are those incredibly bright-painted, long-legged, probing birds, the Avocets, and the black and white Stilts, the big Oyster-catchers, and the seemingly endless pattering ranks of less gaudily garbed wading birds such as curlews, plover of many kinds, sandpipers, phalaropes, and so forth. Then there are the gulls and the terns and the skimmers, whose upper bill is much shorter than their lower, all of which congregate in vast numbers on the seaward sand bars. When you are among the coastal lagoons of this province you would have to be a callous citizen indeed if you did not respond to the endless beauty and mystery of these countless armies of delicate creatures, minding their own business and going about their ordered lives.

Alps, Deserts, and Canyons

The South Montane Block with the Colorado and Wyoming Basins and the Sacramento–Guadalupe Ranges

15 The main body of this province is divided into three great upland and mountain blocks, which may be called the Colorado, Utah, and Arizona. These ring a large upland plateau, shaped like a complex fern leaf, which comprises the drainage basin of the Colorado River and drains into the Grand Canyon. These lands, along with the Wyoming Basin, and the Guadalupe–Sacramento mountains to the southeast, form a unit in the middle of what is commonly called the West—an ill-defined area that presents on physical maps a bewildering mass of mountain ranges, plateaus, valleys, and other structures. How-

Above: A typical lizard of the Utah deserts—a Collared Spiny Swift. Right: Bryce Canyon, probably the most exotically fashioned canyon in the Southwest, is carved into the south of the Utah mountain block.

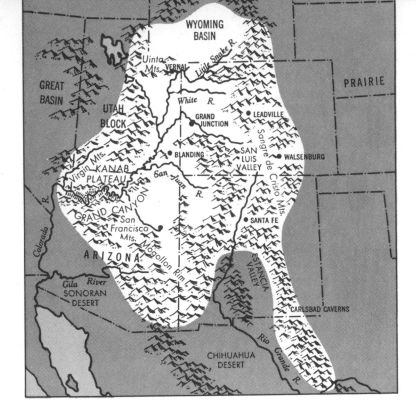

a single river system—the Colorado. It is formed of five great subprovinces, including three mountainous ones which may be called the Colorado, the Utah, and the Arizona blocks, and two major basins—the Wyoming and the Colorado "Plateau" or better, Platea. The three mountain blocks form a complete ring around the latter, with narrow connecting causeways in the north, west, and east. Oddly, the main river cuts right through the northern of these, but, instead of doing the same through the western on its way out of the platea, it has cut the mighty Grand Canyon through almost the widest and highest stretch of the adjoining mountains and left to one side a natural outlet dammed by only a narrow neck of highlands.

Its boundaries are almost everywhere as precise as seacoasts. On the east is the edge of the Great Prairie plateau, from which the mountains rise as from an ocean. (Incidentally, the Continental Divide, of which so much has been made, runs down the middle of the east mountain block. Apart from being a watershed, this has no significance and affects neither fauna nor flora.) Its northern edge is equally abrupt and is formed by the southern face of the North Montane Block. Its western edge is a sudden wall-like drop onto the arid Great Basin. Its southern border, from the mouth of the Grand Canyon around the Arizona Block to the upper Rio Grande, is clearly defined topographically but is not so abrupt and is more indented and steplike. In New Mexico its edge turns north and then east across the heads of the Rio Grande and Estancia valleys and over low mountains to the central plains. South and east of this latter line, there is a string of mountain ranges that reaches far to the southeast—the Sacramentos to the Guadalupes. These are clad in the same vegetation as this province's upper mountain slopes and could be classed with it. However, they have closer affinity with the ranges that stretch across the north Mexican desert to the Sierra Oriental, and should be regarded as a transitional subprovince.

The Wyoming Basin with its many marginal basins is a strange physiographic entity, but from the phytogeographic viewpoint is in no way abnormal, being low in altitude and hence covered with scrub. It is connected on the one hand with the central prairies, and on the other, by a narrow channel winding to the northwest, with the Great Basin.

This province displays a great number of the major vegetational belts and zones to be encountered on this continent because at least half of it stands on the true deserts, whereas some of its peaks are high enough to support year-round icefields. It is also unique in that rock strata representing all known geological ages from the Pre-Cambrian of 750 million years ago to the present are somewhere to be seen on its surface. It is a large, isolated, and well-defined province, being some seven hundred miles from north to south and six hundred miles at its widest. Mount Elbert at the apex of the Colorado area is over 14,400 feet high.

That part of it which is not in the desert is wholly contained within the North Scrub Belt, and this produces some weird effects. Although either wholly mountainous or high plateau, it is edged by pockets of lowlands, it contains one great (the Wyoming) and sundry smaller basins, and its whole center is composed of a sort of fern-frond-shaped gutter drained by

---

ever, one may readily divide the West into a number of clearly defined natural provinces, each having a unique flora, fauna, climate, and to a great extent geological structure and history. There will nevertheless be two pieces, as it were, left over, and these may be tacked onto this province and described with it. The first is the Wyoming Basin, a scrub-covered, almost circular depression lying north of the province, between it and the North Montane Block. This connects with the great plateau of the central part of the continent on the one side and with the upper region of the Great Basin on the other by means of a narrow, winding gorge. The second appendage is of quite another nature.

NO-MAN'S LAND

Going west from the East Chaparrals and following the North Scrub Belt, we proceed up the valley of the Rio Grande via Eagle's Pass which actually lies in the Desert Belt. Somewhat northwest of this point we re-enter the scrublands, while the

desert swings away to our left. This scrub continues for some three hundred miles in a slowly widening belt to the southern edge of the South Montane Province, between the Great Prairies and the Chihuahua deserts. The vegetation in this strip is sparse and stunted, and usually clumpy, with thorny shrubs and bunches of desert grass. It has rather an unusual fauna, including pronghorns, enormous numbers of jack rabbits, and some rather specialized lizards.

As we travel northwestward this vegetation clothes the escarpment to one's right or north side and becomes progressively arid from the foot of Edwards Plateau to that of the Stockton Escarpment. Here the desert comes up to meet us once more, leaving only the Big Bend Mountains to our left. If we climb this escarpment to the upper Pecos valley on the great plateau

These softly colored dunes are piled against the mighty Sangre de Cristo Range, in the San Luis Valley in the southern Rockies. They move and alter form constantly.

of the prairies, we will pass through wonderful Dantesque gullies, filled with bulging, brightly colored rocks and dotted with junipers, piñons, and little oaks, which every now and then open onto small verdant flood plains with lovely groves of willows and cottonwoods interspersed with thick mesquite clumps. These valleys are filled with twittering flocks of birds. Arriving on the top we come onto a level and more or less bare plain stretching to north, east, and southeast, while to the west a great barrier of glowering mountains, usually cloud-covered, rises up like the edge of a continent from the sea. These are the Guadalupes, Sacramentos, and attendant ranges that sprawl for a hundred miles to the north.

These stand in a sea of scrub, and this low vegetation runs far up their flanks, turning into a typical chaparral. Above this the piñon pines close up to form a transition zone with oaks and some other stunted broad-leafed trees; then these give way to a forest of Ponderosa Pines which increase in thickness and height till at the highest altitudes they are replaced by typical boreal forests of spruce, fir, and aspen. On their western flanks, these mountains descend abruptly onto the Tularosa Plain or Basin, which forms the northern part of the Chihuahua deserts. This vegetational "no-man's land" lies in the North Scrub Belt but partakes of both desert and prairie features, contains forested mountains, and yet does not belong specifically to any one of these provinces. Moreover, it contains some unique features of its own.

LIVING TORNADOS

Among the lowest foothills of the eastern face of this range the entrance to the Carlsbad Caverns is situated. This has many miles of passages and is notable for its vast colony of bats.

There are a number of so-called bat caves dotted about the southern periphery of the great central plains. Besides Carlsbad Caverns, the best known is perhaps Ney Cavern on the Edwards Plateau. These contain colonies of almost countless numbers of a small insect-eating bat known as the Free-tailed Bat *(Tadarida mexicana)*. These bats sleep in the caves by day, during which they continually eliminate so that there is a constant rain of their dry excrement, composed mostly of the hard parts of insects, dropping on the floor. Since this has gone on for millennia, enormous guano deposits have formed. This is high in ammonia content, forming one of the finest fertilizers, and has been extensively mined for this purpose. Disturbance due to these operations, together with the draining of swamps and anti-malaria spraying, have greatly reduced the numbers of the bats, but they are still an impressive sight as they stream out in close-packed masses each eventide. Accounts of the discovery of these caves all run about the same: some lone cowboy sees what he thinks is a prairie fire on the horizon one night just before dark, with a huge black smoke plume reaching into the sky. Every evening it appears again. Finally the cowboy goes to investigate and finds that the cloud is countless millions of bats streaming out of a hole in the ground.

The sight is still impressive, and the noise is deafening—having been calculated to surpass in decibels the amount of noise made by a four-engined plane taking off. But more amazing is the fact that collisions are nonexistent, though it was once estimated that two billion bats came out of Ney Cavern—the entrance to which is not much over fifty feet across—in less than half an hour. The animals spread far and wide to feed at night, and they once formed a major control of the mosquitoes and other noxious insects of the region. I mention these colonies here not because they are typical of either the prairies or the deserts but are rather a special feature of both the North and South Scrub Belts.

THE ROOF OF NORTH AMERICA

The natural entrance to this province is via the Estancia Valley, which leads directly from the no-man's land just described. This is a northern prolongation of the Tularosa Basin and penetrates deeply into the Colorado Block. In fact, it is a continuation of a trough in the surface which splits that block from south to north and which continues up the San Luis Valley almost to the towering pinnacle of this continent near Leadville, Colorado. This means of approach is not only most "scenic" but also most highly instructive to those interested in the construction of our continent and the types of flora in which it is clothed. As one proceeds up this valley, all the major belts of vegetation to be found north of the deserts are laid out to left and right along the sides of the mountains, and each dips slowly and peters out in succession—first the scrub, then the grasslands, then the parks disappear, until one enters a beautiful transition zone around Santa Fe. Meantime the mountains on either side

Left: The Puma is still fairly common in large areas of the West and quite numerous in parts of this province. It is generally retiring and not dangerous.

Right: The upper slopes of the Colorado Rockies are clothed in true alpine flora with massed conifers. The higher ridges and peaks—"the roof" of America—are barren or snow-covered all year.

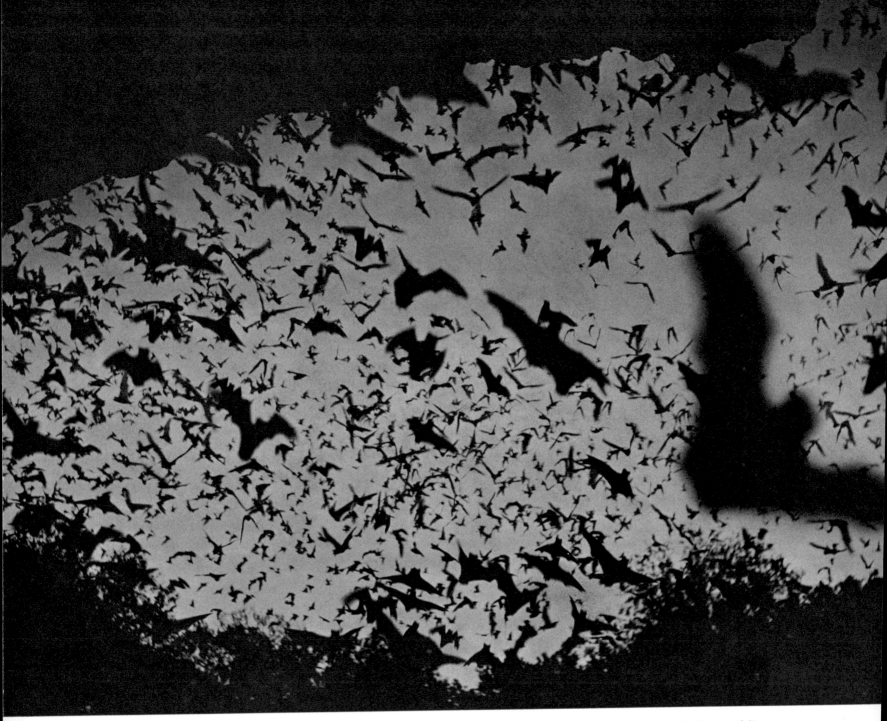

The evening flight of bats from limestone caves in the southern plateau area is one of the world's wonders. Millions issue forth in half an hour, entirely without collision.

show clearly first the boreal forests, then alpine meadows and tundras, and finally bare rocks coming in above. Finally, one bursts onto the San Luis Valley, and there in the distance are mighty snow- and ice-covered mountains, range beyond range, straight ahead. This valley is low enough to be prairie-clad with pleasant parklands around its edges, but it sinks to the north (relative to its latitude) so that some very dry scrub basins occur therein.

It is well worth turning to the right about halfway up this valley, going over the La Veta Pass and down to a place called Walsenburg. Here you run down onto the real prairies, on which pronghorns may be seen grazing, while off to the south stand the towering twin Spanish Peaks. These are isolated ancient volcanos, and all around them on the great sweeping grass-covered gutters that run to their feet are some remarkable geological structures known as dykes, which look like enormous, black, man-made walls, sticking straight out of the plain and all running like spokes of a wheel toward the peaks. These dykes are the

remnants of deep lava flows that were pushed up through great cracks in the earth's surface. There are also, dotted about, some cone- or tooth-shaped structures known as volcanic plugs, which are the fillings of old secondary volcanic throats whose cones have been worn away by erosion.

The fauna of these mountains is large and varied—elk, deer, puma, bear, and all the lesser fry, with a tremendous emphasis on colorful birds, notably the Mountain Bluebird. The lower slopes are clothed in piñons and junipers, the middle slopes with massed ponderosa pines, and the upper with spruce, fir, and aspen. The peaks have a wide belt of alpine tundra, then are bare and finally snow-clad. A similar arrangement of zones prevails all the way north throughout the Colorado Block, rising to a crescendo about Mount Elbert, where there are high suspended valleys clothed in alpine meadows running up to dense fir forests just as in Switzerland. But we should again turn aside, this time to look at one of nature's oddest sights. This lies at the foot of the Sangre de Cristo Mountains in the San Luis Valley.

Here we find some twenty-five square miles of sand dunes, of a beautiful, smooth, pale brown color, some of them topping six hundred feet in height, piled against the feet of the great mountains. These dunes have a remarkable form, sharp-edged along their crests but often with strange double crests or perfect subsidiary crests on the windward side. They are naked but for some tiny patches of two vivid green herbs—Lemon Weed (*Psoralea lanceolata*) and Indian Rice-Grass (*Orisopsis sp.*). These dunes march about constantly changing shape, and their movements are said by those who live there and tend them (it is a national monument) to look as if they are clawing at the foothills and trying to climb them. They have swamped large tracts of tree growth to considerable heights.

The San Luis Valley was once the bed of a sea. After being elevated to a height of some seven thousand feet, parallel cracks appeared along what are now its sides, and while *it* sank, great blocks of territory to either side rose almost a mile high to form the present mountains. Then the south end of the valley was blocked by an outpouring of volcanic material and it was virtually sealed in and dried out. As a result, its fine surface soils were whipped off by the powerful prevailing winds from the southwest. But these winds, while rushing up and topping the Sangre de Cristos at most places, were sufficiently stalled above this point to drop their loads of dust. Thus the dunes were formed.

THE GIANT'S CAUSEWAY

At the north end of the Colorado Block you can trek out onto one or another of a series of great mountainous fingers overlooking the Wyoming Basin, or you can turn sharp left to one of nature's grander achievements. The best route is down the Yampa River valley, leaving the mighty Park Range on the east and going down between the Elkhead Mountains to the north and the White River Plateau to the left. This takes you through a marvelous succession of massed spruce, then alpine meadows, and then through pine forests and a lush park zone, down to a lovely valley prairie in which are some remarkable volcanic plugs towering up like black teeth. Following the river down farther, you debouch onto an arid scrub-covered plain between low gray hills on the left and a rampart of saw-toothed mountains on the right. The latter soon begin to rise precipitately into crazy uptilted ridges of bare rock of brilliant colors, one behind the other. If you could climb onto these and scramble westward, you would presently be confronted by one of the most terrifying gorges to be found anywhere, at a point appropriately called Split Mountain. Through this the Green River flows to join the Yampa. Beyond lies a formidable oblong block of rugged wild mountains known as the Uintas, which form a natural causeway of gigantic dimensions leading to the western or Utah Block. Hundreds of lakes nestle among the peaks of these mountains.

The Utah mountains reach from the southeast corner of Idaho to the southern border of the state. They are formed of a high steep spine facing the Great Basin, inside which parallel ranges step down toward the Colorado Plateau, with several upland plateaus between them, the most notable of which is the Wasatch. Here are peaks over twelve thousand feet high, but on the whole they are more subdued than the Colorado Block. They are clothed in much the same types of forest but here the more southern species of conifers make their presence obvious. Among them are Rocky Mountain, Utah, and One-seed Juniper; some Douglas Fir higher up; Alpine, Corkbark, and White Fir; Blue, Englemann's, and White Spruce; and Bristle-Cone, Whitebark, Ponderosa, Lodgepole, and Piñon pines. Many canyons have cut into this block, the best known being Bryce Canyon in the south, which is filled with weird pinnacle-like formations and is "painted" a vivid combination of colors. This and other canyons, such as Zion, cut north into a great wall of rock known as the White Cliffs, which faces south onto the Kanab Plateau. This plateau rises slowly to the south and then pitches over the Vermilion Cliffs, after which it rises again steadily to the northern rim of the Grand Canyon. This plain is heavily forested to the south; its eastern end is cut off by the barrier of the Kaibab Plateau at eight thousand feet, its western end by what are called the Hurricane Cliffs; and beyond this lie the narrow ridges of the Virgin Mountains, which form another great natural causeway leading from the Utah to the Arizona Block. This would seem to be the logical place for the Colorado to have drained from the plateaus but instead it cut the Grand Canyon.

THE GREAT UNEXPLAINED

Quite apart from being a world wonder and almost breath-taking in its immensity, the Grand Canyon presents a great mystery. It is four to five thousand feet deep from its more or less horizontal rims (which are the two edges of a bisected plateau), triangular in section, from four to eighteen miles wide at the top, and 217 miles long. It cuts through a large number of horizontal strata of various ages and colors that give it much of its natural beauty. Most of these are comparatively soft and some are hardly compacted at all, but in its depths the river has carved down through considerable thicknesses of extremely hard Pre-Cambrian rocks. Now rivers cut deepest and fastest when they are running at maximum speed and carrying an overload of silt, and they run fastest of all when they are pitching down the steepest slopes. When their seaward descent is gradual they do very little digging, and if they then hit really hard rock in any quantity they pond behind it and cascade over it in the form of falls or rapids; their waters by then are clean, having dropped their load of silt in the pond, and so they do little if any cutting back. But the Colorado River appears not to have learned its geological or even its mechanical lessons very well, for it seems to have done everything quite otherwise.

This river is the only outlet for the drainage of an enormous area fed by rivers descending from the snows of the Colorado and Utah mountains, plus what rainfall there is on the Arizonas. It also drains much of the Wyoming Basin via the Little Snake and Green rivers. It is a fairly big river, and it carries a great deal of silt even during the long periods between the annual melting of the snows. Thus in normal circumstances it might be expected to do considerable digging and ditching. In its present condition, however, it cannot and does not, all the silt being derived from gutter erosion at the very heads of its smaller tributaries, and itself being an old and rather sluggish river, and one which even "meanders." This latter is the sign of old age and mechanical weakness in a river that simply has not got the strength to cut a straight channel for itself. Yet it has obviously cut a five-thousand-foot canyon, not only through uncompacted strata of old dried-out muds, clays, and sands, but also for considerable distances and to great depths through some of the

Overleaf: Although by no means the largest canyon or the greatest hole in the earth's surface, the Grand Canyon of the Colorado River in Arizona is a natural phenomenon of endless mystery.

densest of known rocks. As you stand on the rim of this most magnificent of nature's spectacles, you may well ponder these facts; and the more you do so, with the object before you, the more mystified you will become.

Geologists have done this for a century, but they have not, in my opinion, as yet come up with any satisfactory explanation. The theory usually propounded is that this block of mountains started rising only about a million years ago and that, as it did so, the Colorado River managed to counteract the rise by cutting this vast gorge over 200 miles through its midst. Now this could conceivably have been the case if the river had had to deal with only soft muds and clays and an occasional thin layer of sandstone or other sedimentary rocks; but it just could not in those circumstances have done what must have been done to the very hard rocks at the bottom, at which point its cutting power was at its lowest ebb. One thing is sure—the Grand Canyon was not formed entirely during the Pleistocene, even if there was a great enough volume of water bearing enough sediment to carve it out during all the interglacial periods.

The Colorado River followed that channel long before the Pleistocene, and there is reason to believe that it had been doing so since the beginning of the Eocene, some fifty-five million years earlier, and that it had already scoured out an impressive gorge by the beginning of the Pleistocene ice advances. The whole of this province, along with the rest of the Rockies, had been steadily rising since the beginning of the Eocene. Moreover, strata laid down later than that period, though massive both to north and south of the Colorado Plateau, are today entirely absent from it, though there is every reason to suppose that they once existed all over it as a continuous blanket. Where did all this vast mass of material go? Could it all have been carried away by the meltwater from the modest glaciers and icefields of the surrounding mountains in less than a million years?

Furthermore, the whole area is said to have been lower at that time, yet this river cut through the hardest rocks when it was at its lowest level. How was this physically possible? Then again, all evidence from the rocks laid down around the plateau

The Sage Grouse, better called the Sage Hen (Centrocercus urophasianus), inhabits the scrub belt between the Cascade–Sierra Nevada ranges on the west and the Rockies on the east. It is also found all over the Colorado Plateau and in sagebrush and semidesert areas throughout the southern Rockies. It is an impressive bird, but is rather lum-

indicates that the climate there was at no time wet, indeed was fairly arid at least till the comparatively brief pluvial periods of the Pleistocene. To have cut the canyon, therefore, either the whole area must have been at a vastly greater elevation to give the river sufficient power, or it must have taken much longer to form. Neither the melting of the montane glaciers nor the pluvial periods of the Pleistocene could have provided enough water to do the job without getting ponded, and if they were thus contained temporarily, they would have cut a straight rather than a meandering channel through the mountains when they burst out. The drainage pattern left on the plateau certainly seems to indicate ponding and sudden drainage, for it exactly resembles that left on the floor of any pond that has suddenly been emptied by the bursting of a dam. Yet none of these suggestions really explains this vast natural phenomenon, and especially how it managed to form into a serpentine gutter and still cut through the hardest of rocks for scores of miles to a considerable depth at its base level.

It gives one an almost eerie sensation to ponder such almost planetary concepts as one stands on the rim of this great canyon at sundown and strains one's eyes through the pink and mauve miasma that here so confuses the last slanting rays of the sun. There is a great and vast calm and stillness that usually fills the canyon to its brim. Above may be blue sky, wheeling swallows and eagles, and all around on the plateau are stately pine forests, alive with raucous piñon jays, industrious sapsuckers, and busy chipmunks, but in that chasm there seems to be nothing but diffuse color and a great going down. Here indeed is something of the olden times, stately, ponderous, somewhat exaggerated and perhaps even a bit gaudy, but utterly magnificent.

bering in flight. The group courtship displays of these birds are among the most spectacular in the animal kingdom. During breeding season, the colorful air sacs at the sides of the necks are (as shown above and below) inflated with air to a remarkable size. Its trial introduction into other areas has not been successful.

ANOTHER HOLE IN THE GROUND

To the south of the canyon rise the multiple peaks of San Francisco Mountain (12,800 feet), and from this the famous Mogollon Rim runs east to the lava-covered uplands of New

Mexico and forms the northern flank of the southern or Arizona mountain block. This massif is arid though clothed all over its upper reaches with either open or closed coniferous forests of pines and junipers. It contains many upland plateaus, and large parts of it are still true wilderness. If we descend from its northern rim onto the central plateau and start up the course of the Puercos River, we may turn aside to visit another remarkable natural phenomenon. This is the largest and most readily accessible meteorite crater in the United States and one of the most prominent and most recently formed in the world.

It is an enormous bowl-shaped hole, 4150 feet across, three miles around the rim, and 570 feet deep, sunk in the middle of a slight rise on a more or less level plain. It was not recognized as being of meteoric origin until almost sixty years after its discovery in 1871, but it was the first crater on earth to be so recognized. Since then, similar phenomena have been discovered, or reappraised for what they really are, in increasing numbers all over the world. Most active in this novel exploration recently have been the Canadians who, stimulated by the discovery of the enormous Chubb Crater in the Ungava Peninsula (see Chapter 2) from the air in 1948, worked over their aerial surveys and found a dozen more. Some of these are so ancient that they are completely filled in and can at first be recognized only by their distinctive shape and the fact that different types of vegetation grow around their rims, whereas others are filled with lakes that form parts of circular depressions. Later borings and other investigations have confirmed their nature.

The debate about these phenomena, since they have been accepted as such, has centered around the method of their formation. At first it was believed that a large meteorite too big to burn up in passing through the atmosphere, crashed into the ground with such force as to smash its way into the rocks until it came to rest, like a bullet ploughing into a tree trunk. An immense amount of time, money, and labor was spent in probing for buried meteors in the hope of being able to mine them, as they are usually composed of almost pure nickel-iron. No such great metallic mass has even been located, let alone excavated from under any of these big craters. The next theory was that the craters were formed by swarms of little meteors that bombarded a single point on the earth in a stream, breaking up the rock surface and scattering to form crater-like cones, just as you may do by shooting a shotgun shell at sand. At first there seemed to be considerable confirmation of this idea, for, although no whole meteorites were located under craters, a lot of meteoric iron has been detected both in and around many of them. In this Arizona crater—the Barringer, as it is now named—a large amount of such iron has been located by gravimetric methods about a thousand feet below the south rim, and much more is scattered widely all about, the total calculated to aggregate some three million tons. This would form a sphere about five hundred feet in diameter. I may add that this iron would be valued at about a hundred dollars per ton today.

Recently, however, it has been pointed out that a meteorite of this size, hitting the earth at a terrific speed, amounts almost to the proverbial irresistible force meeting an immovable object; and that, on approaching that impossible situation, a number of strange things happen. At the exact moment of impact of the leading edge of the meteorite with the surface of the earth's rock crust, the meteorite is indeed virtually an irresistible object; while the earth, being the greater mass, is an immovable one. The latter therefore absorbs the shock and stops the movement of the meteor, but this occurrence releases a fantastic amount of pent-up energy that has to be absorbed or disseminated. This is mostly in the form of heat, but heat so great and so suddenly

produced that it becomes explosive—molecularly and in extreme cases even atomically—so that electrons are actually blasted from their orbits. (This has been done under experimental conditions by pressure alone.) However, during the split second before this condition is created in the meteorite, that body has penetrated some distance into the rock surface of the earth, both shattering it and subjecting it to unimagined pressures. As it comes to a stop, the meteorite blows up like a monumental bomb, its energy of movement or momentum having all been converted into heat; and it "goes off" in all directions, not only downward. This, aided by the spring-back of the rocks, results in a minor "volcano" on the surface—which causes the crater and explains the masses of shattered rock and the bits of meteoritic iron that are found scattered for miles around. It also explains why there is no single solid meteoric body below.

It is now believed that in some cases the entire meteorite may be thus volatilized, leaving practically no solid residue. In 1908 one estimated to have weighed more than a million tons struck in Siberia. This appears to have been a multiple meteor or a shower; for, although all of it was apparently volatilized, ten large craters, the biggest 165 feet in diameter, and a host of smaller ones were formed. It landed in daylight, but it was seen hundreds of miles away and its heat was felt for fifty miles. Four hundred miles away it rocked a railroad engine to a stop, and all trees in the dense taiga forest where it landed were knocked down for forty miles all around.

The Barringer Crater today is an austere thing to look at. It is without any natural beauty or charm, and it gives one the impression of being just what it is: a vast shell hole or bomb crater. It obviously did not grow on this old earth, and it seems somehow to be a rude imposition.

A FOREST OF OPAL

Sixty miles east of this crater there is still another fascinating sight. This is a vast petrified forest. These phenomena are found all over the world and there are many on this continent, but this is a most spectacular example and perhaps the most instructive. These trees are incredibly ancient, having been dumped into saturated ground or into the silt at the bottoms of rivers or lakes when they were waterlogged in what the geologists call the Triassic Period, some two hundred million years ago. These deposits are today called the Chinle beds and are in some places three hundred feet in thickness. The individual layers often show, on their surfaces, mud cracks such as one sees around drying lakes today, ripple marks, and even giant rain spots. The theory is that these trees grew elsewhere and were washed down in freshets and dumped into shallow lakes. Although this is possible, it seems improbable, since many of them have considerable portions of quite slender roots and branches still in place and undamaged, and almost all of them still have their bark complete and perfectly preserved. What is more, many are really very big trees, and it would take more than a mere freshet to float them without scouring them completely. It seems much more likely that they grew *in situ* and were blown down from time to time by hurricanes, as the great trees of today sometimes are, and fell into a nearby river and then sank, just as today the great cypresses do into such rivers as the Suwannee in Florida.

The South Montane Province has almost every variety of growth—even massed forests of Quaking Aspen on its higher mountain slopes.

Monument Valley, one of the most bizarre of nature's efforts on this continent, is blood-red in color and sculptured into shapes of the utmost fantasy for miles.

Moreover, some obviously lay about and rotted before they were engulfed in the muds and silts that preserved them, and these must have been immersed gently during prolonged floods or more likely by permanent subsidences of the land; otherwise they would have been smashed apart.

Today all the strata laid down above these Chinle beds have been eroded away, and the wind, rain, and other forces are now at work on the beds themselves. The result is a group of low hills with small, shallow valleys meandering between them, sometimes forming miniature canyons and modest cliffs made of the upper strata of these ancient lake and stream beds and containing these trees in a petrified condition. As the softer material is washed away, the logs slowly emerge and many pieces of them roll down into the hollows, where they now form jumbles that look like the back lots of a giant sawmill. On closer inspection, these logs provide a host of further surprises.

They are, of course, composed of solid stone, for the most part a form of quartz known as chalcedony, which looks like glass but is really composed of an aggregation of minute crystals. This material is formed by deposition in cavities in other materials; and, if traces of other minerals are present in the solution, the resulting crystals come in various colors to which distinctive names have been given—carnelian, sard, chrysoprase, bloodstone, and so forth. When alternating light and dark bands are laid down, agate, onyx, and sardonyx result. Between these are often related minerals of the opal group, which in a few rarer forms are gems. Opals are among the few minerals that are not crystalline, and they are really dried-up deposits of a substance known as silica jelly. They contain from 3 to 10 per cent of water. These ancient trees, after being buried in the silt, were subjected to a long process of nature whereby they were, as may be said, taken apart molecule by molecule, the cellulose and other materials of their wood being replaced by these chalcedonies and opals. However, since each part of a tree, often down to each of its rings, contains varying amounts of different trace minerals like iron, sulphur, and so forth, the quartz became stained in different colors. The result is that, though now of solid stone, these trees display every detail of their structure down to the microscopic, in varied and often contrasting colors. The thick bark is usually a rich, smooth, reddish brown; the interior of the trunk a pale mauvish gray; and sections of roots often bright yellow. But the variation is endless, and all kinds of beautiful and grotesque kaleidoscopes of color turn up, especially in places where the trees were cracked, where lightning struck, or where they were otherwise wounded in life.

As you wander about among these stone trees, you will find all manner of unexpected things, like whole stumps with the butts of their roots sticking up to the sky just as if they had been uprooted only the day before. All these trees are broken into neat sections by clean, transverse fractures, though in many places all the sections of whole trees lie exposed on the surface together and in proper order. It is said that this almost regular cracking is due to the rhythmic vibrations of ancient earthquakes. But there are tides that follow each other daily round and round the earth through the rocks, just as ocean tides run through the waters of its surface, so that all rocks are actually stretched and compressed a little twice a day. These tensions and pressures are exerted virtually in all directions, unlike those of earthquakes which travel in one direction, and would be much more likely to cause the regular sectioning; for the logs lie pointing in all directions.

The trees have been identified as conifers related to an ancient group known as the Araucarians, now confined to the southern hemisphere. In some of the associated shale beds, however, are also found the perfectly fossilized leaves and other parts of various cycads, horsetails, and ferns. The three tree species have the tongue-twisting names of *Woodsworthia* and *Schilderia,* the relationships of which are unknown, and *Araucarioxyla.* Of animals of their period, besides a crocodile-like reptile called a

Phytosaur, there are found the remains of creatures called Dicynodonts, which were primitive reptiles showing distinct anatomical tendencies toward the mammals, and of large amphibians shaped like enormous flattened salamanders, called Labyrinthodonts. Also, there was a lungfish, a creature of which there are still three living types found in Australia, Africa, and South America, and which inhabit stagnant water, obtaining their oxygen by gulping air into primitive lungs. Encased in balls of dried mud, they can rest in a form of suspended animation for years.

The name "Colorado Plateau" is misleading. This meandering leaf-shaped upland-lowland is shaped like a platter rather than a plateau. The Spanish word *platea,* meaning the orchestral pit of a theatre, would be much more appropriate, especially in conjunction with the word *colorado,* which means ruddy or red and which is most fitting. If you drive up the middle of it you may pass through some places that are so fantastic you can hardly believe them. The two most typical lie along a route—it is not a road and is not at all to be recommended to average motorists—that leads from a point halfway between Holbrook

211

and Gallup on Route 66, due north for 120 miles across the Navajo Reservation to Route 60, and thence by that road via Mexican Hat on the San Juan River to Blanding in Utah. The first lap of this trek follows the east face of the Black Mesa.

This is a seemingly endless barrier of mountains which runs north for mile after mile. Throughout its length it is carved into a giant phalanx of pagoda-like objects interspersed with fine natural imitations of the temple of Angkor Vat in Cambodia, and is of all colors from a dull puce through grays and glowing browns to a sanguinary red. For a long stretch there is a parallel wall about a mile away, but this is in reverse, being eroded into a succession of notched gullies the sides of which are slashed with bands of glaring white alkalinity. The valley between is clothed in considerable scrub and some shrubbery which at the bottom forms a thick, pale blue carpet made up of a kind of sage. A dry river bed meandering through the valley is whiter than new snow under an alpine sun, due to an accumulation of this alkaline substance.

This valley finally opens out, and you come out upon a vista of low, rolling downs clothed in scattered dusty sage going off to the horizon. But no sooner have you advanced a few miles onto this rolling plain—named the Defiance Plateau—than the ground drops abruptly away from beneath your feet, and you find yourself looking straight down into a world which is completely incredible. Here the land has been gouged away along another wall-like rampart fronting a level, olive-colored plain. This rampart also is red but with a distinct purplish tinge, and it is sandblasted into smooth curves, bulges, and vertical potholes of gargantuan dimensions, some forming globular caves. It goes off both ways as far as the eye can see. But what adds the ultimate touch of fantasy is that, between the bulges of its face, there are here and there vast cones of fine, blue-gray dust and small pebbles that seem to have been poured over the rampart by some monstrous wheelbarrow. Yet there is no such material anywhere above today, either on top of the cliff or, as may readily be seen, in the towering red mountains beyond. Wandering about among these intricate miniature canyons that lead back into the upper plateau, often via natural arches of winding, smooth-walled caves, one finds oneself in a terrifying sort of sandstone nightmare. The floor is absolutely level; there is no life to be seen in the daytime; the silence is profound; the heat is so terrific you can both see it and move it about by making hand-passes in the air. Here our world of living things, blue waters, and green grass seems to disappear altogether.

The *platea* as a whole is not just arid: it is in many places and over vast stretches frankly naked and often apparently skinned to boot, so that you see not only the ancient skeletal structure of the earth itself but masses of its very entrails, so to speak. There is an area down in the Arizona part called the Painted Desert which, at sunset, looks as if it had been splashed with blood, but there are other much more striking places that are heaved and contorted into the most awe-inspiring masses of geological chaos. One is the Hovenweep National Monument, just north of the San Juan River. This is a succession of swooping plains, clad in red dust and speckled with little tufts of scrub, separated from one another by vast walls, barriers, towers, and other natural edifices of red rock, all sculptured in shapes so fantastic they defy description. Some of these mon-

Arizona's most notable petrified forest is composed of logs consisting of opal and jasper lying among miniature canyons of pale gray and mauve-colored dried clays and congealed muds.

strosities stand about singly; others mass together but have narrow "doorways" through which you may peek into further canyons beyond—all lifeless, painted, and shimmering in the glutinous heat.

GREEN EYRIES

But the *platea* is not all like this. On its surface stand several isolated volcanic peaks clothed in lush forests—such as the 11,440-foot Abajo Peak just north of this ruddy desert—and there are great tongues of forested uplands stretching onto it from the mountains all around. Probably the most lovely trip I have made in the United States was on the terrifying little boulder-strewn dirt road that crawls up the almost perpendicular sides of mountains over the Douglas Pass between Grand Junction and Vernal, Utah. The road starts out well and enters a sort of diminutive badlands of bare clay cliffs, followed by a narrow valley choked with a sort of chaparral of dense tall bushes. It then deteriorates into a gravel track, but it goes up and up to a magnificent fir and spruce forest on top. The pass is knife-edged, and beyond stretches a vast valley filled with lakes at various levels, all surrounded by massed forests of all manner of coniferous and broad-leafed trees. The air is here filled with golden eagles: I counted ten on the wing at one time.

The valley leads down through a lush series of meadows, each with its own groupings of bushes, sedges, and flowering herbs. Here are massed willows and alders, wire and swamp grasses. On the slopes are dry meadows crowded with Colorado chipmunks, golden-mantled ground squirrels, and flickertails. Magpies, piñon jays, blackbirds, and cowbirds are everywhere, and there are many ravens. Slowly, junipers and piñons come down the slopes and sage takes over the valley bottom, and then one comes upon a grove of great cottonwoods that line the banks of the White River. After this, desert scrub is met on the top of a bluff composed of fantastic rock formations. Beyond is the Yampa River, also lined with patches of cottonwoods. Here we come once again to the gateway to the north and the Wyoming Basin. And here we find what is perhaps the most remarkable exhibit in this incredible province. This lies twelve miles east of Vernal, where the Green River emerges from Split Mountain.

GRAVEYARD OF THE MIGHTY

The feet of the mountains here are composed of a most unlikely-looking jumble of different rock strata, alternating between hard massive sandstones and materials so soft that they are often little more than dried mud. All these strata slope inward toward the ragged peaks beyond, like a disorderly shelf of different-sized books, tattered and dog-eared and some of them reduced by monstrous termites to mere piles of dust. These rocks are of many colors, ranging from smooth pastel grays to pinks and even greenish blue. They are for the most part bare, but some of them support a stunted growth of greasewood and sage, and gnarled junipers dot the surfaces of the cliffs or cluster in hollows. It is here, among these lesser foothills, that nature saw fit to establish a most extraordinary graveyard some hundred and thirty million years ago.

It appears that, at that time, this place was the delta of a large river, probably on a flood plain bordering a lake rather than a sea. This seems to have been of considerable extent and to have supported a lush flora. There seem to have been marked seasons, for there is much evidence of floods during which coarse-grained

Right: Woodhouse's Jay, a local variety of the California Jay, is in some places common among the piñons. *Below:* The Piñon Jay, another colorful member of the crow family, inhabits the same zones but a slightly different habitat.

material was washed downstream and deposited here; but, alternating with these, were long periods when fine silt and mud accumulated. This was in the middle of what we now call the age of reptiles, or the Jurassic Period, and the sandstones then formed make up what we now call the Morrison beds. During floods, the corpses of the animals that inhabited both this delta and the surrounding lands were from time to time carried along by the waters, and were deposited on sand bars, just as the bodies of domestic animals are today by the Green River. Then, as the flesh was eaten by scavengers, the bones sank into the sand and were entombed. Fortunately for us, many of those so buried in this place were fossilized.

Several great changes later took place, the whole area having, among other things, been covered by a large sea or part of the ocean for a long period. But eventually the land rose again, and erosion went to work on the now upended and exposed sections of the deposits formed in the ancient delta. Again very fortunately, a scientist happened to spot some of these fossilized bones during a field trip in the year 1893 and recorded the fact. Fifteen years later one Dr. Earl Douglass made an extended search which finally brought him to the place of which we speak.

Any citizen may now stand here and gaze upon the skeletons of dinosaurs, both monstrous and minute, still embedded in the sandstones of the ancient delta where they once lived and died. Here the past stares you in the eye with a kind of knowing twinkle, as if to say, "So you didn't really believe what you saw in the museum, did you?"; and this can be most disturbing. You begin to think of elephants and rhinoceroses and other unlikely-looking creatures; and then, perhaps shrugging, you turn to contemplation of the mighty dinosaur commonly called *Brontosaurus,* and you realize that it is only a bit less likely. Then other strange thoughts come to mind.

These creatures, being reptiles, almost certainly laid eggs; and, as far as we know from the few of these found, these were comparatively very small. Did baby dinosaurs, which need not have been much bigger than baby alligators when they first popped out of their eggs, frisk about in the bright sun, or did they dig themselves into the sand, or dart for water before one of their larger cousins could snap them up? There is so much more we would like to know about these fabulous creatures. What for instance did they eat? What color were they? Did some of them have flaming red heads, iridescent green bodies, and bright blue tails, such as one lizard has today? Or were they all just great drab-colored beasts like elephants and rhinos? The very idea of baby dinosaurs is in some respects rather startling, especially when you contemplate the remains of their vast parents. But there were also little dinosaurs—quite apart from baby big ones—that were not much bigger than chickens. One *(Laosaurus)* that was first found here had an over-all length of only two and a half feet, including its long, reptilian tail, and it apparently rushed about on its hind legs just as the Basilisk Lizard of Central America does today. But there are other even more intimate things to be seen here.

Prominent among these are considerable quantities of pebbles, mostly about the size of your clenched fist, that are polished as if by a jeweler. No known natural process can so polish a pebble, for even the finest powdered dust leaves tiny scratches that render the surface dull, while chemicals only etch it. These stones were a mystery until a clutch of them were found occupying the position once held by the stomach of a small fossil reptile known as *Protiguanadon.* From this discovery it became apparent that many dinosaurs, like birds today, might have had

Bristle-cone pines. It has been discovered that some specimens of these gnarled, scrawny-looking pines in California's White Mountains are about four thousand years old, and thus among the oldest living trees.

to swallow pebbles to aid in the grinding of coarse food in their stomachs. And that would be the one place where such pebbles could be so brightly polished. This seems to bring these impossible-looking reptiles much closer, for it gives us one more point to understand about them. The ultimate in getting to know the dinosaurs was probably achieved by Roy Chapman Andrews in bringing to light a dinosaur nest containing its eggs, some of which had within them little dinosaurs about ready to hatch.

The remains of some three hundred individual dinosaurs of a dozen different species have now been extricated from the sandstones of this place. Among these are more than two dozen skeletons so complete that they have been mounted as a whole in museums. In addition to dinosaurs, two kinds of crocodilians, one a real pigmy, and a very ordinary-looking tortoise have come from the same strata. Among the dinosaurs are the vast brontosaur now known as *Apatosaurus;* its more slender relative *Diplodocus* with its horsy head and strange, slender teeth; and the long-necked *Barosaurus;* two kinds of *Camarasaurus;* and so many remains of the fabulous *Stegosaurus* (which probably lived on the drier uplands) that the diggers became frankly bored with them. Of bipedal plant-eaters there are three; and there are two flesh-eaters, one called *Antrodemus,* with a body about the size of a mule and two-inch teeth with serrated cutting edges.

Towering Peaks and Gushing Geysers

The North Montane Block or the
United States Rockies, and the Blue Mountains

Bears are very dangerous creatures. They are also a nuisance, as a memorandum handed to visitors to the national parks in this area indicates. This states, among other useful hints, that "metal chests with good locks make fair storage receptacles although experience has shown that not all metal chests are bear-proof." The Black Bear, whatever actual color it may be, can also look very appealing, in several senses of that word, and the young ones, especially when standing on their hind legs and begging,

16

Left: The Yellowstone area is a hotbed of subvolcanic activity, with geysers, steam vents, and mud flows. The trees here are encrusted with minerals leached from the warm waters. Below: Geysers "blow" both regularly and unpredictably. Hot water accumulated in natural wells in the rock is ejected when it turns to steam.

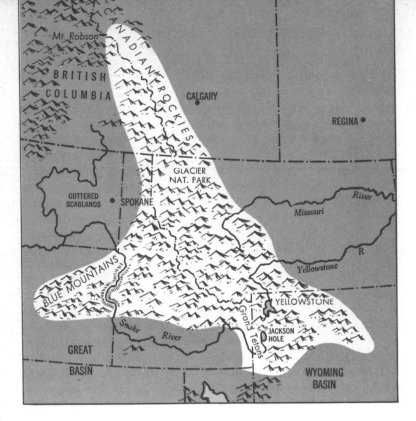

The position, conformation, and boundaries of this province may be seen on the map by reference to the international and state boundaries and the limited stretch of coast that is shown. It is entirely mountainous; it is some 850 miles long from Mount Robson in the north to Wind River in the south, and some 600 miles wide from the Big Horn to the Blue Mountains at its widest.

The reason for treating it at this point is that, as may be seen on both the general map and the province map, it lies wholly within the North Scrub Belt. In fact, any land within its confines that lies below one thousand feet in the south or two hundred feet in the north—though there is only a little at those elevations around the periphery of the province—is clothed in typical scrub. It is the best example on this continent of how little, if any, effect altitude has on the distribution of the major vegetational belts.

The northeastern face of this province is the great barrier that slices this continent from the mouth of the Mackenzie River on the Arctic Ocean to Vera Cruz in Mexico. The Big Horn Mountains form an outlier. On the northwest, it marches with and in part coalesces with the northern extremity of the Cascades, which are clothed in a special type of montane forest related to the northwest Pacific "rain forests" of British Columbia and Alaska. South of this, on its west face, its periphery forms a sharp line of demarcation with the Scablands, which its extension, the Blue Mountains, cradles on the south. The province's southern face is turned to the North Scrub Belt and Gray Deserts of the Great Basin.

The dividing line between this province and the Southern Montane Block is very distinct: it runs south of the Caribou Range and north of the Preuss Range on the border between Idaho and Wyoming and just north of their junction with Utah. Immediately to the east of this narrow gap lies the almost circular, scrub-covered Wyoming Basin, which connects eastward with the Great Prairies.

To many people this block represents the "Northern Rockies" as opposed to the Canadian Rockies, while the Southern Montane Block constitutes the "Southern Rockies." These are sound definitions, since they serve to distinguish these complexes of mountains from the coast ranges, but it must be remembered that about a third of this province lies in Canada and neither plants nor animals recognize political boundaries.

---

seem to be made for cuddling. But this can be most misleading. We have already met the brown or dish-faced bears and, let us hope, got them and their grizzly-coated representatives sorted out. In doing that we had occasion to mention the Black Bear (*Euarctos americanus*). This is one of the commonest and perhaps the most widely distributed of all our mammals, ranging across the boreal forests of the north from Alaska to Newfoundland and south via the mountain ranges of the west to both the Sierra Occidental and the Sierra Oriental in Mexico, and via the Appalachians to Georgia, Florida, and Louisiana.

The whole question of black bears is almost as complicated as that of "brown bears," for they come in various shades of brown, gray, and black, at any season and often in the same litter. But there are races that are always brown and some that are white—the Kermode Bear from Gribble Island and the Kitimat Arm of Douglas Channel in British Columbia, which is pure white except for an ocher wash on its head and along the midback. Then in the region of the St. Elias Mountains in Alaska there is a form that is blue-gray. It would seem reasonable to suppose that a black bear should be black, and a brown bear brown. Unfortunately it does not work out that way. However, the animal now popularly called the Black Bear is quite distinct from all those animals called brown bears and from all other bears for that matter. The best way to recognize it, as we pointed out in Chapter 3, is by the up-arched or convex upper ridge of its snout as seen in profile. This may not seem to matter, but it will if you go wandering about in the mountains of this province.

There are still in this area grizzly bears, some of which are of a pronouncedly dark tone. There are also some large black bears which in old age and at certain seasons may be considerably silvered and lack any white on their snouts. The non-specialist on a camping or fishing trip may well mistake the one for the other in poor light. Although all bears should be given as wide a berth as possible and never encouraged with offers of food, evasive action in face of a grizzly on a foraging foray should be quite different from and more energetic than that in face of a black bear. The Black Bear is very inquisitive and bold, and if tempted and then frustrated can be terribly dangerous because it can outrun most horses, climb trees, and move with unbelievable speed. It slashes with its paws, hugs, bites, and bulldozes, and it is an infighter and terrifically strong. On the whole, however, it keeps its distance from humans.

Grizzlies may behave in quite a different way, and one shouldn't be misled by the gallant tales of hunters. Grizzlies are bolder than black bears in their own territory, and they may actually attack. The best thing to do, should one appear, is to get into the nearest bear-proof shelter and wait till the animal goes on about its business, which it will do. Failing a shelter, present a united front and don't run. Best of all, don't go into grizzly territory without taking the advice of either officials in charge of the country or the best local professional hunters. But beware also of black bears, even along roads. Today these animals have taken to wandering about highways in this province like tramps looking for handouts. They block traffic, stand up and beg, and

Both White-tailed and Mule Deer are found in this province. The does of the two species are not easy to tell apart. These are Whitetail Deer.

shuffle over to peer fixedly at you through your car windows. They have learned that tourists usually carry food and like to hand it out. But they are so shortsighted they may not distinguish your hand from the food, and when you run out of food they may take umbrage and become very unpleasant.

I was once driving through one of the national parks here— accompanied by an authorized person—to write a story on these bear beggars, when we met a brownish black bear on a road running along a sheer cliff face—a place the bear had cunningly chosen because nobody could get away from it, and thus had to stop! My companion opened one window just a crack and tossed two slices of bread to the animal. The bear ate the bread, then came to the car, stood up, and put its claws over the glass of the window and refused to let go until more bread was tossed out. If there had been no more bread, it might have started ripping the window out. The window was then closed, but the bear immediately climbed onto the roof of the car! To dislodge it we had to perform some rather complex maneuvers.

Yet these animals are of immense interest. I will never forget coming across two bear cubs in a small bush in this same country. Although they stood only about thirty inches on their hind legs, it did not seem possible that the slender twigs of the berry bush could support their weight; yet they were some ten feet aloft and were reaching out to pull the fruits toward them with their paws, stripping them with their tongues, and munching away happily. When we came on them, one immediately slithered down the bush, tramped up to us, and stood up on its hind legs begging with its paws and peering intently into our eyes. These were perfectly wild animals, so we shooed the little creature back to its bush, which it ascended reluctantly and rather clumsily while we sat back to watch. About ten minutes

later, I happened to catch some movement in the thick bushes off to our right. We beat a hasty retreat—and not a moment too soon, for the mother marched out almost immediately with a very authoritative air. Fortunately we had not touched the cubs nor given them anything unnatural, for she scolded them down out of the bush and sniffed them carefully all over while keeping one small, bloodshot eye full upon us. Bears are not fools.

THE IMPERIAL HART

Bears are almost everywhere, but it is perhaps in this province that the average person may have the closest view of them at home in their own territory. The same goes for several other of our more outstanding big game. One of these, an animal that is known at least by name to almost everyone, is often regrettably overlooked. This is the Elk or Wapiti, which is the North American representative of the Red Deer of Asia and Europe, of which there are many recognizable species and races. However, it attains to its most magnificent proportions on our continent and, although not ever as bulky as the Moose, it may truly be said to be the king of the deer. It is not so much the size of the creature or its beautiful "lines" but the really enormous yet perfectly proportioned, shaped, and balanced antlers of the larger stags that are so impressive. This deer is today again spread over a considerable area, having been reintroduced to many suitable

Overleaf: The waters of Yellowstone's geysers are heavily charged with various minerals. These are often deposited by evaporation and create incredibly fantastic scenes.

Travertine terraces formed by the outflow from a geyser-like spring in Yellowstone. These crystalline formations may cascade down whole mountainsides but are usually destroyed by earthquakes or landslides.

places such as the mountains of southwestern Colorado. There are still some of the original dwarf race in California, and descendants of others are spread all over the mountainous regions of the West from Alaska to Arizona. The great show place of these animals is the Jackson Hole country in what is now Grand Teton National Park, Wyoming. There the animals spend the winter in the National Elk Refuge near the town of Jackson, moving up into the highlands surrounding that valley in the summer. When snow again covers those highlands they return. These herds are almost domesticated today, and it is perhaps more interesting to meet them away from the partly artificial though excellent administration of the conservationists.

Elk have a kind of majesty not possessed either by our other deer or by any other animal on this continent, and a large stag with a full set of antlers is a most arresting sight. In the fall, large males may often be encountered alone in the mountain glens of this area. Although shy animals with a keen sense of hearing, these lone ones seem not to be difficult to approach. Although they probably become aware of you before you see them, they may remain perfectly still with ears held wide so that you come upon them staring directly at you. The Moose is almost a monstrosity, and the little Mule Deer is almost fragile, whereas the Reindeer is frankly gawky; but the Elk's body is a perfect symphony of construction and proportion. In movement it has a grace that surpasses that of the most delicate of the gazelles, yet it may exceed a large ox in bulk. I once saw one jump a rocky stream almost from a standing start; it soared over with its forelegs bent back almost to its chest, exactly like those deer depicted on vases and ceramics of the classical period.

MOUNTAIN CAPERS

This area is also the home of two other ungulates that many have heard about but probably never seen. These are the Bighorn or Rocky Mountain Sheep and the so-called Rocky Mountain Goat. This latter name is not strictly accurate, for the animal is not a goat but belongs to a genus known as the rock-goats or *Rupicaprinae,* which includes the Chamois of Europe and the gorals and serows of Asia, but these pure white, shaggy-haired creatures are entirely goatlike in appearance, even to having a beard. They are among the most daring climbers in the animal world but look to be extraordinarily clumsy. They live on the tops of the steeper mountains and seem to be especially fond of screes; across these they rush headlong and with apparent abandon. Their hoofs are odd, being of the consistency of tire rubber but encased in a hard sheath forming a sharp edge around the undersides, so that each is a kind of cup with sucker-like qualities. Their antics are not quite so hair-raising as those of the European Chamois, which will sail out into the air and land on a prominence about the size of a man's hand, but they negotiate precipices that look perfectly smooth and vertical, and they can cover ground at unexpected speed. They almost always go uphill to avoid danger and seem happiest when above the grass line. In fact, their principal food is the montane tundra mosses and lichens, and they stay in these wind-swept altitudes all year round.

The young stay with the parents for a year, and then, in November, numbers of families get together for a brief mating period. After this they separate again; the young are born the following spring. They are fairly common animals in Alaska, the Yukon, and British Columbia. There are some on the Cascades, but otherwise they are found in the United States only in this Northern Montane Province, where their numbers are now given as about ten thousand.

The Bighorn Sheep has a much wider distribution, being found from northern Alaska to the Sierra Madre Occidental in Mexico. It is found in isolated areas throughout the Southern Montane Pine Province and in western Texas and New Mexico. It used also to inhabit many lower ranges, even in the Dakotas. The last one in the Sierra Nevada is said to have been shot in 1909, but skulls are still occasionally found on the mountain heights. It is a true sheep but has a thick coat of hair instead of wool. Both sexes bear horns, but those of the males are much larger. They are grazers as opposed to browsers, and they drift about all year following the best grass growths; but they can subsist on mosses and leaves, and they dig down through the winter snows to get at food. In their northern range they perform regular migrations up to the mountain tops in summer and down into the valleys in winter. They once probably did this everywhere, and the habit may have been the cause of their extinction in so many areas, for they have always been mercilessly hunted at lower altitudes.

A large proportion of individuals of this species show, in captivity, what appears to be high intelligence. They are strangely discerning and learn to accomplish some surprising things readily, such as opening mechanical locks on gates and so forth. In this respect they seem to far surpass their relatives such as the Mouflon and the Aoudad, and amongst domestic animals they are matched only by the very strange Badian Sheep that were originally brought from Africa (though where in Africa nobody has ever found out) to Barbados in the West Indies.

Unlike most animals, especially hoofed animals, the herd or flock leaders are males; and, although several rams may get along peaceably in a flock, if two of the leaders meet they more often than not indulge in rather preposterous contests though very few animals, if any, ever "fight" to the death as men may do. Even their battles at mating time are more in the nature of contests which end as soon as one or the other is down or simply quits. Bighorns, however, go at it for hours and seem to enjoy the clash. The unbelievable thing is how any of them manage to survive, because these tests entail a pair of three-hundred-pound animals backing away from each other for a dozen yards or so and then charging head down at full speed, which is possibly as much as forty miles per hour. The resulting impact—at twice that speed—results in a considerable "explosion." But the animals just shake their heads, back off, and charge again. Why it does not break their necks or curdle their brains I do not know. On one occasion I was present when a captive bighorn ram was being led through a zoo to its new pen, which necessitated passing that of another ram. The latter became annoyed at the presence and charged the gate, which was of four-by-two pine timbers set between cedar posts four inches in diameter, sunk three feet into the ground, and attached to heavy-mesh wire on either side. To our horror the animal came right through, smashing the cross members of the gate and tearing it and one of the posts right out of the ground.

Mountain sheep are not easy to see, and not only because of their neat protective coloration. They are altogether more elusive than mountain goats, and they have a habit of lying down in secluded spots by day, when they are extremely difficult to spot even with a telescope.

CIRQUES AND ICE CORBELS

Searching for these animals is, however, probably the best way to see this magnificent country. Many parts of it, not only in the three great national parks, are positively breath-taking. The mountains here are aggressively steep and for the most part well vegetated. In the valleys are usually beautiful blue lakes, while above the tree line there is lush montane tundra and a profusion of alpine foliage. On the highest peaks are many little incipient glaciers. Most of these are really no more than what are called *cirques,* or bowl-shaped hanging valleys filled with ice. Nevertheless they display many interesting glacial features—notably those of slow death.

High in these mountains in summer, the snow remains till fall in great pancake-shaped blobs in the better-shaded parts of steep slopes. These melting patches of snow display some odd features due to a rather exceptional circumstance. In most places where snow lies on the ground all year, be it polar or mountain, the air is clear and clean. Here there is often a lot of dust, due to the province being surrounded on three sides by appallingly dry prairie, scrub, and desert areas. This fine dust settles on the snow but tends to concentrate along any sharp edges. Now, as compacted snow melts on steep slopes, the meltwater tends to form tunnels underneath, and into these you can walk or crawl from the downward side. They often lead into a maze of ice caves and passages, all of which have domed ceilings. The strange thing is that these ceilings are not smooth but are evenly pitted with large, shallow hexagonal indentations like a vastly magnified section of honeycomb. This is a common phenomenon in

The northern Rockies are almost infested with black bears. They have poor eyesight and look rather stupid but can move with surprising rapidity and have more cunning than the fabled fox.

Ten Peaks and Moraine Lake, near Banff in the northern tip of this province, are in an area of alpine scenery and great beauty extending for hundreds of miles.

snow tunnels, but here it becomes fantastic because the dust outlines the ridges so that the whole looks like a corbeled roof in a Gothic cathedral.

THE AMERICAN ALPS

The forests are for the most part coniferous. In the north there is fir, spruce, and lodgepole pine, western white pine, and Douglas fir and the juniper, which is here usually called "red cedar." In the valleys there are larch, aspen, birch, and alder, and in some places quite large stands of cottonwood. Farther south the combination is lodgepole, limber, and whitebark pines; alpine fir, Douglas fir, Englemann spruce, and juniper, with aspen, alder, and cottonwood in the lower valleys. The southern edge of the province constitutes an almost complete break in vegetational type, so that most of the species do not spread south at similar elevations but only at higher elevations. A wonderful feature of this land is that as soon as the snows begin to melt at lower levels flowers begin to bloom, and then as the snow retreats up the mountains one stratum or zone of vegetation after another blooms; and this continues until early fall, when the alpine flowers are in full color. Here in the space of a few miles, due to altitude, there are often four of the major vegetational belts, including all the north temperate forest zones one upon the other.

The upper slopes are of great interest because of their very abundant fauna. The clear air of these fastnesses may often ring incessantly with plaintive whistlings that seem to penetrate your brain. These noises are made by small furry balls called variously pikas, conies, or whistling hares. Although these animals (Ochotona) are distantly related to the hares and rabbits, they in no way resemble those long-legged creatures. (The term "cony" is most misleading, since the animal referred to in the Bible by that name is the hyrax, a distant relative of the elephants, while the name is also applied to rabbits and to certain other animals in other parts of the world.) Pikas are most engaging little things, shaped like an egg when they squat down, and covered in fluffy gray fur. They live mostly between the rocks of screes rather than in excavated holes, and they line these retreats with great masses of dried grasses and other soft vegetation. But screes are by their very nature full of holes, and the homes of the pikas invariably leak when it rains. As soon as the sun shines again the little animals therefore laboriously haul all their bedding out to dry and then tote it all back again. They may do this day after day, and they are then so preoccupied with their labors they seem to forget their natural caution and often fall prey to martens, fishers, weasels, bobcats, and even day-hunting owls. They live in large colonies and may start up their whistling when they are all together underground. This produces a most eerie effect.

There is another mammal of these mountains that I find most interesting. This is the Yellow-bellied Marmot, which here replaces its close relatives, the Hoary Marmot of the northern Rockies and the Groundhog of the East and the lowlands. These are large and often grossly obese-looking characters that delight in sitting upright on their fat bottoms on stumps and prominent rocks, with their forepaws on their corporations, blinking and mumbling to themselves. In places where people are unknown or are rare they seem to adopt an aggravated air at your approach, refusing to move and glaring at you down their long noses, while they sometimes even chatter and growl at you. Unlike the Groundhog, they are very adept climbers and prefer hollow trees to earthworks; like squirrels, of which they are a giant form, they can scamper up large trees to some height. They are also adept disappearing artists, being able to squeeze themselves into holes that often don't seem to be as wide as their skulls. Marmots are powerful creatures, and they can give large dogs a pretty rough time if cornered. I have not only heard of, but once witnessed, one of these animals attacking a man; nor was the animal rabid. They are rather splendid individualists though unutterably pompous in mien and apparently rather grumpy in temperament.

THE WATER FLIERS

Then there is a bird that lives about and even in the mountain streams of this area in considerable numbers. It is really quite common, but few people pay any attention to it and even persons born in the country where it lives often will not believe that it behaves as it does. It is a compact, plumpish, plain gray bird with rather long legs and short tail. It lives by the water and never flies far from it. Its food is aquatic insects, and to obtain these it flies down under the water—and I do not mean that it dives in and out again, but that it actually flies into water, using the same wing motions below the surface as in the air. It can also sink to the bottom and walk about there for considerable periods of time. There is hardly a more ridiculous sight to watch than one of these birds tramping along the bottom of a clear pool, pecking away between the pebbles for all the world like a small chicken in a barnyard. It then literally *flies* out of the water.

This bird is known as the Water Ouzel (pronounced *oozle*) and sometimes as the Dipper. It is a great songster, being undeterred by the worst winter weather when all other birds give up completely. In fact ouzels are immensely hardy and will dive under the ice and bounce around in the snow. They lay four or five pure white eggs in a dome-shaped nest made of mosses and other green stuff. Their favorite nesting spots are underneath waterfalls, through which they fly unconcernedly. The young have an enchanting habit of sitting in a row on a rock and "curtseying" to their parents when they want food.

Another bird with some strange habits is common on the lakes of this province. This is the Loon, a large black and white bird with so much "forebody" and its legs so far aft that it always seems to be toppling over forward when on land. The majority of them spend the summer up in the Arctic on the sea, where they dive for a living. In winter these birds move down into the continent and take up residence on lakes; however, a certain population seems to stay on the lakes here all year round. When at sea they are silent, but when inland they utter awful noises which have often been compared with insane laughter. They lay rather unpleasant-looking oily brown, elliptical eggs on prominent mounds of reeds and so forth, and often on floating masses of debris, and treat them with singular indifference.

Loons have long, very strong, and extremely sharp beaks, and they can use them with deadly effect. There are few animals that will tackle a loon, though large pike sometimes make the mistake of grabbing one by a leg and usually end with a large hole in the top of the head for their trouble. Loons are like the

Above: A young bobcat, the more southern, short-furred form of the Lynx. It is very common and found all over the continent but is not often seen. Below: The Yellow-bellied Marmot is one of the Western, mountain-dwelling forms of the large ground squirrels otherwise known as Woodchucks or Groundhogs. It is a great climber.

early rocket planes in that they have a very difficult time taking off and landing, but once they get air-borne they travel like shells. To watch a loon land on a large frozen lake is positively breath-taking, for it comes down breast first and, with hardly any change in speed, goes roaring off into the far white yonder. One that has just had a large meal and ends up in the middle of a frozen lake often cannot get air-borne again until it has digested, and so flounders about squawking in frantic frustration, for these birds cannot stand up on ice when overladen.

THE BELCHING EARTH

Contained within this province is an area of volcanic activity. It is an isolated area a little outside of the great belt of crustal instability that rings the Pacific Ocean, but it displays many interesting features. The most obvious and active of these are now confined within Yellowstone National Park. (Incidentally, Yellowstone is the oldest of the national parks, having been established in 1872.) Here there are over ten thousand individual holes in the ground that belch hot steam, water, gas, or mud. These holes are distributed among a number of mountain basins —the average height of the whole park is about 7500 feet— named the Norris, Lower, Midway, Upper, Heart Lake, and Shoshone. Among these natural phenomena are many geysers, including the famous "Old Faithful."

We have run into volcanicity already and we shall meet it again several times before our journey is over, but it is a large subject and one of great variety. It might seem that any hole in the earth out of which anything belches either continuously or irregularly is much the same as any other, but this is not so. Material comes up out of the shallower depths of the earth in various forms and manners. There are places where molten basaltic rocks—not lavas—have flowed out over the surface and spread for hundreds of square miles; there are other places where similar deep-down *rocks* have forced their way between strata to form huge lenticles; there are still other places where they have formed wall-like structures called dykes. Then there are the true volcanos, some of which, like Mauna Loa in the Hawaiian Islands, are enormous pits into which molten lava sometimes wells. There are other types, such as Vesuvius in Italy and Mount Rainier in Washington, that are vast mountains of lava rock, and other materials built up over millennia by eruption. Next there are the cinder cones, of which the best known in modern times is Paricutín in Mexico, which appeared suddenly in a cornfield as a small hole in the ground from which clinker-like material started spouting, built up a thousand-foot mountain in ten months, but which has now been reduced by rain to six hundred feet.

Going down the scale, we come next to the mud volcanos. These are truly volcanic outpourings, but of water, usually hot water, containing so much finely divided mineral material that it constitutes a sort of gooey mud. This slops out in all directions and then begins to flow downhill. As it does so, it gradually dries out and forms smoothly curved and rounded terraces following the contours of the land surface and so may often produce the most bizarre effects.

Then finally, there are those holes that belch water and steam. These are known as *geysers,* from an Icelandic word *geysir,* which means a "gusher" or "rager." The original *geysir* (or *hver,* which means "hot spring"), known as "The Great Geysir," is in Iceland, and all other similarly spouting hot springs have

Bighorn or Rocky Mountain Wild Sheep is one of the commoner large animals of the upper mountain pastures and alps. They are very wary creatures and great climbers.

derived their common name from this. Geysers are found all over the world, notably in Iceland, Indonesia, New Zealand, and South America.

In Yellowstone there are over a hundred true geysers, four of which are notable. The best known is undoubtedly "Old Faithful," which has been spouting away almost exactly every hour on the hour for five minutes ever since it was discovered by white men and, if the Amerindians are to be believed, for centuries before that. (Even during the somewhat violent earthquake of the summer of 1959 in this region, Old Faithful continued to spout with perfect regularity.) This geyser spouts hot water some 100 to 150 feet into the air. The star performer, however, is named the Giantess; it spouts a massive column to a height of about 60 feet, which then throws up a jet that reaches some 250 feet. Another, known as the Castle, is very variable both in timing and effort but makes the most tremendous rumpus about it, roaring like an open furnace and shaking the whole earth.

Geysers are a product of volcanicity, which is to say the presence not too far under the surface of the earth of a large pocket of molten rocks. Whether such pockets are upward extensions of a generally molten substratum that underlies the whole crust of the earth or are just big vesicles within the crust itself is still not determined, but in either case these pockets are under pressures other than and in excess of the normal ones due to the mere weight of the rocks above them. Volcanic areas are places where the earth's crust is under stress and is being either compressed or stretched apart, or is shearing. If there happens to be much water present in the rocks in such areas, it will be the first substance to be pushed out, and it will be hot. The Great Geysir has a surface temperature of some 190 degrees Fahrenheit.

In certain kinds of rocks the minerals dissolved in hot water form, when redeposited, a solid flinty material that resists further solution. Thus a pipe may form where hot waters reach the surface and superheated water is constantly pushed from below. As this water wells up it cools, so that the upper layers in the pipe are substantially colder than the water at the bottom. The latter may be well above the boiling point and be constantly heated from below. Eventually, when the vapor pressure rises to a critical point, the superheated water at the bottom suddenly turns into steam, which entails its sudden expansion and pushes upward the whole column of colder water above it. As this spills over the edge of the basin at the surface, its weight on the superheated water below is reduced so that more hot water flashes into steam; and, with a roar, all the water is blasted sky high. Then everything settles down till the funnel fills once more and the whole process starts over again.

Geysers often build wondrous formations on the surface all around their mouths. Sometimes the hot waters are filled with all manner of minerals in solution which are deposited when the water cools and which form rim-stone basins, frozen cascades, crystalline walls and domes, and other beautiful creations. There are several fine examples at Yellowstone as well as some eerie scenes that look like settings from Dante's *Inferno* as depicted by Doré. There are countless hot springs in addition to geysers, and the waters of some of these encrust everything with pure white or softly tinted crystals, making them look like something out of a fairyland.

Saline Lakes and Alkaline Flats

The Great Basin or Gray Deserts, and the Guttered Scablands

17

The first white men to see the edge of this great deadeye were sixteenth-century Spanish scouting parties sent out by expeditions which were working northward through the coastal ranges and the South Montane Province. They looked at the edge of this appalling waste and promptly decided to go around it. Later, they learned from the Amerindians that theirs had been a wise decision, for even these latter had long abandoned most of it as worthless or too dangerous even as regular hunting grounds. When Anglo-Saxon Europeans began to infiltrate the west coast from the sea, and later across the prairies and over the mountains from the east, they likewise stood on its rim and wondered. Those coming from the west stopped at the eastern edges of the Cascades and the Sierra Nevada, whereas those from the east skirted the Basin, either to the north or to the south. Those going north reached the coast by following the Snake River and the Columbia; those that went south had to make a dash across the foothills of the Arizona mountains to southern California. Although a few bold souls ventured out onto this terrifyingly dry and seemingly endless region by a process of lake-hopping, it was not until the great Mormon migration that it was really colonized or even penetrated.

A glance at any physical atlas will quickly show why this province was left till the last by settlers, for it is a desert in every sense of that word. Even a physical map does not make clear that the rather numerous lakes dotting its northern, western, and eastern edges, and especially those clustering at its center, are of no use to travelers, for almost all of them are either saline or alkaline. Political maps are no more useful, though they do reveal a dearth of roads, towns, and place names. Only a visit to this province will demonstrate that while most of its surface is relieved by some variation of topography, it is as sterile in appearance as one could expect any land to be. The whole place is undeniably a desert. But is it a "Desert"?

WHAT IS A DESERT?

This is one of the most troublesome geographical questions that can be asked. Nonetheless, it must be asked and, if possible, answered. For sooner or later, every Easterner who crosses the hundredth meridian asks it; and every Westerner gives a different answer; and all foreigners, including even Mexicans, will probably disagree with all the answers. The trouble is not just geographic or even phytogeographic, but semantic, and profoundly so.

The word "desert" does not mean the same thing to Americans as it does to Englishmen, or even to Canadians, Australians, and other English-speaking peoples. To each of these it means something different, and to all of them something other than the word *desierto* means to Spaniards. According to Webster, "desert" denotes "a deserted region; a region left unoccupied"; and as a second choice, "an arid region lacking moisture to support vegetation." The Oxford Dictionary, on the other hand, ignores the connotation of desertion or abandonment and gives simply "uninhabited, desolate; uncultivated, barren," and leaves it at that.

Now it so happened that the Spanish got to the American "deserts" first. They hailed from a cold, upland, wind-blown kind of desert, and they carried their term to the New World and applied it to both the *altoplano* of the Andes and the uplands of central Mexico. Later, when they went north into the Chihuahuan and Sonoran regions, they applied this term to those regions as well. The Anglo-Saxons, however, having no deserts in their homelands, brought with them a traditional concept of deserts as being endless, completely vegetationless sand dunes such as are found in some parts of the Sahara. And this is how they naturally pictured the *desiertos* of the Spaniards, and what they therefore expected to find covering the whole Southwest. The notion has persisted, so that Easterners arriving in California via Route 66 may even now be heard inquiring what happened to the Mojave Desert.

None of these definitions has any real validity. A desert is not necessarily a deserted place, and it need never have been deserted by either plants or animals or men; and it is seldom unoccupied by all three of them. Moreover, it is only in some cases an arid region—therefore necessarily moistureless—but hardly if ever so lacking in this respect as to be unable to support life. In fact, deserts swarm with life. Only moving sand dunes are more or less sterile, but even in the midst of large areas of these (see the White Sands of the Tularosa Basin, for instance) there may be some vegetation and a good deal of animal life.

The geographer sees deserts as comparatively dry places, or rather places that receive little rainfall—the polar deserts being waterlogged, as we have seen. The geologists separate hot from cold deserts—the first as areas where subaerial action dominates and hydrodynamic factors are at a minimum, and where red-colored soils and deposits predominate; the second as places where precipitation is low but the ground is frozen. To botanists and zoologists, deserts are regions where certain environmental features differ from those of all other regions and where plants and animals of certain kinds and special structures live. To the vegetationist—which is to say, us—there are three kinds of deserts—polar, montane, and torrid. These have no common features. The polar is cold, has a low rainfall, but is waterlogged; the montane is cold, has a high precipitation as a rule, and usually has moist soils; the torrid is hot, with a very low rainfall and almost no ground moisture.

The only way these three types of deserts can be defined is by reference to their position in the sequence of the major vegetational belts. And, by this token, the Hot Deserts are those lands

Salt flats bordering Great Salt Lake in the Great Basin area. These deposits are over ten feet deep and cover hundreds of square miles of former lake bottom.

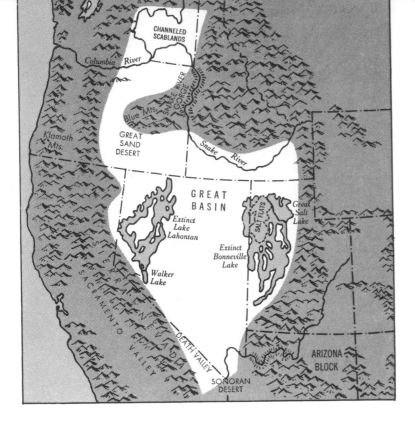

This province is so clearly defined in most respects that it is widely recognized as forming a unit within the otherwise complex terrain of the West and has acquired a popular name—the Great Basin. It is not strictly a basin, either geologically or in structure, for it does not slope inward from its subcircular periphery but is nearly level, though its surface is covered with ranks of mountain chains. It is almost entirely ringed by steep, high mountain walls. It can be divided into three not too well defined subregions, and has an appendage to the north—an area commonly called the Guttered Scablands.

Its boundaries are formed on the east by the Utah block of the South Montane and a portion of the North Montane

provinces; on the north by the southern face of the North Montane Block plus the Blue Mountains, which lie entirely within its confines; and on the west by the barrier of the Cascades to the northwest and the Sierra Nevada to the southwest. Its southern boundary appears to be arbitrary on a map but may be outlined by the zone of change from the red soils of the Sonoran Deserts of the south to the gray soils of the Scrub Belt of the north. The Great Basin as thus defined is some eight hundred miles long from north to south and five hundred in width. It is shaped like a human heart.

This is an odd province in many respects. First, it is geologically rather new as a physiographic unit and is still changing somewhat rapidly. Second, unlike all other provinces on this continent, its nature and appearance, although still basically dependent upon its position among the major vegetational belts, is much influenced by secondary forces. Prominent among these is absence of rainfall, due to mechanical factors—namely, the almost complete atmospheric moisture trap formed by the Cascade–Sierra Nevada barrier to the west, which cuts off the prevailing moisture-laden winds from the Pacific. Third, it has no indigenous drainage system apart from the Snake River in the far north, which today merely carries the runoff from the Northern Montane Block through its territory. The Scablands form a distinct subprovince.

The body of the area is hilly, but the northwest forms a level and rather featureless platter, whereas the northeast portion, comprising the Snake River valley, is a wide, almost flat gutter. The remainder of the province, south of the forty-second parallel, is roughly triangular, is lined with north-to-south parallel strings of small mountain ranges, and drops to large depressions on either side. These were once the sites of the huge lakes today named Lahontan, on the west, and Bonneville, on the east. This subprovince is excessively arid and may be included in the Desert Belt. For a further note on the limits of desert belts, see "An Explanation and Glossary."

that occupy a central position in the belt between the Prairies and the Savannahs. Just where they begin and end in relationship to the Scrub Belts is definable only by changes in the facies of the flora and fauna.

WHERE ARE OUR DESERTS?

This question is almost as troublesome as the preceding one. Deserts were unknown to the first English settlers. Then it was learned that the lands of the Spaniards in the Southwest were called by their colonizers *desiertos,* and it was immediately concluded that most of Mexico and the southern "West" were covered with waterless and completely unvegetated seas of sand. However, after the Louisiana Purchase and the beginning of the drive to the West, a reaction to this set in. Early travelers reported, quite legitimately, that many places which were supposed to be covered with "deserts" were not only fertile but even supported considerable forests.

The government deliberately fostered these tales, in order to encourage mass immigration in the shortest time possible. The famous Major Powell, the first scientific explorer and surveyor of the Southwest and the founder of the United States Geological Survey, fought this propaganda for half a lifetime and lost. Not

until after his death did the truth of what he had so steadfastly contended became obvious—namely, that the Southwest could not be made to produce even low-grade meat and vegetables unless something substantial was done to augment its rainfall of less than ten inches a year. Its "desert" reputation was consequently revived.

The next phase came when the Southwest had been populated and roughly surveyed, and scientific investigation and precision became general practice. The deserts then began to shrink again —in time almost to the point of disappearance—so that statements may be found in official literature to the effect that, at least technically, there are no real deserts in the United States or even in North America. This seems to be in part a reversion to the old north European idea of a desert as a sandy waste—coupled, I would suggest, with a misconception of the Scrub Belts or a simple failure to recognize that these exist.

Nonetheless, there are vast arid areas on this continent, either with scant vegetation or with none at all, which are commonly referred to as deserts and which by proper scientific definition

The sand dunes of upper Death Valley are unique: they not only come in many colors but often are banded or neatly striped, their grains being sorted by the wind.

should be so called. Yet there are great parts of the lands lying within the true Desert Belt that are neither barren, sandy, unvegetated, nor even particularly hot or arid. Most are covered with stunted drought-resistant plants, some with bunched coarse desert grasses, a great many with thick cactus groves, and not a few with veritable forests of mesquite, palo verde, and other plants both woody and herbaceous. Completely bare rock, stony, or especially sandy areas are rare indeed. On the other hand, there are large and frequent areas of all of these in the North Scrub Belt, on the Colorado Platea, in the Wyoming Basin, in the present province's northern regions, and even in the Sacramento Valley. Among those in the Great Basin are some of the worst *desiertos* in the world, and more or less the whole of this province may, in fact, be so designated.

UNEXPECTED DESERT ANIMALS

There is only one consideration that casts doubt on the classification of the body of this province as being in the true Desert Belt. This is its fauna. The faunas of deserts are among the most highly specialized combinations of animals there are; so that, while scrubland or even prairie and woodland types may occur in a desert under favorable local conditions, true desert animals are very seldom found outside deserts. The fauna of the Great Basin is particularly provocative in this respect, for it is not primarily or essentially a desert fauna but is made up mostly of animals found in adjacent areas or of close relatives of these. This fauna, moreover, is very extensive.

Over 80 species of mammals are recorded from here, some 150 resident birds, 44 reptiles and 10 amphibians, about 30 fishes, and a large number of insects. In the northern part—the Scablands, the Blue Mountains, and the Snake River valley—there is of course a less arid climate and more vegetation; and here we

Right: Mono Lake on the western edge of the Great Basin is a fabulous natural basin of ever evaporating alkaline waters in which sundry strange mineral formations grow. Below: A saline pool among the rocks of the Nevada desert. Violent evaporation creates crystalline deposits.

find such animals as a water shrew, the Raccoon, Short-tailed Weasel, Otter, Red Fox, Mink, Beaver, and a whole galaxy of other rodents not found in the more arid southern regions. But in the latter the list of mammals alone is extraordinary. There are no less than 17 species of bats; both the Desert Wood Rat and the Rock Rat; the Muskrat; three voles or "field mice"; a small shrew; a jumping and a harvest mouse; the Porcupine; a pocket mouse; two kangaroo-mice, four species of kangaroo-rat, two grasshopper-mice, and five types of white-footed mice; the Golden-mantled, White-tailed Antelope, and three other kinds of ground squirrels; the Yellow-bellied Marmot, three chipmunks; five kinds of pocket-gophers; the Pika, the Brush Rabbit, two kinds of cottontails, and two jack rabbits; the Mule Deer, the Pronghorn, and the Bighorn Sheep; the Puma and Bobcat; the Coyote, the Gray and Kit Foxes; the Striped and the Spotted Skunk; and the Badger. Less than half a dozen of these are either typically desert animals or confined to deserts other than in this locality.

Almost all groups of birds are equally well represented, and the marshes are often crowded with many kinds and many families. Ducks of a dozen species are plentiful, and there are many waders such as the stilts and avocets. Gulls and pelicans play a considerable part in the natural economy, as we shall see; and the number of crows, owls, swallows, swifts, goatsuckers, and birds of prey, plus the scavenging vultures, signify a large animal food supply. The rest of the roster of resident birds reads like a catalogue of the avian fauna of the Southwest generally, just about the only species not present being those most typical of the Sonoran Deserts.

The reptiles, however, show more pronouncedly desert affiliations, led by the Desert Tortoise. There are twenty species of snakes including the Desert Gopher, the Sidewinder, and two other rattlers found only in this province, as well as the Mojave Rattler. Of the twenty-two listed lizards, most are typical desert forms; but a skink and a gecko are to be found here, the latter quite surprising because it is a moisture-loving form, here isolated from the rest of its kind. But most surprising of all is perhaps the abundant frog and toad population, including a tree toad, a spadefoot, four typical frogs, and four species of toads.

The mammals, as usual, for the most part keep well out of sight, but those that are about by day are naturally more evident in open, sparsely vegetated places. The birds, on the other hand, are very obvious and bold, and the insect-catchers and predators appear as if by magic in swarms at dawn and dusk, while even in the more arid areas owls seem often to hunt by day. The reptiles are all well camouflaged and are hard to find; they also shun direct sunlight. (A Gila Monster forced to stay under the midday sun on open ground died of heat prostration in fifteen minutes!) Reptiles are dependent upon external heat and go into a sort of coma if deprived of it, so they come out and sun themselves in the morning. They then pass the day in the shade and start hunting in the evening, when insects also are out in force; and they often carry on late into the night while their body heat lasts. The amphibians, on the other hand, stay near water, since they have to lay their eggs therein, and have porous soft skins through which they must to a considerable extent do their breathing.

BOWLS, PANS, AND BASINS

Most of the animal life of this province congregates around the lower parts of depressions in the land surface due to the availability of water there. Such depressions are numerous, widespread, and of all sizes in this country; in fact, they are a feature of it, and are mostly of the kinds known as bowls, pans, and basins. These are rather rare topographical features in other areas and have been brought about here by the odd history of this region.

The whole province, which is basically a fairly flat plateau about four thousand feet above sea level with long, wide, but

Below: Vast colonies of White Pelicans live on islands in and around Great Salt Lake. Here on Gunnison Island the birds line up for "inspection" before going fishing.

shallow gutters down each side, owes its existence to major geological faults that define its east and west borders. Outside these, the whole land surface has risen to form the North and South Montane Blocks, and the Cascade—Sierra Nevada ranges. The Great Basin has for long, and still is, being squeezed between these, and this has caused a great deal of subsidiary faulting in the basin itself, along with consequent mountain building, so that today the whole province is covered with parallel strings of mountain ranges. These are all about fifty to seventy-five miles long and six to fifteen wide, but rise only some three to five thousand feet off the plateau. Apart from the Snake River, which really only passes through the area, there is no drainage system leading out of it, and precious little leading into it. What rain falls on it cascades down these little mountains into the depressions between and either sinks below ground or evaporates. Were there enough rainfall, this water would find its way downhill over the surface until it formed a river system going to the sea. As there is not enough and has not been for a very great time, other mechanisms have had long enough to become effective.

The infrequent rains are often torrential, and, falling upon such bare ground, they wash enormous quantities of material down the mountains to form great fans and outwashes in the valleys. Further, the great differences between day and night temperatures, especially during the winters, crack up the rock surfaces and cause screes of exceptional dimensions. All of these structures may meet across valleys and create dams and barriers, so that the level land between the mountain ranges is formed into strings of bowl- or basin-shaped depressions. These become little catchment basins for whatever surface moisture there is, and those lined with fine sediments and clays may retain water in the form of shallow lakes. A large percentage of the whole province is covered with these structures, and a great many of them contain either permanent or intermittent lakes or dried-out lake floors. Two of these are of enormous size but of most irregular outline and are filled with "islands." These are the ancient or "fossil" lakes today called Lahontan and Bonneville.

The depth and size and even the very existence of these lakes and incipient lakes are entirely dependent upon the amount of rain that falls. This varies from year to year and in various longer cycles; it has also varied very greatly during the geologically recent ice advances and retreats, notably during the latter, when great volumes of ice on the surrounding montane glaciers melted.

LAHONTAN AND BONNEVILLE

The Great Salt Lake of Utah is the largest natural inland body of water in the United States west of the Mississippi, but it is a paltry remnant of a much greater body of water that not too long ago rivaled the Great Lakes of the east. So big was it, and its sister Lake Lahontan to the west, that both figure prominently on the accompanying map. These lakes are really only areas that are lower than the surrounding territory and have no outlets. They are formed of checkerboards of the smaller bowls and basins and pans described above. Both are alleged to have been created in the first place by the melting of snow and ice on the surrounding mountains. Bonneville was once 350 miles long and 150 miles wide and some 1000 feet deep. Lahontan was about 250 by 100 but was only 500 feet deep. Today the former has shrunk to the Great Salt and Provo lakes; the latter, which was always of more irregular outline and contained many more islands, has left numerous remnants, notably lakes Honey, Pyramid, Winnemucca, North Carson, and Walker.

Both lakes Bonneville and Lahontan were initially fresh, and they went to depths of 910 and 320 feet respectively. They then went through a dry period when they became saline, but this was followed by a wetter period when they rose to 1000 and 530 feet in depth. At this time Bonneville found an outlet over Red Rock Pass to the north, and some 375 feet of its water drained off in a very few years into the Snake River. Then the snows stopped melting and/or the rains came less torrentially on the mountains, and the two lakes started evaporating, thus becoming increasingly saline. The exact heights to which the waters rose can be determined from altitude measurements of the noticeable wave-

cut platforms that were once beaches, which now circle these lake areas along exact contours. There are three prominent and many subsidiary platforms around the Lahontan basin, at 320, 530, and 110 feet, and it is thought that these represent the ends of the three major glacial periods, in that order.

Evaporation is intense in this area and has now reduced Bonneville to the Great Salt Lake, which is only 13 feet deep on an average and 35 feet at its deepest. In the year 1873 it was 18 feet deeper than it is today, but so flat and shelving is the basin—or rather "pan"—in which it lies that a rise of only 10 feet will spread it over an extra 500 square miles. This fact acts as regulator on and preserver of the lake; for the greater expanse of surface it presents, the more it evaporates, and it seems that its present size constitutes a balance at the current average rainfall over the years.

NATURE'S CHEMICAL PLANT

The Great Salt Lake is today slightly over 25 per cent pure salts. This surpasses all known natural waters except for the Dead Sea in Palestine, and causes some odd and often amusing things to happen. You may enjoy morning coffee on its waters while floating beside an ordinary wood table, provided you don't create waves. However, larger birds are so buoyant on it that they find the greatest difficulty in staying upright, and after constantly capsizing they become encrusted with salts and water-logged, and cannot get air-borne. Some of us are naturally very buoyant (I happen to be among these) and can float endlessly even in fresh water; we people should beware of such waters as these, for we have such a low Plimsoll line that it is almost impossible for us to prevent the heaviest parts of our bodies, our heads, from going downward like a lead weight. Oceanic water, even in the tropics, runs only about 3.5 per cent of salt, as opposed to more than 25 per cent here.

Almost all the lakes of this province are not fresh, but neither are all of them saline: many are alkaline. Nature's chemicals come in three principal forms, called acid, alkaline, and salt. The last is the stable result of neutralizing the other two by mixing. Most surface rocks contain concentrations of or are themselves basically one of these three forms. When they are eroded and washed away into lakes or the sea, many of the substances of which they are composed are dissolved in the waters. They are therefore in due course concentrated in oceans and lakes that lack outlets. (One of the ways of calculating the age of oceans is by estimating the rate of concentration of their salts.) Acid waters are rare except in swamps and bogs, which contain tannic and humic acid derived from plant roots, though there are, of course, highly acid rocks. Alkaline strata (or rocks containing dissolvable alkaline substances) are fairly common, but saline ones are commoner due to the fact that rain water is acid (through picking up carbonic acid from the atmosphere and thus tending to neutralize the alkaline). There are, however, a surprising number of alkaline lakes in the Great Basin, and even more alkaline flats left by lakes that have completely evaporated. The great flats alongside Great Salt Lake, covering 180 square miles to a depth of four feet, are saline and composed of gleaming white crystals, mostly of calcium chloride.

Left: Death Valley is an appalling desert at the southwest edge of the Great Basin in the shadow of the southern Sierra Nevadas. It is in many places guttered and sculptured by wind erosion.

239

Calcium chloride and table salt are not the only substances deposited here. Also present are Glauber's salt, a hydrate of sodium sulphide; gypsum, or calcium sulphate; Epsom salts, or magnesium sulphate heptahydrate; magnesium chloride; potassium chloride; and others. There are estimated to be over seven billion tons of salt in this basin. When fresh water does find its way here from the mountains and the infrequent rains, it floats on top of the salt water and only slowly mixes with it, and in winter miniature icebergs may form on the surface and ride about. In some of the dry basins there are incredible beaches and accretions of salts and alkalis that look just like snow and ice.

It is curious that the name "salt bushes" has been given to plants that happen to be tolerant of high concentrations of alkalis, not of salts. It is a fact that plants—which can readily manufacture acids—can cope with alkalinity by neutralizing it but are unable to cope with the more stable salts. Thus there is a dearth of vegetation around salt pans but often a quite profuse growth around alkaline deposits, notably any that still contain water.

ELECTRIC PLANTS

Much of the Great Basin, where it is not entirely bare due to these chemical deposits or marching sand dunes, is covered with a rash of stunted plants, growing well separated as if planted deliberately. This continues to the tops of most of the mountains and looks at first quite homogeneous. Closer examination, however, shows an astonishing variety of different plants, all growing in much the same way and looking surprisingly alike. All of them have minute leaves or none at all. Almost all bear thorns or prickles or veritable spikes, often all over and in great density. Such structures are prevalent in the floras of deserts and other arid regions in warmer latitudes, but not in circumpolar regions. Prickles or spikes on plants present an interesting puzzle.

While temperate regions have their share of thorny plants and equatorial areas are rife with spiky things, neither can display anything to compare with the prickles and spikes of the arid regions. In our deserts and drier scrub zones we find all manner of spiky plants apart from the cactuses, such as the mesquite, the huisaché, the cat's-paw, the bull thorn, and countless others. The purpose of these spines has long been debated. It is manifest that thorns and especially hooks on seeds or bits of plants that may proliferate are valuable, in that they may become attached to animals and so disseminated. Also, the spiny cover of a barrel cactus has been shown to cut down the amount of heat striking the skin of that plant by as much as 20 per cent. Further, although spikes and spines may deter some animals from eating such plants as bear them, most larger animals of dry areas, even the worthy cow, seem to be able to chew such indelicacies happily all day long. But none of these reasons explains the profusion of such devices. Some more adequate explanation is needed, and one most interesting suggestion has been made.

Plants with leaves breathe through the tiny pores called stomata on the undersurfaces of their leaves. These can open and shut to regulate evaporation of water vapor from within. Constant evaporation at the tops of trees causes a drop of pressure within the plant so that sap rises. This process, called

Utah's gulls are famous for their role in the founding of the Mormon settlement in this arid region and are now in the Utah state seal.

The Collared Lizard, one of the commoner denizens of the arid Great Basin area, often basks on rocks.

suction-pressure, enables very tall plants to raise water to great heights. The roots of these plants are absorbent, their tops porous. In desert plants, on the other hand, conditions are reversed, in that evaporation from the plant above ground is neither needed nor possible if the plant is to survive in such dry air. Therefore all desert plants are encased in tough waterproof skins, often coated with impervious wax layers, and they have little use for leaves. But they need water just as much as do other plants, and it also has to be lifted up into the head of the plant. If there is no breathing-suction apparatus above to do this, how is it accomplished? This is where the spikes seemingly come in.

Plants growing in intensely dry areas, isolated from each other as here and with roots in soil that is desiccated most of the time, build up a considerable electrical potential over and above the normal prevailing between the air and the ground. The parts of these plants in the air are, as we have said, often coated with wax, a highly efficient nonconductor, whereas their roots are designed to extract every last molecule of water from the soil. This moisture does rise to the heads of the plants, and in the process these become highly charged with static electricity, having received free ions from the roots below. Now electric overpotential is most readily discharged from fine points or spikes, as in lightning rods. It seems that these plants have developed spikes for just this purpose, and this proves to be another way of "pumping" fluids up to points above that to which capillary attraction and atmospheric pressure will force them. There are many references to strange crackling sounds in very dry scrub that are otherwise unexplained, and at least one traveler in southern Arabia speaks of bushes sparkling at night.

The effects are the same as those produced by combing your hair in the dry atmosphere of an artificially heated room.

AN AZURE PARADISE

The existing permanent lakes of this strange world have a quality all their own. Their waters look as cold as those of man-made reservoirs, which for some reason I always feel look colder than any natural body of water, yet they are warm and brightly colored, seeming to reflect even a pallid sky with great vividness and intensity, and moving all the reflected light toward the blue band of the spectrum. This coloration is in marked contrast to the surrounding hills, which are always of subdued shades and often pallid or glaring white. Visibility is here high, so that the white gulls and pelicans that invariably wheel above or bob on the surfaces of these lakes stand out like glaring beacons even when seen from great distances. Then very often these lakes are either wholly or partly rimmed by vivid green sedges and water grasses.

One of the most beautiful and typical is Lake Walker, a remnant of old Lake Lahontan. The present shore of this lake is ringed above by several pronounced and large platforms due to past lake levels—one at a height of over five hundred feet—and below by line after line of curious tiny strands of puce-colored vegetation due to recent minor changes in water level. The lake itself is of considerable extent and slightly saline. It usually reflects dark blue of a hard, gem-like hue. Seen under a blazing, cloudless sky, backed on one side by tangled crags and on the other by a fairly wide, gently sloping, brown plain leading up to subdued brown mountains, it has a slightly out-of-this-world quality. Water of any kind in the dry immensity of the Great Basin is always a shock.

Walker Lake provides the naturalist with a number of most pertinent questions. Upon its sapphire surface quite a number of pelicans may be seen bobbing up and down on the small, choppy waves. There are also many gulls floating along its shores or idly flapping over its waters. For miles around there is nothing but rock, heat, dust, and miserable little clumps of spiny scrub. The birds have to eat something. The question is, what? The obvious answer is fish. What then do the fish eat? A visit to the lake's edge will reveal the answer to this. First, the shore all around supports a fringe of vivid green water plants of a slimy and stringy consistency. These sprout from everything right to the upper limit of the lapping waters. The beach immediately above the waters appears utterly sterile, and it is; but if you turn over the boulders at the water's edge and look closely, you will see an astonishing profusion of small life. The most prominent are crustaceous creatures known as amphipods; these swarm everywhere. They are aquatic animals that lie on their sides and progress by jerks; on seashores we call them "sandhoppers." Then there are countless small white worms wriggling among the water vegetation and hosts of larvae of various insects. Curiously, there are also innumerable small spiders and little beetles, both of which we normally presume to be purely land-living forms. Yet here they dwell under water.

In other words, a vast amount of fish food can be found in these lakes, and enormous numbers of fish. Upon these the pelicans, gulls, and other birds feed—so well that some of them, like the pelicans, take the trouble to fly all the way from the Gulf of Mexico to these isolated, desert-locked waters each year to breed and fatten. The Great Salt Lake is renowned for its massed flocks of White Pelicans, and its gulls have become pro-verbial. Almost everybody knows the part they played in the

A flicker of life amid the sun-baked desolation: a lone poppy.

grim first days of the Mormon settlement upon this inhospitable land. As the story goes, a vast horde of large "crickets" (actually grasshoppers) fell upon the first crops of these industrious people, in numbers so great that they threatened to devour every leaf and seed and stem. But the Mormons prayed and the gulls came, and in fairly short order they gobbled up all the insects and the crops were saved. This actually happened, and the gulls responsible are now enshrined as the emblem of Utah. Yet gulls in a super-briny lake in the middle of a continent, in one of its driest areas, seem out of place and are a surprise to the uninitiated.

The fish can also, in certain circumstances, provide us with more than a little surprise. Among the almost innumerable lakes, near-lakes, drying lakes, and almost ex-lakes of this baking basin, a very high percentage contain fish. These are not special fish; they are the same species that are found in surrounding areas. They have not had time to alter their constitution or even their bodily form to comply with the exceptional conditions in which some of them now live. However, *some* of them seem to have developed, or otherwise found it within themselves, to

counter one of nature's most deadly traps and to survive in conditions so extreme that it defies comprehension.

There are animals—certain nematode worms—that live comfortably in vinegar or acetic acid; there are larvae of certain flies that customarily flip about in petroleum; and there are crustaceans that live in almost saturated brines as in the Great Salt Lake. In some places in the Great Basin there are dying lakes that all but evaporate entirely in the summer, but these still contain fish. As the water evaporates these fish must either die or concentrate more and more into what is left of the water. This some of them do; but they sometimes continue to do so until all that is left of the water is little stagnant rills, often highly alkaline, contained between bare rock, which during the hours of direct sunlight may rise in temperature to as much as 175 degrees Fahrenheit (considerably above the point at which even a human hand can be left submerged). It is stated that they sometimes survive even greater temperatures, reaching very near the boiling point of water. These fish have nowhere to go out of the broiling sun, yet they survive.

Hummingbirds and Kelp Beds

North America's "Mediterranea" in Southern and Baja California

18

It may seem a big jump from the barren gray aridity of the southern parts of the Great Basin to a land so lush in appearance, so verdant, and so balmy yet always freshened by ocean breezes and filled with flowers and palm trees and clouds of hummingbirds. And it is indeed a leap, though not a great one in space, as may be seen from the map; nor is it one in fundamentals, as a little closer inspection of the country will show.

In the Great Basin we were in a desert in the widest sense of that term, but we were in the North Scrub Belt. If we follow this belt on its ever westward progress from that area, we see that it plunges under the south end of the Sierra Nevada and then emerges onto the lower end of the Sacramento valley, where we find country similar to and little less arid than that which we have just left on the other side of the mountains. But then, right athwart our path, we find another barrier of mountains. These are the multiple ranges of southern California, which stretch along the Pacific coast from Point Conception southeast to the region of Los Angeles and then run inland to the San Bernardinos. These mountains are green and fully forested, but their feet are girt with lovely yellow grasslands above which are parks dotted with bushy oaks. Our scrublands extend right to these mountain feet and there give way to the grass; which is to say, they "plunge under" these mountains also—but only to appear once more, for the last time on this continent, on the shores of the ocean beyond.

To the south of the Scrub Belt lie the Hot Deserts, and before the coming of the white man the dividing line between the two emerged onto the coast about the valley and narrow coastal plain in which Los Angeles is now situated. Thus, although these mountains and others lying to the south of that point are green, the lowlands were from there on to the peninsula of Baja California originally much more arid. Today irrigation has been initiated on an enormous scale throughout this area, but wherever it has not been, you will find at sea level places of a most desolate nature, clothed only in stunted and clumpy scrub and cactuses and inhabited by the typical fauna of the Sonoran deserts.

Thus the two mountain blocks which compose the greater part of this province are seated upon the North Scrub and the true deserts, their feet being bathed in a sea of chaparral, as it were. Above these in most areas are rather sterile-looking grassfields,

seen typically along the coast, especially between Los Angeles and San Diego, and in the inner valleys. But these montane prairies are narrow, and, as one ascends even low hills, they merge rapidly into beautiful parklands dotted at first with individual evergreen oaks and then clumps of them. In the eastern and southern ranges the chaparrals are more extensive and profuse, and in many places they merge above with the montane temperate zone, squeezing out the grassfields and parklands almost entirely. The upper slopes of all the ranges are clothed in the most beautiful mixed forests of evergreen broad-leafed trees, shrubs, and conifers of various typically southern varieties. On the tops of the highest peaks and ridges there are still pure stands of northern types of conifers with a typical boreal type of undergrowth.

THE ANCIENT ISLES

Lying off the coast between Point Conception and Los Angeles are a number of interesting though rather barren islands. These form two groups: in the northwest, San Miguel, Santa Rosa, Santa Cruz, and the Anacapa Islands; in the south and west, the three larger isolated islands named Santa Barbara, Santa Catalina, and San Clemente. Today these islands are put to various purposes, and some of them are "off bounds" to all but the Coast Guard. Each is of considerable interest to the zoologist on account of its lesser fauna, notably the rodents, lizards, and insects; they are of equal interest to the botanists because they support some unique plants, as well as others which are found also on the adjacent mainland but which have developed into special and in several cases dwarf forms on these islands. They are, however, perhaps of greatest interest to palaeontologists and especially to palaeoanthropologists—i.e., those who study the fossilized or other ancient remains of Man.

The Santa Barbara Natural History Museum has for several years now been carrying on excavations on the north shore of the island of Santa Rosa, where there are modest earth cliffs leaning landward in large steps and intersected by deep gullies. Working around these, the excavators have brought to light hearths made by very ancient tribesmen along with a great number of artifacts in stone and bone. The bones of several animals also have been brought to light, among which the most interesting are those of a pigmy form of elephantine related to the Mammoth, if not indeed a tiny kind of that species. Such very small examples of this group of elephantines have not been found anywhere else in the world—though equally small relatives of the African "Elephant" or Loxodont have been unearthed on the island of Malta. From this palaeontological evidence and that of some of the living plants and animals, it seems that these islands have not been connected to the mainland for a very long time. Pigmy island races of many animals are known, and it is conjectured that their small stature develops slowly to conform to limited space and food supply after the animals have been isolated. However, some small island races might well be survivals of an original short-statured stock from which their larger relatives later evolved on the mainland.

These pigmy mammoth or elephant bones have been found in considerable quantities, and there is evidence that their

A Rufous Hummingbird helicoptering before a flower. This province abounds in these gemlike birds that dart about and flick their wings like tiny whips wherever trees, shrubs, or herbs flower.

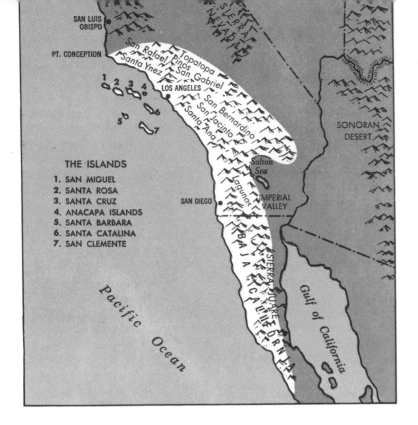

THE ISLANDS

1. SAN MIGUEL
2. SANTA ROSA
3. SANTA CRUZ
4. ANACAPA ISLANDS
5. SANTA BARBARA
6. SANTA CATALINA
7. SAN CLEMENTE

olives, madrones, and so forth. Grasses are rare, and the ground surface is usually rather bare and sandy or rocky. Incipient deserts may occur in them. Their soils are rich though desiccated, and they are notable areas for growing fruits and herbs.

The present province is quite distinct. It lies athwart the North Scrub but extends into the true deserts. It consists basically of two blocks of moderate mountains, both composed of several ranges. Between these are long, narrow, meandering valleys and, in places, a very narrow coastal strip or plain. These valleys were originally covered with arid scrublands or deserts, but today most of them—such as the San Bernardino valley—are verdant as a result of irrigation or sprinkling, and are highly productive. Artificial watering has also crept up the mountain slopes in many areas, while all manner of foreign trees, shrubs, and herbs have been introduced and spread widely. Prairies start at a low altitude due to the nearness of that belt to the north, and may run up above the "forest" at sea level, for the latter is what is called chaparral—actually, just a giant growth of the bushes of the Scrub Belt. Above the prairies come narrow montane parklands, and then the usual succession of temperate broad-leafed, mixed, and coniferous forest zones. No true alpine facies exists in this province.

The boundary of this province is the northern face of the Southern Californian mountains from San Luis Obispo to the region of Eagle Mountain. From that point it turns due south, west of the Chocolate Mountains, the Salton Sea, and the Imperial Valley, and then continues down the peninsula of Baja California to the southern end of the Santa Catalina Mountains. The northern mountain block includes the San Rafael, Santa Yñez, Piños, Topatopa, Santa Susana, San Gabriel, and San Bernardino Mountains; the southern block, the Santa Anas just south of the Los Angeles valley, the San Jacinto, Santa Rosa, and Laguna ranges, and the Sierra Juarez, the Santa Catalinas, and the great upland mesa between them in Baja California. Off the coast are several strings of islands of considerable intrinsic interest.

The term "mediterranean" (meaning "middle of the world"), applied by the Romans to the sea which lay in the middle of the world as they knew it, has today acquired a much wider connotation. It is applied to a type of climate and vegetation found all over the world on the edges of hot desert belts—in Mesopotamia and Persia, China, southwestern South America, the tip of South Africa, and Australia, as well as in Florida and the southern and Baja California areas. (We use here the Spanish word baja, meaning "low" or "lower," to distinguish the peninsula of that name from the most southerly portion of the state of California.) Mediterranea lie in the scrub belts and are distinguishable by their forests of small-leafed evergreen trees—both pines and other conifers, small oaks, and such trees as

carcasses were brought to these particular places by the men who made the fires and charred some of their bones there. These hearths and the strata in which they are found represent a considerable spread in time, during which these little elephantines continued to be obtained in fair quantities; so that some have wondered how they managed to avoid extinction, especially if they were hunted by seemingly most competent groups of humans. Since there is much volcanicity along the whole Pacific coast, and earthquakes and long-term earth movements are common, it has even been suggested that these islands are only the remnants of a much larger land mass or series of much bigger islands that existed off this coast for a long time but was never again connected with the mainland after it was separated from it. Many specimens of material dug from these sites have now been submitted to radiocarbon dating, and some, which were associated with men's work, turn out to be more than 14,000 years old, while other of the material has been otherwise estimated to go back as much as 32,000 years. There is evidence that men and the pigmy mammoths were both there at a very early time, and if they were hunting at the latter date this is nearly if not the earliest date so far established for the presence of Man on this continent—though some much earlier ones have been claimed, notably from the San Diego area. The

date 32,000 B.P. (that is, before the present) would mean that these hunters were active on these islands at the beginning of the last major ice advance, yet had quite a well-developed culture. If the dates given for the San Diego and certain other finds are authenticated, it would put Man's presence on this continent back into the interglacial stage before the last-but-one ice advance, and yet he would even then appear to have been a competent toolmaker. It would also make him almost an indigenous part of the fauna. We would then very much like to know what manner of man he might have been, and whether he evolved here from some even more primitive race or himself crossed over from eastern Asia carrying prototypes of his tools with him via the Bering Strait.

THE CREEPING HILLS OF PALOS VERDES

We mentioned that earth movements are a feature of the coastal regions of this province. Considerable stretches are subsiding at a rate that is causing real concern, especially around San Diego. But just south of Los Angeles there is something much more startling to be seen. The coastal plain south of what is now Redondo Beach moves inland behind a headland of high grassy hills named Palos Verdes. On the seaward side of this there are cliffs several hundred feet high, in places dropping straight into the sea, in other places descending by steep slopes. Upon a stretch of the latter a pleasant residential area was laid out only a few years ago, with a beach club and many fine homes, surrounded by ornamental trees and shrubbery. Today the entire site is a grotesque shambles.

The whole face of the cliff is slipping or creeping downward to the sea at a pace that, although it cannot be observed by the eye, is remarkable. Roads are half fallen away; drainage pipes stick out of the side of cliffs and then start again way below; some houses are twisted or even completely upended; others are cut in half or have been taken apart in great angular chunks and the chunks then piled up crazily. The inhabitants have just left everything as they installed it and gone elsewhere. Notable is the fact that the vegetation seems not to be so adversely affected as the works of man. A few trees or shrubs have been overthrown and some now grow at sharp angles; otherwise they seem to creep downward with the earth, so that some may be seen growing merrily in the middle of colorfully furnished living rooms or thrusting through garages.

The same type of movement is going on over the greater part of the earth, though much more slowly. Here it is merely a slipping of uncompacted surface material; in other places it is an inexorable creeping of solid rock strata. And, if you want to appreciate how much solid rocks can flow, obtain a geological map of England and Wales in color, and you will clearly see that strata which were once about Liverpool have now bulged south-ward between the mountains of Wales and the Pennines in England almost to the Bristol Channel, some sixty miles away. An even more impressive piece of evidence is a huge block of hard sandstone, shaped like a shallow shoe box, that is in the Geological Museum in London. This was balanced across a steel beam about three feet from the floor in the year 1909. By 1930 its two ends had bent down to rest on that floor. Incidentally, there is a kind of sandstone called Carolinite that, when cut into thin slabs of about the size of a pocket notebook, can be bent back and forth as though it were paper. This is an odd phenomenon, and it is due to the loose arrangement of the molecules of which the stone is composed. Then it must not be forgotten that earth tides, causing an expansion and contraction of all surface rocks, flow round and round the earth every day just as ocean tides do through the water.

THE DEATH PITS

Another product of crustal instability may be seen in the middle of the modern city of Los Angeles—the famous La Brea Tar Pits (the word *brea* means "bitumen" in Spanish). These are great funnels in the earth filled with bituminous pitch or asphalt that keeps welling up from below. The material has a consistency somewhere between firm taffy and frozen butter. It may be cut or dug out with a sharp, strong instrument and the hole will always fill up again. It is black and of smooth texture. Throughout the soil in adjacent areas may be found small patches, lumps,

In Ice Age times, the famous Tar Pits of Los Angeles, now in a city park, were traps of crude-oil seepage in which hundreds of animals died.

before going upon it, and being able to extricate themselves from deep mud and even quicksands. As a man will just float in water, he will only go down about halfway in quicksand, which is much denser: it is his upright gait and his panic that cause him to work his way down. Animals, being horizontal and not panicking, tend to "float," and then usually manage to paddle their way to a firm bottom. However, oil and pitch lakes are often covered with water, under which there may be a fairly firm crust rendered slippery by the water; and animals may march out onto this, break through, and then be caught in a viscous mass with the tenacity of glue. This would account for the trapping of the larger, heavier animals, especially those with narrow, tapering limbs. Once so mired, these would attract the carnivores such as the saber-toothed cats, who in turn might get bogged. The birds, on the other hand, probably fell from trees growing around or actually in the "lakes," sank to the bottom, and were slowly engulfed. There are voracious little fish in the water on some of these asphalt "lakes," though the temperature of that water may rise almost to boiling point during the day in direct sunlight, since the asphalt, being black, absorbs every bit of heat. These fish feed upon algae and some plants that manage to grow in these waters; they also attack any small animal that drowns therein, and soon take it apart, so that its bones sink to the bottom and are gradually engulfed.

WINGED JEWELS

This province has a vast avifauna, since it is a meeting place for the species of the northwest from as far away as southern Alaska, and a certain quota from the subtropics, while floods of migrants pass through almost all year. It also has some unique types, the most notable being the Californian Condor, of which only some hundred are estimated to be still alive. This is the largest land bird that can fly, having a wing span of up to ten feet and weighing about 20 pounds. It is related to the brilliantly colored King Vulture of the Andes—where it has also an even nearer relative in the Andean Condor—and belongs to the same group of birds as the Turkey Buzzard and the Black-headed Vulture. Actually, these birds are not true vultures but belong to a family named the Cathartids which is confined to the New World.

Most typical of this land are those marvelous little creatures, the hummingbirds. They are everywhere by the millions, heard more often than seen, chittering away like small electric fuses blowing, and streaking through the sunlight. One, the male of the Broad-tailed species, even makes a high-pitched keening noise with its wings as it slices through the air. I remember a place among the foothills of the Santa Yñez Mountains, bathed in sunlight and surrounded by many flowering bushes and massed vegetation of almost tropical appearance, where I sat with a companion for four hours while five species of these extraordinary little ingenuities of nature whirred about us from bloom to bloom. There were the Black-chinned, Anna's, Allen's, the Broad-tailed, and the absolutely unbelievable little Calliope with its glittering, iridescent red and platinum throat.

Hummingbirds are birds of the western hemisphere, and over 300 species of them are known. They are the smallest of all birds, and among them are some of the most exquisitely colored.

and pancake-shaped bits of this substance, dried out to about the firmness of hard rubber. These "pits" are found in a number of places about the earth, the most notable being one of the same name on the island of Trinidad.

Asphalt is a sort of end product of oil in nature, just as tar is of crude oil in industry, being what is left after lighter oils have been distilled off from the crude. Oil pockets in surface strata of rocks may be pinched by earth movements and burst through to the surface, and if this happens in the bottom of a depression, the oil forms a sort of lake. There, exposed to the air and washed by rain water, the lighter oils which naturally rise to the surface eventually run off and the asphalt or pitch is left. The most interesting feature of the Los Angeles pits is that they contain large numbers of bones and even complete skeletons of extinct animals. Among these are the bones of the Imperial Mammoth, probably the largest elephantine that ever lived; of mastodons; the giant ground sloths; a tapir; a camel; bison; the remarkable saber-toothed cats; and of numerous birds. These pits were discovered in 1769, but no use was made of them until 1875, when the owner—a Mr. Hancock—discovered the skeleton of a sabertooth. Digging or mining of the asphalt continued until 1906 before any proper scientific excavation was undertaken. So much of interest was then found that Mr. Hancock deeded the pits to the County of Los Angeles in 1915, and subsequently a great collection of animal remains was recovered and housed in the Los Angeles County Museum.

A popular notion once gained credence to the effect that these hapless beasts of the Pleistocene or "ice age" had fallen into pits constituted just as we see them today. A moment's reflection, however, will dispel any such idea, for the asphalt is so firm that on the Trinidadian "lake" a railroad track is laid across it to serve in the transport of material dug out of it. The animals must have sunk into it when the area was filled with semi-liquids of a much lighter density. It has been pointed out that animals, especially elephants, very seldom if ever become mired in the wild, having an uncanny knack of knowing the nature of treacherous ground in advance, usually testing it carefully

Fourteen species have been recognized in the United States, and one migrates as far north as Alaska in the summer. They have long, slender bills, and obtain their food, which consists of both nectar from flowers and, in many cases, small insects, by helicoptering in front of the blooms and dipping their tongues into their recesses. They build exquisite little nests, often only about the diameter of half a hen's egg, composed of delicate materials neatly woven together into a cup. These they delight in placing on the crowns of tiny seedlings about three feet tall. The mothers are not only bold but fearless, and will buzz at you or even dive-bomb you if you disturb them or approach their nests too closely or touch their two tiny white eggs. The chicks when hatched are about the size of the nail of your little finger, and the full-grown birds, deprived of their feathers, may, in some smaller species like the Calliope, be about the size of a large bumblebee.

Yet these minutenesses migrate back and forth between North and South America annually. In full flight hummingbirds have been observed to have a speed of thirty miles per hour or more for short distances, and they may average more than sixty miles per hour with strong tail winds. Most migrating birds "hedgehop" on their tremendous journeys, staying by the courses of rivers or along coasts, but some—among them certain hummingbirds—cross seas and parts of oceans. Some, on the west coast, apparently cut straight across from the region of Jalisto on the Mexican coast to Ecuador in South America—a distance of some twelve hundred miles over the ocean. How, we would like to know, does an object only the size of a bumblebee store within itself enough fuel to produce the energy to keep its wings beating at the rate of about ninety "revolutions" (or ups-and-downs) per second long enough to traverse this distance without stopping? This is a question that has not been answered and that, like the flight of the bumblebee (which aerodynamicists have "proved" cannot fly at all but which has been doing so for geological eons), does not at present fall within our understanding of mechanics or even of logic.

The mammals in this province are not often seen, though there are plenty, and some extremely odd ones. Jaguar occasionally wander north into this province; and there are ocelot, a small blotched and spotted cat; jaguarundi, an attenuated, low-slung, long-tailed, dark brown cat; coatimundis, a form of the raccoon family; as well as puma and cacomistles or "ring-tailed cats," another member of the raccoon family. These mostly live in the isolated and forested uplands of the southern block of mountain ranges.

Despite its dense chaparrals, scrub-covered deserts, and montane forests, this province is most intimately connected with the ocean that bathes its shores, and from which daily mists roll inshore. Though storms are just as furious here as in the Atlantic, the Pacific does indeed usually seem to live up to its name. Sometimes its surface is absolutely smooth for days on end, so that the multitudinous pelicans, ducks, and other diving birds that cruise up and down its beaches leave an endlessly dissipating network of V-shaped wavelets upon its surface. The sea here is alive with subaqueous life.

MARINE FUNSTERS AND FIGHTERS

While the waters off the coast of this province teem with both commercial and game fish, it is another group of sea creatures that here most forcibly imposes itself upon the attention of even the casual visitor; and more so here than anywhere else around the edge of our continent. This group is the cetaceans or whales.

If we use the second and commoner of these names for these mammals, everyone immediately thinks of the vast leviathans that are hunted commercially—the mighty Blue, Finner, Sei, Humpback, and the other rorquals, the Sperm, the Bowhead, and the black Right Whale. Most of these, including even occasionally the Blue, do appear off this coast, but they are seldom if ever seen from shore. However, there are other members of the order of Cetacea that are in almost daily view. These are of two kinds: the Gray Whale or Devil Fish, and the dolphins.

The former, which grows to a length of about forty-five feet, used once to migrate annually down and then up the whole length of the Pacific coast of this continent in enormous numbers, keeping among the great kelp beds or even between them and the shore. This is one of the most primitive whales and belongs to the group having baleen instead of teeth—i.e., the rorquals, rights, and the Humpback. However, it lacks a back fin and it has only two or four deep longitudinal folds under its throat. The young when born are about seventeen feet long and have regular lines of hairs all over their heads. In color these animals are mottled or dappled gray, and they are often also covered with many pale scars, since they delight in rubbing themselves against rocks to get rid of whale lice and other external parasites; and unlike almost all other whales, they come right inshore and gambol in the surf. These mammals used to pass these shores in enormous numbers twice a year and were the basis of a special whaling industry during the latter half of the last century. The commerce so depleted their numbers that they became "extinct" on our coasts in 1895. However, there apparently had always been two great groups of them, one of which used the North American coast, the other (discovered by Roy Chapman Andrews in the 1920's in Korea) the east Asiatic.

Shortly before World War II they again put in an appearance on our coasts and now, due to careful protection, are once more quite numerous and have become a regular sight as they pass to and fro between the Arctic Ocean and the Gulf of Baja California, where they winter. In the latter confined area they have been rather intensively studied in recent years, notably by Dr. P. D. White, who has endeavored to record their heartbeats and to study their other physiological processes. These whales were called "devil fish" by the old-time whalers because they put up a terrific fight and are mean and dangerous, especially when among the kelp beds. Unlike most other whales, they would deliberately attack the small whaling shallops, particularly those that were painted white, and they both used their heads to ram and their tails to flail men in the water.

It is the dolphins, however, that are most prominent among the whales of this area. Any day hundreds of them may be seen, both close inshore and out at sea, leaping in what appears to be pure exuberance. There are numerous species here too, including the Killer Whale and the Blackfish (both of which are only large dolphins or *Delphinidae*). Most numerous is the Common Dolphin *(Delphinus delphis)*, which is a prodigious jumper, but is beaten handsomely in this respect by the little slender Spotted Dolphin *(Stenella graffmani)*. There is an excellent sea aquarium at Palos Verdes where blackfish and these two species of dolphins were kept in a huge tank. All three showed a high degree of intelligence—in fact, scientists today claim that cetaceans rank next to humans in this respect—and performed all manner of agile tricks on demand to the delight of visitors. The Common Dolphin can jump to a height of twenty feet to take a fish from

A White-winged Dove, an inhabitant of the dry valleys of the southern and eastern part of this province.

250

a keeper's hand, and they are trained to do this; the Spotted Dolphins, however, had to be prevented from doing so because they were so quick and jumped so much farther that they started leaping right out of the tank.

THE RETURN OF THE GIANTS

There is another huge sea beast that once lived in enormous numbers around islands both in the far southern parts of the southern hemisphere and on the islands off this coast. It too appeared to have been exterminated at the end of the last century, but it also has comparatively recently reappeared rather mysteriously from nobody knows exactly where. This is the mighty Sea Elephant or, alternatively, Elephant Seal *(Mirounga)*. The males may measure eighteen feet and have a fifteen-foot girth; they are equipped with an eighteen-inch trunk which normally flops down over the muzzle but which, being connected with the nasal passages within, can be inflated and raised almost upright. When alarmed or mating, the bulls rear the forepart of their bodies vertically, raise this trunk, and give rise to tremendous bellows and roars. They feed on a combination of fish, cuttlefish, and seaweed, and they are quite mobile if not agile when in the sea, but they spend a lot of time on land sleeping and snoring loudly, after lumbering laboriously out of the water. The males maintain harems, and once a year these creatures indulge a remarkable habit. They are normally clothed in short, sparse, grayish brown hair, and like other mammals they go through regular molts; but instead of just shedding their hair piecemeal as the next season's growth comes in, they shed the whole outer layer of their skins. As a result, they present a quite revolting sight, being bright pink and naked and looking as if they had been skinned alive and parboiled, a fantasy augmented by their endless moaning, belching, and snoring.

These vast corpulent mammals have now made a fine comeback and have large colonies on the Guadalupe, San Benito, and Cedros Islands off the coast of Baja California, and they have even appeared on the islands off the coast of this province. The Southern Sea Lion also occurs along this coast, and there are now also once again a few of the small Southern Fur Seal or Sea Bear.

HONORABLE ANCESTORS

Each time we have touched on the Pacific coast, we have had occasion to mention *kelp beds*. Though most people have heard of these beds, and although we are taught that kelp is a seaweed, very few of us realize the significance and uniqueness of this phenomenon.

There is nothing like this anywhere else in the world. To explain, it is an almost continuous strip or belt of seaweed stretching for thousands of miles, a little offshore, from Alaska to Baja California and, in isolated patches, a bit farther in both directions. It is a result of the combination of a narrow continental shelf and a cool current cutting south through a warm ocean, and nowhere is this more prominent than off the coast of this province. Under bright sunlight, stretching to the horizon up and down that coast, and when the ocean is so calm it

A Washingtonia, the only indigenous palm in this province and one of the grandest on this continent. Often the dead leaves clothe the whole trunk to its base.

appears more like pale blue oil, the kelp looks alive. All that can be seen is a serpentine mass of heaving shiny things, like billions of giant snakes, out beyond the surf.

The bed is composed of huge ribbons of a firm brown stuff that looks and feels like wet rubber but breaks like a stiff jelly. These ribbons are attached to firmer fibrous stems that are often tens of feet long and end in a small cone of branching roots that may grip small pebbles and other material on the bottom. These obviously vegetable things are seaweeds of the group known technically as *Fucales,* or commonly as Brown Algae. (The huge algae group is conveniently divided into four great subgroups—the green, blue-green, red, and brown.)

Now, there is something rather special about these Brown Algae or seaweeds. A prominent and highly respected scientist recently put forward the staggering suggestion that we and all other animals are descended from the same ancestors as these dull vegetable things. This is to say, both all other animals and ourselves are but animated "vegetables," and part of one great kingdom of life on this small planet. I find this theory—even if it be merely a theory—fascinating, and I found it most significant when sitting on a cliff top on this coast watching the endless mass of apparently insensate vegetation heaving up and down on the Pacific swell.

The kelp has other strange connotations. Its large "leaves" just float upon the surface whereas its stems are anchored on this comparatively shallow sea bottom, but its stems can be measured in the hundreds of feet. Actually, the lengths given for species found in the Antarctic sound fantastic and would, if accurate, make them by far the largest living things on earth, surpassing the greatest trees by hundreds of times in length (that is, height) and perhaps even in bulk.

In this province you must sooner or later become aware of the kelp: either you find it cast ashore on the beaches or you see it floating out to sea. If you are an angler, you will come to know of its use as cover for all manner of desirable fish, and if you are a sailor, you will come to curse it both in darkness and in fog for its clinging qualities. On the other hand, if you are a commercial fisherman, you will bless it for the home it provides for just what you want.

EXOTIC PLANTS

This province is notable as the home of a large number of exotic plants of various groups and kinds. First, it is the principal habitat of a fine palm known as *Washingtonia,* which, because it is the only palm indigenous to the area, is often erroneously said to be the only palm that was in this country before the coming of the white man. This is not so, as vast areas of the Southeast are covered with various palmetto palms; and there are other species in Florida, the most odd being the *Paurotis,* which grows only along a narrow belt between the fresh and salt-water marshes. The Sabal or Cabbage Palm is also indigenous to that area. A large number of other palms have now been introduced to this province and flourish there. These have been brought from all over the world and include both subtropical and many true tropical species.

Another tree that is now widespread throughout the valleys of this province and also grows over much of lowland California and in many other states today is a eucalyptus. This was brought from Australia about the middle of the last century by the builders of the Santa Fe Railroad, who needed timber for ties in treeless areas of the West. The particular eucalyptus chosen—for there are hundreds of species in Australia—is a hardy, fast-growing type that is able to thrive under a minimum rainfall and to survive long periods of drought. It is also a parkland species and can grow isolated or in copses even in very arid soils, while it also grows among other trees and even in deep shade and under a high rainfall. It has taken hold vigorously in the Southwest without, it seems, unduly upsetting the natural vegetation. It is interesting to note that several Australian parkland trees and shrubs, including such as the mimosas, are readily adaptable to this northern hemisphere province. Not only is the general climate equivalent in the two countries but the two belts where these plants are now found correspond in their basic vegetational form. The eucalyptuses have been welcomed by the indigenous fauna, particularly by the hummingbirds, which may be seen feeding on and around them in clouds at certain times of the year.

Eucalyptuses belong to the myrtle family (Myrtaceae) of which there are over four thousand known species in Australia but only one in Europe, whereas in North America they are represented by an allied family, called the *Rhamnaceae,* often called lilacs. One on the eastern seaboard used to be called the New Jersey tea bush. Most true eucalyptuses produce in their leaves fragrant oils such as eucalyptol and geraniol. These are highly volatile and inflammable, so that fires in eucalyptus forests are the most furious known. Not only do the flames leap along faster than anything can move over the ground below, but they can jump canyons and even wide valleys by means of great fireballs of flaming oil particles so fine as to create a mist or gas cloud which may suddenly burst into flame in mid-air. Another peculiarity of many eucalyptuses is that they produce one oil for part of the year and another kind during the remaining months, and that one of these oils may be highly toxic to certain animals. The little "Teddy Bear" or Koala of Australia is one of these, and if it is feeding in a grove of such trees when they make the change-over, it must come to the ground and trek off in search of other species that do not so change and are then suitable to them. Incidentally, the right species of eucalyptus for these fascinating animals have now been planted in this province, so that they can for the first time be exhibited alive in this country.

Apart from the many introduced exotic plants, the most notable feature of the indigenous flora is what are collectively called "succulents." These do not form a special family of plants but are examples of many families which grow in a particular way. Unlike ordinary herbs, or woody shrubs and trees with leaves, they are either fleshy throughout both stem and leaf or in the leaf only; or they may not even show any distinction between leaves, branches, and stems. Like cactuses, they can store water, so they may live in arid regions marked by long droughts between rains. Also, there are forms that can grow where there is excessive salinity, as on salt flats or on coastal beaches bathed in spray. These plants manage to survive because of the very high concentration of salt in their own bodies. Many people, especially in California, make a hobby of collecting succulents and maintain a wide variety of both indigenous and imported varieties in their gardens or in their homes. These plants may be propagated from small random cuttings, and they form a fascinating study.

The Empire of the Cactuses

The Sonoran and Red Deserts

19

It is night. The heat is still glutinous and no wind stirs. The whirling "deedees" have died away to the east as the glowing orange orb of the sun has drifted to the west in a purple miasma. The dust that filled the air in a swirling curtain has also miraculously vanished and, after a period of intense silence and utter blackness, some seemingly mechanically constructed insect has started up like a lone buzz saw. Now the moon comes sailing out over the nearby dry mountains. It has been heralded by the aerial glow that we might expect, but one minute it is utterly dark, the next, platinum beams are fingering out over the endless plain and filtering through desiccated ocotillos and the stark, poxed skeletons of things that were once fleshy and green. Rapidly, a fairyland comes into being.

The desert can be a dreadful place and it can be both ugly and boring—just an endless array of stones and coarse, colorless dust. At other times, parts of it can be extremely beautiful and soft. Then sometimes come fantastically painted scenes, so gaudy that they upset the uninitiated but bring ineffable peace to those who know them. Even under a glaring noonday sun, the bare bones of the deserts seen through a shimmering curtain of "ningning" may seem glorious to some and may indeed contain most wondrous sights, but never under such conditions do they display the beauty they disclose by night. Under the light of the moon they come alive in a quite unearthly way.

Many people believe that deserts represent nature's lost causes—those parts of the land surface of the earth where she has simply given up the struggle. Even many of those who have visited these areas feel this way, and see nothing but the bare rocks and stones, the grit and the dust, and the seemingly lifeless vegetation. This is sad, for the deserts are places of somewhat ebullient life, even if it be only of marching sand dunes and rocks that explode in the night. Moreover, the seemingly lifeless vegetation is a miracle of vitality that, in its way, rivals the tangled, seething competition of the tall equatorial forests. Plants —and animals—not only survive but thrive here in conditions that would extinguish those of more salubrious climes. Here, both have developed more extraordinary aids to survival than anywhere else, and as a result their over-all tonnage and variety is remarkable.

The most outstanding of these plants in our hemisphere are members of the family of the cactuses. But these, which are not by any means all desert plants, are not the only ones that have developed in a special way to cope with the extreme environment. In our western deserts representatives of many families of plants have done this. Notable among them are the lilies, in the form of the yuccas such as the Joshua Tree and the Spanish Dagger, and the agaves, which include the Century Plant. There are also the ocotillos, which are represented here by spiny-stemmed cactus-like shrubs with many long, slender, whiplike stems that flaunt little scalelike green leaves only after rain but that bear beautiful scarlet blooms at the tips of their stems every spring. There are also places within the confines of the Desert Belt where true trees are found; the mesquites, the palos verdes with their green trunks and branches, and the thorny Ironwood. These, however, are more specifically plants of the scrublands.

Cactuses form a family of plants of unique habits and of exclusively New World origin. They have now been carried all over the world as ornamental garden and household plants, and some species have become widely established in Australia, Hawaii, Palestine and other Mediterranean countries, and elsewhere. There are over sixteen hundred known species of cactuses, which range from the Strait of Magellan to Canada. At least one of them is now found growing wild in every state in the union except Maine, New Hampshire, and Vermont. Some grow on forest trees in wet tropical jungles, and some in the Everglades in southern Florida grow with their roots in brackish water. But their headquarters are the true Hot Deserts, notably that belt in the northern half of the western hemisphere; while many species now spread over both the North and South Scrub Belts in both halves of the western hemisphere. About three hundred species are indigenous to the United States, but nearly three-quarters—or some twelve hundred kinds—are found within the confines of the North American continent as defined in this book. Cactuses are "traveling" plants in that bits of them, aided by their hooks and spines, can readily be transported long distances by animals, and their seeds may be carried by birds. They will take root in a surprisingly wide variety of climatic conditions. They are hardy, and they have developed methods for surviving frost that are almost as efficient as those which they possess for overcoming prolonged droughts.

Though cactuses are found over a wide area of our Southwest, in the driest parts of Texas, and in the East Chaparral and all over Mexico in great profusion, their headquarters are in these Sonoran Deserts. Here they attain their greatest size and dominate not only the vegetation but the whole landscape. They come in a bewildering variety of shapes and sizes, arrayed with all manner of plumes, hooks, spikes, spines, scales, prickles, hairs, and bristles. Once a year they burst into gorgeous bloom. Taking them as a group, the beauty and color of their flowers probably surpasses that of all other forms of plant life. Take away the cactuses and this province would indeed be a dreary, sterile place, and probably a true desert throughout its length, for without them much of the other vegetation could not survive and most of the fauna would not be present. Thus a description of this province becomes almost synonymous with an introduction to the cactus family. The cactuses may legitimately—if not strictly scientifically—be divided into five great groups: the Opuntias, the Barrels, the Hedgehogs, the Pincushions, and the Cereuses (*Cereus*-es) or Cerei.

The Opuntias are divided into two distinct and well-known types called the Chollas (pronounced *choiyas*) and the Prickly Pears. These are the jointed cactuses that often form bushes or trees; but Chollas have stems that are round in section whereas the Prickly Pears are oblong, each section forming an oval "pad."

A Century Plant (Agave americana), *a kind of aloe related to that from which sisal hemp or henequen is made. The plant's flower is seen in the center.*

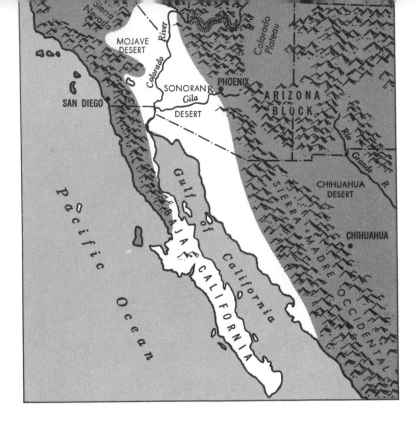

This is a somewhat complex province, geographically speaking. As a belt, it would under theoretical conditions run across the lower half of the latitudes it now occupies—that is to say between the twenty-eight and thirty-first parallels—but, because of the major ocean and atmospheric currents, it is today pushed north to the thirty-sixth parallel, about the region of the Mojave and Death Valley. At the same time, it extends south farther than it should (due to a set of lesser factors) and includes the whole central section of the peninsula of Baja California. In fact, it here runs almost due north to south.

Its boundaries are ill defined. To the north it merges with the "gray deserts" (as defined by the soils) of the Great Basin. To the west it disappears under the coastal mountain ranges of Southern California but appears again on the coast from Los Angeles south to Baja California. To the east it likewise disappears under the Arizonan or southern block of the Southern Montane Province, but it shows itself again on the Colorado Plateau. To the south of this upland massif, it peters out about Phoenix, Arizona, and from there to the Gulf of California on the Sonoran coast it merges with the Southern Scrub Belt. Southward, it hops the Gulf and cuts right through the peninsula of Baja California.

Its isolation from the central or Chihuahuan Desert Province is occasioned by the northward swing of the Southern Scrub Belt and by the fact that the subtropical grasslands (savannahs) and the orchardbush likewise approach the north Mexican border, while there are many mountain ranges that connect the Arizonan block to the Sierra Madre Occidental athwart this neck. Many of these mountains rise high enough for montane conifers and even other forest growths to maintain a footing on their peaks. There is, in fact, a broken bridge of uplands connecting the two, which, combined with the scrublands, completely separates the western or Sonoran from the central or Chihuahuan Desert Province.

The Sonoran Province is composed of lowlands through which flows only one substantial river—the remnants of the Colorado—though the Gila is not altogether insignificant. Upon its surface, however, there lie a great many mountains, both isolated and in chains, and the backbone of Baja California is sharp and in many places precipitous. To the northwest, there are some true deserts such as the Mojave, culminating in the sunken, sub-sea-level Death Valley. The province as a whole is a sort of vegetational sink, the inner recesses of which are drier and less vegetated than the periphery, which merges with the scrublands on all sides. Here may be seen as typical desert conditions as anywhere on this continent.

In the Barrels, the buds arise from special protuberances, called areoles, just above the *ordinary* areoles that produce the spines. (Areoles are unique structures in the plant world, being special areas of tissue from which joints and spines are developed and from which flowers may arise, while roots will sprout from them on bits of cactus that fall to the ground.) In the Hedgehogs, the flowers erupt from the skin of the plant just above the older spine-bearing areoles. In the Pincushions, the flowers grow between the skin tubercles or from their upper sides and have no connection with the spine-bearing areoles. The Cerei are the most difficult to define; they range in size from the three biggest cactuses, the Giant or Pringle's, the Organpipe, and the Saguaro, to tiny vinelike things no thicker than a pencil. Among these last are the famous night-blooming cactuses. All these produce their flowers at or just below the tips of their limbs.

As mentioned earlier, cactuses are encased in impermeable coats of special leathery tissue usually plentifully supplied with wax, and they sometimes have a waxy external covering besides. Everything about them is devised to store water, so that, even without a fresh supply of it, they maintain themselves for long periods, in some cases for years. There are places where they live that have on occasion remained without a drop of rain for as much as four years. However, too much water can kill them, and they must have rest periods when they do not absorb any through their roots. It may therefore be thought curious that many of them live in saturated jungles. Cactuses therein are, however, epiphytes—that is to say, they grow on other plants (but are not parasitic on them)—and they straggle about on the branches. In these forests they would "drown" in the saturated air were it not for their impermeable skins. Then again, in many of these areas of very high rainfall there is often a prolonged comparatively rainless period or one when the rain comes down in sudden great spurts of short duration. As soon as it stops, the tree limbs dry off completely.

DESERT DEVILS

The Chollas, which tend to develop into treelike forms, are constructed like branching strings of green sausages with little

Facing page, above: The Mule Deer, shown here apparently alerted by the flash of the photographer's strobe light, is at home in the desert and is quite common in the Sonoran region.
Below: The little Spotted Skunk or Spilogale has silky fur and hunts small nocturnal desert animals. Like all other members of the skunk family, it has what are euphemistically called "scent glands."

A cactus wren on a cholla.

Facing page: The mighty Saguaro Cactus and the fuzzy-coated Cholla dominate the Sonoran deserts.

A pack rat on a barrel cactus. These mammals romp about among the most densely spined cactuses.

spirally arranged rows of lumps all over them. Like all cactuses, they contain a sort of skeleton—in this case a cylindrical tube perforated all over with spirally distributed lines of irregular-sized holes. This tube is woody and is filled with pulpy material and wrapped around outside with a considerable thickness of soft tissue, which in turn is completely enclosed in a leathery skin armed with masses of spines on the lumps. The "sausages" break off readily at the constrictions between them and fall to the ground, where they may shrivel and die or may put out roots and start a new plant. There are twenty species in this province, among them the "Chain Fruit," the "Staghorn," and the "Jumping" Cholla. This last is a devilish creature, completely covered in needle-sharp spines, the sausages of which drop off at the slightest provocation, almost literally jumping at you and then bouncing on the ground. If you so much as brush against one you may get a most unpleasant wound and one that can become infected. But there is a worse one sometimes called the "ramose," or "branching," which looks innocent enough, being covered with strange little shields each bearing a single spine concealed in a deceptive papery sheath. To barge into one of these is exquisite agony.

The other Opuntias, the Prickly Pears, are almost too well known to warrant general description. They are the most widespread of all types, with over 150 species. Their oval, pad-shaped sections are variously armed with spines—few or many, tiny or enormous—arranged in regular clusters. The pads grow one from another either singly, in twos, in threes, or in groups, and at all angles, so that the plant forms great clumps. Sometimes these join up to make impenetrable forests covering acres, as the Australians discovered to their dismay when these plants were introduced to their continent. Perhaps most surprising of all the Prickly Pears are those represented by a species called the Santa Rita, which has orange-spined purple pads, or the Beavertail, which is pale blue with bright yellow spines. Their flowers are among the most exquisitely colored even among cactuses. These are borne along the edges of the outermost pads, sometimes alone, at other times in whole corollas. They come in the most vivid reds and yellows. That of the Beavertail is a glowing, old-rose pink with vivid yellow stamens.

Cactus flowers, as has been said, are "all flower," due to the fact that the sepals and petals are usually indistinguishable and both are colored, while there is, of course, no supporting foliage. They are also very often of comparatively enormous size; some, as in the case of the Sand Dollars (Astrophyton), being as large as the plant that supports them. Those of the largest species, however, are often small and even insignificant. There is one Cereus that has a flower over a foot in diameter. In their natural habitats, cactuses flower at regular periods each year. This has nothing to do with the rainfall, unlike the flowering of other desert plants, which occurs only after rain. In the northern part of the Sonoran Province, the first to come out in April are the Beavertails and some Hedgehogs; in May the Chollas, Prickly Pears, and Saguaros begin to bloom. Most of the others struggle out in June, which is the time for the flowering of the wonderful "Queen-of-the-Night" with its delicate, slender, pointed, multi-rayed white star and central emergent corona of delicate flesh-pink stamens. Some of the smaller Chollas bloom in July and August, along with most of the Pincushions. By September only the Barrels are left. Most individual cactus flowers last only one day, but special atmospheric conditions may keep them opening and closing for several days. The night-bloomers often all come out together if a very hot day is succeeded by a very hot night at the right time of year. Most of these start opening just before sundown and close in mid-morning.

LIVING BARRELS

The Barrel cactuses are really extraordinary. They are mostly tub-shaped structures fluted vertically but usually on a slight bias. The ridges bear lines of nodules from which the spines sprout, but some of them also bear hooks. Some species grow to a height of ten feet, are four feet in diameter, and weigh tons. They are believed to live for upward of six hundred years. Even the biggest have only a slender three- to six-inch cylindrical and central woody skeleton and roots that are very shallow and widespread. When rain comes after a drought, they sometimes absorb water so fast and in such quantities that they swell visibly and get so heavy their roots pull out of the softened ground and they topple over; but they may then put out new roots and just go on growing, lying there like stranded grampuses. Their toppling is encouraged by the curious fact that they almost invariably lean to the southwest, often at an acute angle. It is said that they tend to grow as far as possible with their heads pointing to the sun, which is on an average in that region of the sky for more hours than in any other during the year as a whole in this part of the world. There being more drying of the skin on that side than in the comparatively more shady northeast side, the plants tend to lean that way. It is further suggested that the bias in their fluting, which almost invariably goes sinistrally, is due to the head slewing around, as it were, to follow the arc of the fall, winter, and spring sun as it crosses the southern sky from east to west, getting hotter after noon. However, there appear to be some rugged individualists who twist the other way, and still others that don't twist at all.

The Hedgehog cactuses are small three- to twelve-inch forms shaped like bunches of prickly cucumbers, and some of them are covered in silver mantles like domes of spider web glistening with dew. One species extends as far north as Montana. About thirty of the total of seventy-five known species have been found in the Sonoran Province. The Pincushions, of which there are several hundred known species, arc also extremely numerous. They are mostly small, squat, globular things, sometimes immensely spiny, sometimes quite smooth, and they come in the most astonishing colors and shapes, often looking exactly like sea urchins.

MOON FLOWERS

It is among the night-blooming group of what are called Cerei that we encounter the most impressive and the most odd of all cactuses. Although of great variety, they may be divided into several lots for purposes of recognition; the Giant (known as Pringle's), the Saguaro, and the Organpipe; the long, meandering, snaky or vinelike species; and a number of intermediate forms. Not all night-blooming cactuses are Cerei, but all Cerei flower at night. The Giant and the Saguaro may exceed fifty feet in height. The latter has a single, central, upright stem from which sprout side branches that form elbows and then also go upward. Examples up to fifteen tons in weight and estimated to be almost three hundred years old have been found. They often grow so thickly they form forests. In this province they range from sea level to almost five thousand feet, but there are few in the south and they are found mostly just about the bor-

The Joshua Tree (Yucca brevifolia), *a woody-stemmed type of yucca that may grow to over forty feet, is a prominent member of the desert flora.*

261

der. They have a skeleton of a dozen or so woody rods that may reach two inches in diameter and are immensely strong, to hold aloft the tons of pithy "flesh" and the thick, solid skin.

These giant cactuses are all vertically fluted and carry bunches of spines on series of knots running up their ridges. Those of the Saguaro are of two kinds, one black and stiff, borne by young trees for their first half-century, the other yellow and pliable, developed by older specimens. The Organpipe is the common form of lower Sonora and Baja California, though Pringle's is also found there. The Organpipe is formed, as its name implies, of a number of great pipelike stems, looking not unlike a bunch of enormous upright cucumbers from a distance. These are also fluted but more shallowly, and they are usually ringed or pinched at irregular intervals, a characteristic caused by frosts or periods of low temperature which restrict their growth or temporarily kill their growing points. Organpipes have edible red fruits covered with soft spines that can be brushed off. The fruits of many cactuses are edible and some are delicious; that of the Saguaro is very sugary, of the Prickly Pears excellent. The seeds of some can be ground into a fine meal.

There are about 450 other species of Cerei. Their headquarters are subtropical Central America (that is to say south of the Tropic of Cancer to 10 degrees north); some just reach into the United States. They are numerous in the West Indies, both in the arid areas that cover most of the Greater Antilles and in the wet forests of the Lesser Antilles; they are everywhere up to the montane forests of Mexico; and there are many in South America. Among them are the cactuses which are universally most admired for their blooms and which have been given such names as King-of-the-Night, Princess-of-the-Night and Midnight-Ladies. Personally I prefer the name Moonflowers. These are mostly white, tinged with most delicate salmon pinks and golds, and they pop unexpectedly out of dry, ropelike tangles or from pale blue, fleshy, leaflike straps. Some have a very powerful aroma.

STRANGE FRUITS

As I said above, the cactuses, although the dominant plants of the true Desert Belt, are not by any means the only ones, for in the places of most appalling aridity there is a considerable variety of other families of plants in addition to the ocotillos, yuccas, and agaves. Some of them look rather like cactuses, notably the Candelilla (canday-lee-ah). This is a member of the euphorbia or spurge family, but is very cactus-like. Members of this family replace the cactuses in African deserts. The Candelilla grows in large masses of asparagus-like stems and is known also as the Wax Plant; its scientific name is *Euphorbia antisyphilitica*. It yields a wax which is used in the manufacture of candles, floor and polishing waxes, shoe polish, and phonograph records. In Mexico, as its scientific name implies, it is a recognized item in the treatment of venereal disease.

The ubiquitous Creosote Bush also can exist almost anywhere that a cactus can. This is a small evergreen shrub with small leaves and tiny, bright yellow flowers. Its leaves are sticky and it smells of creosote. Cattle will not eat it, but a lotion used to be made by soaking its leaves and stems in boiling water; this was considered efficacious in treating cuts and bruises of both man and beast, especially saddle sores on horses. Also in the true desert there is some Saltbush, the little acacia known as the Catsclaw, and occasional stunted Allthorn—an apt name for a thing that is literally, when not in its tiny flower, *all* thorns. There are herbaceous plants in readiness to spring up as soon

as it rains, but just about the only one that somehow manages to put in an occasional appearance at other times is a thistle.

Conditions, of course, are altogether different as soon as one passes from the Desert Belt itself into its enveloping scrub zones. Of the Northern Scrub Belt we have already spoken at length in Chapters 14 to 17, and we shall visit it again in the next chapter. The Southern Scrub Belt will be encountered later in its rather specialized form on the upland plateau of Mexico, and has already been described in a still more particular form, in Chapter 14, which dealt with the East Chaparrals. However, there is in the province we are discussing a wide belt of Southern Scrub running down the east side of the desert from the mountains of Arizona to the Gulf of California and then appearing again on the tip of the peninsula of Baja California. This merges with the desert on one side and actually penetrates it to a very large extent. On the other side it merges with the subtropical Savannah Belt, which extends northward from the coast of Mexico and thins out against the Sierra Occidental.

This strip of scrub is significant and rather distinctive. In this, despite no noticeable increase in mean average annual rainfall, conditions are quite different from those of the Desert Belt or the Northern Scrub Belt. The same kinds of plants occur but much more exuberantly, and they are interspersed with a whole host of others, many of a woody nature, such as the giant heather called the Madrone with its coppery smooth bark, as well as mesquites, ironwoods, great groves of yuccas, century plants, agaves, and many herbs. In fact, although the ground itself remains a desert and grass is absent but for a few scattered and minute specialized areas, the dry-stalked herbs, scrubby bushes, small trees, and thorny shrubs actually coalesce to form a forest—and a closed-canopy one at that. If there has been rain of any consequence before the vegetating season in the spring, this heterogenous mass may burst into flower and be exquisitely beautiful, with cicadas whirring and bees buzzing by the millions everywhere.

Passing from this zone westward to the desert in southern Sonora can be almost as startling as stepping out of a tall equatorial rain forest onto the Orchardbush Belt; for, although the two zones merge over most of their range, there are places where you can literally have your right foot in the Desert and your left in the Scrub Belt.

THEY TREAD WARILY

Introduced domestic animals of the larger varieties tramp about in both the Scrub and Desert Belts and do not seem to be much affected by the spines and thorns of the cactuses and other plants. They do not eat cactuses except during extreme droughts, when some prickly pears are rendered edible by the burning off of spines. The larger indigenous fauna, however, seems to find these spiny things rather irksome and treat them with about the

Above left: The Gila Monster, a slow-moving, obese form of lizard. It produces a copious poison which flows out of glands and down its guttered teeth.

Above right: Prominent among the multitudinous rabbits found in these deserts is the little Desert Cottontail.

Below: The Desert Tortoise seems to be immune to heat and desiccation but actually spends most of its time in the shade or under rocks.

Left: Even hawks make use of the cactuses. Here a pair of Western Red-tails has built a nest among the spines.

Facing page: Barrel cactuses are rather odd: their spines reduce the effect of the sun's rays; they grow after they have fallen; and they grow on the bias.

and the Eyra (Jaguarondi)—manage so well in just such growth, getting their food by hunting the innumerable other animals that seem to be totally unaffected by the worst that even a jumping cholla can provide?

This is really a curious thing when you come to examine it. In jumping chollas—which are more or less impenetrable masses of needle-sharp spines—there customarily live hosts of small animals that dart in and out of their mazelike branches, apparently with as much ease as we might cross a country road. First there is the little Cactus Wren, which seems to be more or less symbiotic with the chollas, making its nest therein and skipping through them at great speed. In addition the Goldfinch, Linnet, Verdin, and sundry other small birds also live in the densest masses of spines. Then the Kangaroo Rats make their nests in huge piles of the fallen portions of the most spinous cactuses, and dart in and out of them as if the spines did not exist, without ever so much as a scratch. The Pack Rats also tote these horrendous objects considerable distances and pile them up. How either rodent manages this is not known.

Their basic aim would seem to be to make a rampart against predators such as coyotes; but their worst enemy, the Cacomistle (often called "Ring-tailed Cat"), though a small, soft-furred, quick member of the raccoon family with a long, bushy tail of alternating black and white rings, seems to be able to penetrate these *bomas* with the greatest of ease. Cacomistles are the mammalian world's champion escape artists; for, though the size of small domestic cats, they can wedge themselves into crevices so constricted it is quite unbelievable even when you see them for yourself.

Many kinds of mice, such as the Pocket Mice, gallivant about cactuses of all kinds, rippling in and out among the spines; but I have seen a bobcat shin up one as if it were spineless, while the coatis climb them unconcernedly during their mass forays. All three kinds of skunks—the Hognosed, Striped, and the little spotted Spilogale—bumble about beneath them, and fat raccoons hunt in them. There is a small gray-colored squirrel in southern Sonora in the Scrub Belt that delights in rushing up and down the flutings of the giant organpipe cactus stems *inside* the spines and can somehow safely dart through from one of these flutings to the next. And it is in the giant cactuses—Pringle's, the Saguaro, and the Organpipe—that the most astonishing communities of wildlife may be found. First, the Gila Woodpecker gets his living off insects from under the leathery hides of these plants by making his characteristic holes; he also makes specially large holes in which he installs his mate at nesting time. The cactus responds by lining this with scar tissue. When the woodpecker's family is raised and has departed, the tiny Elf Owl comes along and takes up his abode therein. This delightful little creature is about the size of an overfed sparrow, is incurably inquisitive, and seems not at all afraid of man or beast.

DESERT NIGHT LIFE

The fauna of the desert is extraordinarily plentiful, but it is so adept at concealment during daylight hours that one might think

same respect as a sensible human does when wearing thin-soled canvas shoes. Deer and peccaries mince carefully along between them and always go around them, even when in headlong flight. The large cats and, I have been told, particularly the Jaguar prefer to give all areas where they grow as wide a berth as possible. I have seen puma in dense cactus beds in south Sonora, and it was then pointed out to me that they were always following man-made paths. Experienced native hunters told me that the cats suffer from cactus thorns picked up on the ground as they do from porcupine quills, because both may be barbed. This seems reasonable; but how then do the lesser cats—the Ocelot

264

The Cactus Owl or Elf Owl. Only about the size of a sparrow, it feeds mostly on insects and lives in holes made in the cactuses by woodpeckers.

and eventually more than likely the sound of rapid munching. You may then switch on your previously focused lights and even start to move about a little, for once the denizens of this particular wilderness have found an unexpected pile of delectable food, they often throw all caution to the winds and just eat. What is more, predators may be tugging at the meat while the prey they should be hunting sits munching contentedly not more than a dozen feet away.

There are, of course, lesser folk in the deserts, and it is at night that they too are about. One must be very wary of not a few of these. Just as the desert supports an unusual number of obnoxious plants armed with spines, hooks, and irritants—such as the ghastly Chéchem tree of the Southern Scrub Belt of Yucatan, mentioned earlier, which can produce second-degree burns on human flesh—so also does it seem to favor poisonous animals.

DANCING JACKS

Two of us once spent an afternoon with these engaging animals. Our objectives were for one of us to photograph cactuses, which were then in bloom, while the other was to collect beetles. The first entailed a certain amount of wandering about, for, although cactuses covered the earth for miles, to find the particular one wanted in good light and location called for patience and some ingenuity. Beetle-collecting is easier. Beetles are everywhere on land, in an uncounted profusion of species and individuals, many of them tiny, and you can collect them simply by sprawling on a blanket spread almost anywhere. The ground around this, if raked over and examined carefully with a lens, will usually yield enough material to keep you occupied for half a day.

As we trudged over the arid ground looking for a place where enough different cactuses warranted photography, jack rabbits of monumental dimensions kept popping up, loping leisurely away for a few yards, and then sitting down behind some minute bush. One particularly large one, which walked rather solemnly on its rakish legs somewhat like a newborn lamb, stayed just ahead of us until we found a good spot. Then I spread my blanket, and my partner set up his cameras. The jack watched these operations with an air of sagacity from a distance of only about ten yards. As we concentrated on our jobs, the animal loped off and first went to watch the photography. After circling around and sitting up with its immense ears at the alert and satisfying its curiosity there, it came toward me by a series of cautious approaches and long pauses—but always on the alert.

As I was prone and hidden in a small dell, I ceased beetle-collecting and just watched. The animal first came up and observed me keenly, looking me straight in the eyes, which is most unusual for any animal, let alone a wild one. It then walked solemnly off to my right and beyond my vision. I dared not turn my head lest I disturb it, so I remained quiet, waiting for it to circle me and appear from my left. Imagine my surprise, therefore, when, after about two minutes, I felt something tugging gently at my right foot, followed by a sound like an electric coffee-grinder starting up. I could no longer resist turning my head, and there sat the jack munching on a fair-sized bite from my blanket. But my movement caused him to make only two leisurely hops to the shade of a creosote bush, where he sat down and continued to munch. Nor did he move when my companion approached and took his picture close up. We sat down to watch.

In a short time another jack appeared, and the first one got up instantly and thumped on the ground. We thought we were

it nonexistent. It is at night that one may see it, and there is nothing more interesting than then to find a quiet spot, sweep it free of thorns before dark, and lie there on a blanket or tarpaulin and wait. One should place at some distance various baits, such as handfuls of grain in piles, scraps of meat tied to low but tough bushes by short strings, and piles of freshly watered green vegetables. As the painted sky fades slowly to a soft heliotrope, many small movements will be heard all around witnessing an invasion of territorial rights by another male, but the second animal must have been a female because the two went into a sort of game, approaching each other and almost touching noses and then jumping aside at a tangent. Later, they started actually to jump over each other; and then we noticed that we had fellow spectators to this performance in the form of several other jacks. Soon other games were in progress, and we stayed all afternoon watching, thereby gaining an unusual insight into the way these animals spend their time when not dashing away from danger.

DESERT LOW LIFE

In addition to these lesser fry, the Sonoran Desert has a fine selection of reptiles. First, there are the two species of the large, slow-walking, desert lizard known as the Gila Monster, with pink spots on black, and the Beaded Lizard of Mexico, with white or yellow spots on black. These can give deadly bites. That they ever manage to do so is extraordinary because they live where men do not. Yet year after year misguided persons (and they never seem to be professional herpetologists) insist upon dallying with or trying to handle one of these animals and get bitten. The Gila Monster, when once it bites, hangs on and chews, while a nasty venom pours from its teeth into the wound. The teeth are grooved, and below those of the lower jaw are poison glands. If one is properly bitten, the result is worse than that of a rattle-snake bite; the poison is neurotoxic, speeding up the action of the lungs and heart until, by gradual paralysis of the muscles activating those organs, both stop working.

Then there are the snakes. Of these there are the Coral Snake, several species of rattlesnakes (there are thirty species and sub-species recorded from the United States, about two-thirds of them in the Southwest), and the "back-fanged snakes"—the Lyre Snake and Vine Snake, and three smaller genera. All these are poisonous to one degree or another. The Coral is a crotaline snake related to the deadly cobras, but it is a small and retiring beast with such a small mouth that the danger of being bitten by one should be, but unfortunately is not, negligible. It is ringed with bright red, yellow, and shiny black. The Lyre and Vine Snakes are also small; their venom is borne by grooved back teeth, and they would be hard put to it to inject their poison into a human. The only really dangerous snakes are thus the rattlers, since they are adept at concealment even in bright daylight, and they delight in lying about on preheated open ground after the sun has gone down so that the unwary may well step on them. They strike fairly fast, directly outward; and they have huge fangs that they automatically project almost straight forward so that they gain the ultimate penetrative power. Their venom is deadly. Despite all the playing down of the subject recently, these animals are responsible for many deaths every year in this country and many more in Mexico, where people do not wear such heavy footwear and where they spend more time in the bush.

These snakes are really very interesting creatures—especially, of course, one in this area that intrigues anybody who has ever heard of it. This is the "Sidewinder." This term should be confined to a small species of rattler named *Crotalus cerastes*, or the Horned Rattler. It is a true desert inhabitant, and in traveling over loose sand it casts a loop ahead with the fore part of its body in order to get a grip against which it can haul its remaining sidewise undulations forward. Its progress is fascinating to watch—a sort of jerky, undulating, corkscrew motion. Some other desert rattlers do something slightly similar in their otherwise normal, snaky progression, and are sometimes likewise referred to as sidewinders.

The Sonoran Desert Province contains many other wonders and mysteries. Despite its often austere appearance, especially by day when the deedees whirl and even whole regions may be blanketed by dust storms, its beauty can be almost unsurpassed at sunrise, at sundown, and particularly at night under the platinum iridescence of the moon. Its plant and animal life is enormous, varied, and often beautiful in the extreme but can be, at the same time, noxious and even dangerous. It is just as if nature indeed did abandon the whole place, then changed her mind—not once but several times—ending with perhaps the most remarkable yet bewildering area imaginable.

Brown Rocks and White Sands

The Hot Deserts of the Tularosa and Chihuahua, and the Deserts and Scrublands of the Central Mexican Plateau

20

Between the great deserts and scrublands of Sonora and the East Chaparral Province where these two belts reach the east side of our continent, there lies a land that is customarily referred to as the Chihuahua Deserts after the Mexican state of that name. Much of this is a desert indeed—in many parts even more desolate than any we have so far visited. It is a vast upland country of most odd construction, so that, unless you travel with an altimeter or a map showing the elevations, you would never know that the whole of it starts at some three thousand feet above sea level and rises southward to over six thousand feet. Many atlases show the whole province as just a great upland plain; but it is quite otherwise, being covered with mountain ranges. Apart from the small part that lies within the boundaries of the United States, detailed information about much of this province is difficult to obtain. The northern part of it, in Mexican territory, is a wilderness, with only one or two roads crossing it, and containing several huge areas that are completely uninhabited. Apart from the difficulty of travel in this area, information is hard to come by because of the practice of printing maps, including even road maps and atlases, in such a way that everything ends abruptly on the publisher's side of any international political boundary. This is particularly misleading here since there is no true boundary or change of any kind at this point. The net result is that practically nobody on one side has any idea what the country looks like on the other. On all readily available maps, the country immediately south of the Rio Grande is shown as a smooth blank, just as are lowland plains elsewhere. However, that entire region stands at a considerably higher general level than on the United States side. Moreover, the whole of it, from the region of the Big Bend all the way to Monterrey and the grand Sierras, is covered with strings of mountains and small ranges, rising some four to six thousand feet above the already elevated plain.

Coming from the Sonoran region, we enter this province via the dry, cactus-covered plains of southern Arizona, which run up into the foothills and gorges of the southern block of the South Montane Province. This narrow neck of territory represents the northernmost bulge of the South Scrub Belt, and it winds its way between little mountain ranges that litter its otherwise more or less level surface. These are outliers of the great Sierra Madre

Occidental. Were the whole area some three thousand feet lower, they would form a galaxy of islands like stepping stones between that range and the southwestern edge of the Rockies. These mountain ranges are, in any case, very much like islands, each having its own crown of special vegetation, often containing a fauna that may be unique, including the only parrot (a Conure) native to the United States. The taller these mountains are, the more forest they have on their upper slopes; the farther south one goes, the more these forests come to resemble those of the Sierra Occidental, while the northern-type conifers, of course, rise ever higher on them. This narrow neck of scrubland thus completely separates the Sonoran Deserts to the west from the Chihuahuan to the east, for the deserts pass north under the mountains of Arizona and New Mexico to appear on the Colorado Platea.

The most northerly extension of the Chihuahua Province comprises the Tularosa plain or basin. This is a fascinating area, containing some of the most remarkable sights. It is enclosed between two great mountain blocks—the San Andreas and Oscura on the west, beyond which lies the upper Rio Grande valley containing the Jornada del Muerto desert; and the very high Sacramentos and Guadalupe Mountains to the east. This basin is a long, wedge-shaped depression pointing north and continues on into the Estancia Valley beyond some low hills. If you get up from this plain a short distance, you see two unexpected phenomena. To one side, it looks as if there had been a tremendous snowstorm over a limited area, for a well-defined portion of it glistens so that, in bright sunlight, one can hardly look at it. Somewhat beyond and to the northwest of this apparition, another area looks as if tar had been poured upon it in even greater quantity. This is a large lava flow, jet-black in color, and of comparatively recent date, geologically speaking. The first phenomenon is now very appropriately named "White Sands" and is a national monument.

WHITE LAND

White sands occur rarely in various parts of the world. There are a number in our Southwest that form an arc following the curve of the Northern Scrub Zone and center on a point about the middle Colorado River valley. White sands, per se, originate from a rather special kind of rock laid down around the edges of warm ancient seas that became landlocked and eventually dried out. This rock is composed of gypsum, a hydrous calcium sulphate which, when dehydrated or baked, forms the basis of plaster of Paris. The origin of the white sands in the Tularosa Valley is interesting and serves to explain how most of these oddities come about.

What is now the Tularosa Valley was once the exact opposite—i.e., a long ridge formed by an upfold of the earth's surface that took place some time after the ancient sea had disappeared. This raised the gypsum stratum into a sort of immense elongated shield. Then two vast parallel faults or "cracks" developed along either side of this shield, and the whole strip of territory between them collapsed and sank downward to form a valley or basin, while the blocks of land on either side rose up to form mountains. Then erosion got to work, and the gypsum stratum, which was near the surface of the shield, was quickly washed away.

Great areas of this province, north of Bolson de Mapimi, are covered with massive lava flows. These are scoured and cracked but support a tough flora.

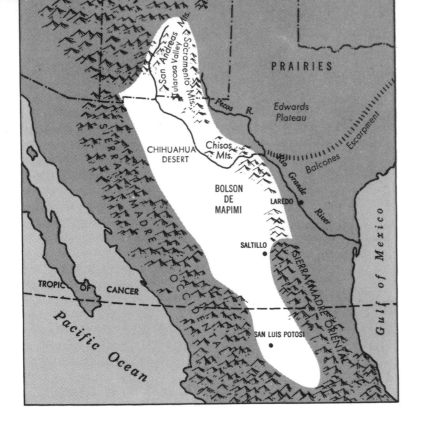

This province, a fairly large one and important from an ecological point of view, is the least well defined on the continent. Yet it forms a distinct unit. It is basically a desert province and is duly ringed with scrublands; however, these are of the South Scrub Belt only, for the following reason. The northern boundary of the province is formed by the steep southern-facing slopes of the South Montane Block's uplands, but the northeastern frontier consists of a thin belt of high mountains. These reach from the Estancia Valley to the escarpment that forms the southern rim of the Prairie Belt on the Stockton and Edwards Plateaus. We passed through that narrow belt on our way northwest from the East Chaparral to

the South Montane Block (see Chapter 15, where we described this as a meeting place of three provinces and somewhat distinct from all of them). The narrow eastern boundary of this province is the eastern edge of the Big Bend district of the Rio Grande valley.

The equally narrow western boundary of this province is drawn arbitrarily across the South Scrub Belt between the Arizona block of the South Montane Province and the northwestern tip of the Sierra Occidental. The rest of the province forms a long tongue extending to the southeast into the central highlands of Mexico between the Sierras Occidental and Oriental. As these are clothed in subtropical montane vegetation and are ringed by orchardbush and the Savannah Belt, we exclude them here, and draw the periphery of the Chihuahua Province along the line between them and the edge of the South Scrub Belt.

The flora and fauna of this province are homogeneous throughout—typical desert forms centrally and indigenous scrubland forms peripherally. The latter may extend to considerable altitudes up the inner faces of the Sierras, due both to the aridity of the central upland plateau and also to the following fact: Under absolutely theoretical conditions, the Desert and South Scrub Belts should run from east to west between about 15 degrees and 25 degrees north latitude. On the west side of this continent, as we have repeatedly pointed out, they are pushed far north. However, here, between those latitudes, they have a chance to assert themselves, and, aided by the exceptional aridity, they perform what is called a major "re-entrance" (from their normal position toward the south, in the form of this long, tonguelike projection).

The province is almost 1000 miles long from northwest to southeast, 500 miles wide at its northern end, and about 250 miles wide between the Sierras, narrowing to less than 100 miles in the south. The northern part is on an average about 3500 feet above sea level, the tongue some 6000 feet high.

However, along either side of the valley it remained as a horizontal bed, running along the upper faces of the mountains. As rains continued to fall upon these mountains, the gypsum was washed down to the floor of the valley, along with detritus from the other strata.

At one point on the valley floor there happened to be a small lake, and in this the gypsum accumulated in solution. Then, during extended dry periods between the rains, this lake underwent excessive evaporation and large, platelike crystals of a glassy, transparent material called selenite grew around its margin. Next, hot and powerful winds blew over these and broke them up into little grains, which rolled away over the floor of the valley. These grains were angular and were also heavier, though smaller, than the other sand grains thereabouts, so that they became segregated and formed dunes, while smaller-grained material was blown onto the plain beyond.

This process has been going on here for thousands of years. The result is a monumental pile of glistening, pure white sand, in dunes that may reach a height of sixty feet, extending in a belt some five miles wide for some twenty-five miles to the northwest of little Lake Lucero. These dunes are perpetually on the move, their grains being blown up their gentle windward slopes by strong winds and then falling over their sharp crests. The dunes sometimes crawl over each other and there are lesser

dunes on greater ones. Their windward faces may be covered with beautiful ripple marks.

We have mentioned many dunes before but most of these were either fully vegetated or supported at least some plants. It so happens that in the Tularosa Valley there are no such plants available. Although the highly alkaline floor of the valley supports stunted growth which can use the subsurface water that is highly charged with gypsum in solution, there is no vegetation here that can root in and live on pure gypseous sand. However, seven kinds of plants have by a most novel method partially adapted themselves to these singular conditions. They grow normally in the soil of the plain, but if a dune approaches them—and the movement of a dune is irresistible—they somehow manage to put on a spurt of growth that just equalizes the rate at which the dune piles up, thus keeping their heads above the sand. Botanists have been amazed to find that some of these plants had roots going down forty feet.

The dunes themselves are of great beauty. They also have a quality that I can describe only as one of friendly eeriness. As you stand among them, especially when only the tops of the greater mountains far to the west and east can be seen over the larger dunes, you can readily imagine that you are on another planet. Yet, despite the total absence of anything familiar, the place is somehow not an unfriendly one. Around the edges of the dune area, especially along its flanks where the sand is just passing by rather than encroaching frontally, the ordinary vegetation makes valiant efforts to grow onto the slopes, and in many places it has actually almost covered them with greenery. The ubiquitous mesquite has gained a foothold in small patches hard by the dunes; and nothing can be more exquisite than one of these trees with its dark, twisting trunk and branches and its feathery bright green foliage dancing above the rim of a pure white dune under an azure sky.

DISAPPEARING MICE AND LIZARDS

The dunes are not entirely lifeless in other respects, for a few small animals have adapted themselves to these exceptional conditions in a most remarkable manner. Notable are a mouse and a lizard. The first is a kind of Pocket Mouse *(Peromyscus)* of a species that ranges quite widely over the whole region. Where it lives on ordinary soil it is of a normal reddish brown color; but on the adjacent black lava flows it has developed an almost pure black form, and on the white sands all the individuals are as nearly white as a mammal can be without being a full albino. Only over their rumps is there a slight creamy wash, while their large eyes remain black and stand out like jet buttons. They are engaging little creatures that literally whiz over the firm crust of the sand, their legs going so furiously they are invisible. They can also jump prodigiously and can dive into and under the softer sand.

These mice live in tunnels dug in the compacted sand either just under the surface or deeper down where there is moisture, but the entrances to these tunnels are often at some depth under the soft surface. To get in, the mice just dive in and bore or "swim" their way down to their tunnels. How they know exactly where these hidden entrances are on what must be, to them, veritable continent-wide stretches without any landmarks (for the sands are constantly shifting) is a mystery; but they seem to go below with unerring accuracy. By judicious probing, moreover, you will eventually find your finger entering a firmly constructed little tunnel. I may say that in doing this once I was greatly surprised to receive a sharp bite from the apparently infuriated occupant.

The other outstanding animal of the white sands is a small lizard about four inches long of the genus *Sceloporus*. This is a large genus with a wide distribution, and the species vary enormously in color and pattern. Those around the dune area are of sundry grays and browns; those on the dunes are almost pure white with a yellow wash only on the back, but they have in and just behind their armpits, on either side, two jet-black spots.

Right: This is the region of the most preposterous-looking of all rabbits, the Antelope Jack. It is among the half-dozen fastest living things.

Overleaf left: The Palo Verde, one of the commonest trees of desert and scrublands, belongs to the pea-and-bean family, has tiny transient leaves, and develops pods. Top right: The strange spiny Ocotillo. Not a cactus but a shrub related to the candlewoods, it bears small green leaves and puts out flame-colored flowers.

Bottom right: The well-known Horned Toad (Phrynosoma), *actually a flattened, short-tailed lizard of the iguanid family, is a very common member of the desert fauna.*

THE BIG BEND

If we travel from these mysterious sands in a southeasterly direction, skirting the south end of the Sacramento Mountains, we will run parallel to the course of the Rio Grande River. This is open, intensely dry, and hot country covered with widely scattered cactus and low scrub and is appropriately known as the Salt Basin. It narrows rapidly to the southeast and enters a considerable pile of mountains forming a complex jumble between the Rio Grande and the Pecos rivers and terminates in the south in what is called the Big Bend. Here are the remarkable Chisos Mountains. To the north of this strip lie granite escarpments with gulley-like valleys filled with small junipers or groves of willows following meandering streams. These gulleys end abruptly on the southern edge of the prairies, which are there (the Tonah Basin) as flat as any in the world.

The Big Bend is the block of territory contained in a great swing to the south made by the Rio Grande. Happily for geologists, zoologists, and botanists, a substantial area at the southern tip of this territory has been set aside as a national park. At the angle in this bend lie the Chisos Mountains, a compact, more or less circular area with two outliers of different formation, standing on the northern bank of the river. At the foot of these on the

west side you may look into the Grand Canyon of Saint Helena, from which the river debouches onto a narrow sand-covered plain supporting a forest of huge willows and cottonwoods. Both natural and some artificial meadows of lush grass border this on the north side. The south bank lies at the foot of a gigantic cliff. That is Mexico.

Most of the Big Bend area is extremely arid, the valleys and the slopes being covered with cactus scrub and some of the taller mountains being completely bald. The rocks sometimes take grotesque shapes, and large arroyos have been carved out of the uncompacted surface strata and the outwash soils. Despite their towering heights, the Chisos and associated mountains are formed of an ancient plateau that "fell" or sank some thousands of feet into the earth between two faults. Later, the middle of this block was upfolded by pressures from beneath; then volcanicity added its efforts, further elevating the surface and pouring out massive strata of lava. Thus, today, the Chisos rise from a hole in a plateau, but to a height that carries their peaks well above its general level.

The Cacomistle or Ring-tailed Cat, a small, soft-furred, and agile type of raccoon found all over the West and Southwest. It can squeeze into tiny crevices.

The rocks of the old plateau were formed under a sea that very long ago extended up the center of this continent from the Gulf of Mexico to the Arctic Ocean and that later formed great lagoons, coastal swamps, and lakes. Coal beds were laid down in these and the fossil remains of dinosaurs are now to be found in them. Above these are later strata of the Tertiary period, the age of mammals, which contain certain long-extinct animals of great interest, known as Hyracotheres. These were nondescript mammals, the size of a large dog, with five toes in front and four behind, all of which terminated in tiny hoofs. They were members of the stock from which the horse tribe later arose. The earliest known member of that tribe is a remarkably similar-looking beast named *Eohippus,* or the Dawn Horse, found in Egypt and North Africa in strata of similar age.

The Chisos Mountains themselves are of extreme beauty. They appear to rise almost straight up in towering red grandeur, and as you go up into them you encounter unexpected growths of all manner of trees. On their summits are pure stands of very fine Alligator Junipers and large Mexican Piñon Pine. There are three species of oak. Higher up still are Ponderosa Pine and even Douglas Fir. In one small place there are great Arizona Cypress, and in another even Quaking Aspen.

No less than two hundred species of birds have been observed here, among them both western and eastern species. The list is outstanding for the number of species of birds, such as eight hummingbirds, fifteen hawks, five doves, four jays, four juncos, seven owls, twenty sparrows, six wrens, and seventeen warblers. Outstanding species are the Colima Warbler and a hawk called the Aplomado Falcon. Over fifty-five species of mammals have been observed, and fifty-four reptiles, including twenty-two lizards and twenty-eight snakes. The Chisos form an outlier of the great mountain chain that includes the Rockies and the Sierra Madre Oriental, and they are a stepping stone from the vegetation of one to the other. Plants grow and birds assemble on their summits from both areas. They form, in fact, a northern extension of the eastern Sierras, as may be seen by the map.

The whole Big Bend area, not just the Chisos Mountains, is a mecca for botanists and zoologists, for even the apparently arid plains and valleys that surround the mountains support a varied fauna. In recesses far from human passings you may find the Pronghorn Antelope, and after dark the Peccary seems to materialize in droves from nowhere. The beautiful and agile little Kit Fox is plentiful, as it has food here in great abundance. Innumerable mice and other small rodents swarm, and the Antelope Jack Rabbit is everywhere.

LESSER DANGERS

There are also in this province two small (two-inch) kinds of scorpions technically named *Centruroides* that are really dangerous. These are slim and light-colored, and they run about rather fast on the open ground at night with their pale, slender pincers held before them at the ready. If they encounter anything that moves or that their senses tell them is animal, they stick their tails forward over their heads and then upward, jabbing a minute, hypodermic spine into the prey. This may well be your leg or any other part of your anatomy if you have left it uncovered. The results can be very serious.

By official record, more deaths occur in Arizona from scorpion stings than from all other animal stings or bites combined, rattlesnakes not excluded. Not all scorpions are deadly. Of over twenty species recorded from Arizona alone, and many others from the southern reaches of this province, most of the larger ones—one reaches five inches in length—are not deadly at all, though their bites are always painful. The worst in this province are the little pale yellow "durangos," as they are often loosely called in Mexico; but there are other non-desert species to the south that are even more dangerous.

There are also two kinds of spider that should be avoided, and there are places in this province where both of them abound. These are the well-known Black Widow, the female of which can be deadly, and certain hairy spiders, properly known as avicularians but commonly and erroneously called "tarantulas," which, though seldom if ever deadly, can produce most unpleasant effects and are definitely aggressive under certain circumstances. The Black Widow is a small, glabrous spider with a shiny black, almost spherical abdomen the size of a large pea; it carries a bright red mark underneath that sometimes is of an hourglass outline. It is a lurker in dark places by day, but at night, like most other spiders, it prowls about, and if disturbed, it may well bite. Like the sting of the scorpion, the hypodermic falces under its head are so fine that they penetrate the human epidermis, which then closes, making local treatment difficult. Cutting, as in cases of snakebite, has for this reason been recommended. The symptoms of Black Widow bite may be learned from many publications and need not be dwelt upon here.

The danger of the avicularian spiders is much less, but it has been both grossly exaggerated and even more grossly underestimated. All spiders are poisonous, but most of them do not carry falces long or strong enough to penetrate the human skin, and all but a very few that do carry such falces have venom that produces only local irritation and perhaps a little swelling. On the other hand, several of the lycosids, to which the Black Widow belongs, are deadly. Among the great host of avicularians distributed all over the world are some positively enormous forms—the biggest is probably a jet-black one (with eight orange-tipped legs) that inhabits the heads of palm trees in the swamp forests of the Guiana coasts, catches small birds by leaping at them, and has been known to kill rats and fair-sized tree snakes. It can jump many feet downward, especially out of holes in trees and banks, and it has a pair of huge, claw-hard falces under the head. Some rather large species inhabit our various Desert Provinces; at night they are hunters and predators and will stand up on their hind four legs, wave their front four, and strike at anything. All this proved too enticing for the writers of horror stories, so that the animals gained the reputation of being one and all monstrous man-killers. This is not the case, of course, but naturalists, in their desire to strip away all this nonsense, have leaned too far the other way. There are extremely poisonous arvicularians, though it is not the great, black, hairy monsters but some of the little, light-colored ones that are the most dangerous. It is almost sure that one in Hispaniola is deadly, and more than one in Mexico are undoubtedly very dangerous, producing dire symptoms in adult humans and critical ones in children, and even causing death at times. They should be strictly avoided but not killed, since they are useful creatures that keep down other even worse pests.

In this province is another member of lowly groups that has,

Right: The mouth of the Santa Elena Canyon, the gorge through which the Rio Grande debouches onto the flood plain surrounding the Chisos Mountains in the Big Bend.

Overleaf: Formed of gypsum grains sorted by the wind, the sands of White Sands in the lower Tularosa Basin are blindingly white. They cover 125 square miles.

in my opinion, been somewhat underestimated. This is the Uropygi or whip-tailed scorpion. The whip-tails are armed with a pair of grapples rather than pincers, and have piercing mouth parts. They hook onto their prey and squeeze it to their mouths so that these protruding devices may puncture its hide. Most Uropygi are small, but there are some in this province that are three inches long. They inject a fluid that, if it gets under the skin, produces excruciating burning sensations and inflammation. They are rare creatures, but no case is, as far as I know, on record of death from them.

INTO THE BOLSONES

If we cross the Rio Grande gorge and travel into upper Mexico we find ourselves in a vast *desierto* that extends across the state of Chihuahua and is traversed by only one north-to-south road. Here we are in the center of the Desert Belt although at an altitude of some three to four thousand feet. The country is very arid, and as true a desert as any on this continent, yet most of it is clothed in quite profuse plant life. The cactus flora is somewhat different from that of Sonora, but the creosote bush again holds sway along with saltbush, some scrub huisaché, and a great many yuccas. As a whole, the cactuses, yuccas, and the creosote bushes here grow below the 3500-foot level and greasewood and sages above these and up to about 5000 feet. Above this comes grass—the montane zone of the subtropical savannahs—and very soon appear small isolated cedars and junipers, which coalesce upward and in turn give way to pines and firs above 7000 feet. The true northern or boreal coniferous zone is represented on the very tops of the mountains at over 8500 feet.

The plateau is a vast level plain with ridge after ridge of mountains running from northwest to southeast. These rise on an average about 3500 feet above the level floor. In between are shallow bowls called by the Spanish *bolsones,* which are shallow lakes after rain but dry dust bowls during the rest of the year. The present topography was formed by extensive faulting, blocks or rather long strips of territory rising up to form the mountain

Trap-door Spiders are found all over the world but their wonderfully constructed hinged door-ways are particularly noticeable on this desert.

ranges, the intermediate belts sinking. Since then, the uplands have been eroded mostly by the occasional torrential rains, wind action, and gravitic creep, and the resultant materials have been slowly spread out over the depressions, filling them to a great depth with recent deposits. The plateau itself was created millions of years earlier when a large section of the bottom of the sea that once covered the whole Southwest was raised and then eroded until it formed a great level plain. The rising of the Sierras and the faulting came later.

These wild, empty lands have an almost mystical charm of their own, unlike either the "deserts" of the West or those around the Rio Grande valley. By day they seem to be only endless dusty wastes with the ever-same yuccas, cactuses, and stunted bushes, though you may enter vast groves of mesquite or huisaché. But at night they come alive, and you find yourself in a sort of zoological garden with all kinds of animals from deer to tiny mice that appear as if by magic. Where the non-burrowing animals hide during the day defies comprehension, and how any of them survive during the long droughts is a mystery. Here, too, you may spend the whole night in one small location and see a different animal every hour in the beam of a single flashlight.

The plateau rises steadily as it goes southward from the huge northern Bolson de Mapimi (see map), the mountains upon it gradually crowd together, and the smaller bolsones become more bowl-like in appearance. These mountains are covered mostly with sparse scrub. Along either side of the plateau are shelflike ranges of foothills. Extreme desert conditions give way to increasing vegetation and ultimately to grasslands. Here we enter the cul-de-sac of this province. Beyond lies the towering string of volcanos that stretches right across the isthmus and forms the seat of this continent as we have defined it.

IN THE CUL-DE-SAC

Here the hand of man has changed the whole surface of the land, and today most of the bottomlands are cultivated. There is much surface water in these bottoms and a great variety of crops can be grown; but, despite occasional oases of massed tall trees, meandering copses of willows, and lines of ornamental and other introduced growth, the country itself remains stubbornly true to its appointed position in the scheme of things. This is the Southern Scrub Zone, and scrubland it remains. Around its periphery and as one goes up into the surrounding mountains, stunted and then taller trees begin to grow naturally, but widely spaced, to form the Orchard Belt. Only on the higher slopes do the trees form closed-canopy forests of magnificent oaks or massed conifers. This intermediate zone, where the arid scrubs vie with the grasses of the Savannah Belt and the first little trees, is an area of great loveliness.

I remember in particular one place that nestled among rounded hillocks covered with short grass and spotted with small cactuses. All around were some curious little craters which we had taken to be of volcanic origin, but which turned out to be a cluster of small meteor craters. Whatever had come down out of the sky had formed a family and had not hit the earth too long ago. They had come down at a slight angle, thumping into the sides of hills and apparently knocking the tops off others. One of these craters formed a pocket that looked exactly like a man-made quarry. The rock from which this had been gouged happened to be bright red in color, with strange white veins of in-

Scorpions are common on the Chihuahua deserts. They go through a nuptial dance and ceremony that may last for days, the female leading the male around by his pincers.

truded material running through it diagonally but irregularly. This crater faced down a long slope to a big shallow lake of creamy bluish water, and from this a grove of willows extended up the slope. My companion and I sat down to eat an outdoor lunch in the crater.

Immediately after we were still and quiet, spots started dancing before our eyes so that we blinked in the torrential sunlight. Then one of these spots came to rest on a straggly dead willow at the mouth of the crater and resolved itself into a living jewel. It was a Vermilion Flycatcher. So were the other spots, and soon a host of these exquisitely colored little birds had come up out of the willows by the lake and were flitting all about, perching here and there, and making trilling noises. We remained absolutely motionless as more and more gathered and as their little white-fronted wives also began to put in an appearance. They were working into the crater where there was deep shade and where countless clouds of gnatlike insects danced. But then suddenly they took to the air and high-tailed it back to the willows.

This made us look round sharply and there, standing at the entrance of a hole high in the side of the crater, was the most incongruous sight imaginable. A glistening white Barn Owl stood swaying back and forth on its long legs in the sunlight, blinking out of its clownlike face and hissing. The moment we moved, it took to the air and alighted on a cactus at the rim of the crater. A few seconds later its mate rushed out of the hole, tumbled into the air, and glided up to a dead mesquite on the other side of the crater. A barn owl perched on a cactus at midday is an unusual sight. We played a prolonged game with these birds, first hiding, then pretending to walk away, and doing everything we could to persuade them that we had left, but they maintained their posts until we trudged off and started up our car, which we found was in sight of the birds. Only then did they fly back into their hole.

The Mexican Sierras

The East and West Sierras Madre and Coastal Plains, and the Sierra del Sur

From scholarly students to humble farmers of the mountains, Mexicans are exceptionally alert to the physical nature of their country. Almost any wayfarer in country districts can tell you just what kind of *bosque* (vegetation) is to be found where, what kind of trees and flowers grow in said *bosque,* and so forth. Similarly, visits to agricultural and forestry departments of universities and state bureaus are a pleasure for biologists and especially phytogeographers, because one almost invariably meets therein enthusiasts of all kinds, working busily at their local problems and integrating their findings with an over-all picture. It is a rather sad commentary, therefore, that the excellent technical reports of this work are rarely translated into English, let alone made readily available outside Mexico. I mention this because I have nowhere else encountered such a volume of published information on the subject that interests me most, while no natural province on this continent is less known popularly than the one now to be described.

Tourists and other foreign visitors stream in and out of Mexico from north, south, east, and now even from the west, but they all do so either by air or along a limited number of roads and railways. If you study a good up-to-date road map of northern Mexico, you will find that only one road crosses the western slice of that country and one the East Sierra—the first from Torreon via Durango to Mazatlan; the second from Huisaché via Ciudad del Mais to Mante (see map). Of course, at the bottom of the plateau where the two Sierras Madre converge and abut onto the volcanic Sierra del Sur, there is a great network of roads, which lace this latter range also, but the main bodies of the two grandest parts of the province are quite untapped. I have penetrated these vast areas at a number of points over the last twenty years, mostly in the earlier days on the' west side on foot or on horseback but more recently by automobile into the eastern Sierras, and what I have seen therein has never ceased to amaze me. I am therefore astonished at the continued absence of published non-technical information on these areas, or even of any mention of them in general works.

All but the outer fringes of the two great Sierra complexes are truly hidden lands. Their very existence is not apparent to people passing along the normal routes of travel. The foothills, and even the outer ranges of these two tremendous mountain complexes on both their inner (facing the plateau) and outer (facing the coasts) sides are generally arid, while along those limited southern stretches, where they come right down to those coasts, they rise so precipitously that travel into them is extremely difficult. The roads snake their way through them by means of the lowest possible passes or along river valleys which are almost nowhere even forested. Unless otherwise informed, nobody driving south on any of the four main roads—the Pacific coast road; the El Paso—Chihuahua—Durango; the Laredo—Monterrey—San Luis Potosi; and the Brownsville—Ciudad Victoria—Tamazunchale routes—would ever suspect that within a comparatively few miles to one side of them lie valleys choked with a tropical type of vegetation, over which parrots and other splendidly colored birds squawk and yell and where glorious waterfalls splash and rumble. Here, cycads and fabulous palms drip in the mists, the branches of the greater trees are loaded with orchids and bromeliads and other epiphytes, and, among other exotica, a great chasm, many times larger than our own Grand Canyon, lies waiting to be properly explored.

Nor, indeed, would even the more adventurous travelers have any conception of the vast oak forests and open pine forests, with a continuous carpet of grass beneath the trees, that sprawl in an immense U-shaped belt around this province from the Arizona border south to the twentieth parallel; thence, right across the country to the east; and then north again, to within sight of Big Bend in Texas. These oak forests are almost as little known as the "jungles" or *tropicales* of the inner valleys. They have no roads; but, instead, little meandering pony trails lead to many still quite aboriginal Amerindian villages. What is more, the traveler is often paced along these paths for lengthy periods by inquisitive but discreet wolves. Here, in the upper highlands, one enters a world the existence of which is never suspected by the average North American and which, be it admitted, is seldom visited even by any Mexicans other than local inhabitants.

North America tapers down at its base to a narrow isthmus that curves off to the southeast and then straight east. It is virtually pinched off at the Isthmus of Tehuantepec, a gutter that runs due north to south, that does not rise above 850 feet, and that separates the massive mountains of northern Mexico from the uplands of Chiapas and Central America. At the outset of our journey we decided to make the crest of the great volcanic range of mountains, sometimes known as the Sierra Madre del Sur, which crosses Mexico from east to west at about the twentieth north parallel, the base of our continent. In the last chapter we approached this line within half a degree down the central upland plateau that extends south from the deserts of Chihuahua. Previously, in the Sonoran and in the East Chaparral provinces, we ranged south across the deserts and hot scrublands on both the west and east sides of the country to the edge of the subtropics. There thus remains to be visited this large cup- or V-shaped block of mountainous territory, lying between these three prongs of dry hot lands. This is in many respects one of the most interesting provinces on this continent, and certainly the most varied and exotic.

Despite its great extent, its wide spread in both latitude and longitude, and its tremendous variations in altitude, it has a certain unity. This is most apparent in the field we are particularly interested in—namely, the distribution of various types of vegetation, their manner of growth, and their order of succession. The exoticism and the excitement in visiting these lands are supplied by the tropical influences, which are, to the inhabitants of temperate latitudes, as bizarre as those of polar regions.

Mighty Popocatepetl and its mate Ixtaccihuatl, the dominant volcanic peaks of the Sierra del Sur, a range that cuts off the bottom of the continent.

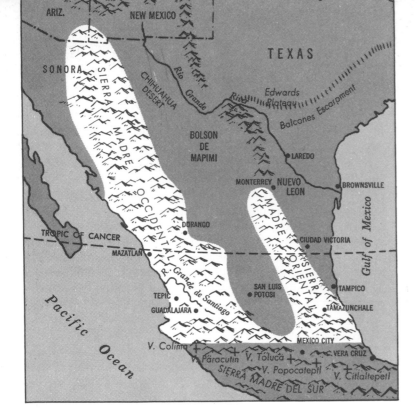

This province is made up basically of four major vegetational belts, and is tripartite in composition. It consists of three large blocks of mountains and two narrow coastal strips. On the mountains all the fifteen possible major vegetational belts between the equator and the poles, plus various transition types of growth, are represented by pronounced montane zones. It forms a large V-shaped structure, lying northwest to southeast with its point thrust into the isthmus of central Mexico. The left-hand, or west, tine of this province is one thousand miles long; the right-hand, or eastern, five hundred miles; the northern

ends of the two tines are six hundred miles apart. The central portion of this triangle is occupied by the desert and scrublands of the Chihuahua Province.

The western part of the V is composed of the great Sierra Madre Occidental and the narrow coastal plain that lies between those mountains and the Pacific. These ranges stretch from just south of the United States border in the state of Sonora to the region of Guanajuato. The eastern part, composed of the Sierra Madre Oriental, starts about Monterrey in Nuevo Leon and stretches southeast to the heights of Hidalgo. Between these mountains and the Gulf of Mexico there is also a narrow coastal plain, which broadens out somewhat in the north where a string of ancient, low mountains are spread along its surface parallel to the Sierra. The third or southern part is composed of the great chain of volcanic peaks and connecting ranges that reach from the Pacific coast in Jalisco almost to the Gulf coast in Vera Cruz. Along this range lie the famous volcanos such as Popocatepetl and Mt. Orizaba.

All three parts of this conjoined province are extremely complex in structure, the individual ranges being in almost every case composed of dozens of individual blocks, each with its own particular features. The vegetational forms, floras, and faunas of these are equally diverse, but the first retains its basic pattern with absolute rigidity and formality throughout. The flora is different from that of any other part of the continent mainly because much of this province lies within the subtropics and consequently truly tropical elements from the south are introduced. The fauna, on the other hand, is almost wholly of North American affiliations, for the great zoological divide between North and South America follows the northern edge of the truly tropical forests at base level. These forests barely finger north to this province through the lowlands of Campeche and Tabasco. The types of birds vary widely.

If you approach this province from the northeast, entering Mexico via Matamoras, and proceed down the fine coast road toward Mexico City, you will cross first the much constricted Desert Belt and then almost two hundred miles of the Southern Scrub Belt (see Chapter 14). The road then winds through a range of low and extremely ancient mountains, one of a long string that lies on the plains from somewhat north of Monterrey all the way to Tampico. These are of very old strata and have been above sea level for a long time, so that they have become a refuge for certain plants that are not found elsewhere and that have relationships only with those of distant places like upland Venezuela. Beyond these mountains, one enters a low, dry valley or gutter still clothed in the typical chaparrals of the scrublands, but ahead one sees the towering wall of the great Sierra Madre rising abruptly to the sky. Nestled at its foot is the beautiful old town of Victoria. Here, if there are no clouds on the mountains, one may lie back in a deck chair and study phytogeography in one easy lesson, for every major belt from the Southern Scrub to the Barren Grounds of the Arctic are plastered as distinct zones across the face of these mountains in regular bands—at the bottom a desert band, then a north scrub chaparral, then an open scrub, then a prairie, a parkland, a temperate forest, a transition zone with conifers coming in, above this a true boreal coniferous forest, then a stunted alpine flora leading to low tundra and finally barren ground. The whole scene, however, is typically "northern."

If you drive on to the south, you mount over some small hills and then descend onto a continuation of the scrub plain covered with cactuses and mesquites and infested with the birds called road runners. This gradually narrows into a valley between the Sierras and the ancient mountains. Then, about fifty miles along the road, there is a modest sign which informs you bilingually that you are now crossing the Tropic of Cancer. Within a mile the hills close in from either side, and you plunge into an entirely new world. You are indeed in the tropics.

Curiously enough, almost exactly the same thing happens a few miles north of Mazatlan, when one drives down the Pacific coast road. In both cases one has not changed altitude and is still passing along a narrow coastal plain between high mountains and the sea when, suddenly, desiccated scrubs with cactuses of a desert type give way to grasses of all kinds (including even bamboos in swampy areas), and bananas and other tropical cultivated plants become part of the landscape. The birds too change shape and color abruptly, and while the ubiquitous crows are still everywhere, birds such as parrots put in an appearance. Real trees line the streams, which again contain water; there are little vines among the bushes; and epiphytic plants may be seen growing on trees and telephone wires.

We have here entered the northernmost outliers of the great tropical Savannah Belt, but it is so compressed and pushed so far north that even modest elevations suffice for trees to come in and form an orchardbush scenery. The stunted mesquites and other scrubland acacias give way to related species and grow taller; and palms appear. Many of the broad-leafed woody plants that were mere shrubs in the chaparral blossom forth as real trees, and in a matter of miles narrow gallery forests appear along waterways. At the same time, since one is going steadily southward, the belts we have left behind rise up the mountain sides, and beneath them wedges of tropical growth begin to slip in. This is the nature of the whole southern Sierra Madre Oriental, which culminates in a montane facies of the true equatorial forests in the gorges between those ranges just a little south of the twenty-second parallel.

THE TROPICS

I have never been able to fathom just why the regions of the world between the tropics and the polar circles are called the "temperate" zones. By comparison with other regions, they are the most *intemperate,* having just as widely fluctuating over-all climates as the polar regions and a much greater inclination to sudden changes in short-term weather than the tropics. Contrary to popular opinion, it is rarely if ever too hot in the tropics; the regions of great heat lie in the desert belts to north and south, while over considerable areas in the tropics it can often be much too cold for comfort. Further, high humidity is not unhealthy nor, except psychologically (or unless one must wear unsuitable clothes and work in buildings designed for sub-Arctic winters), is it really uncomfortable. Much more uncomfortable is the desiccating effect of the super-dry atmosphere of deserts, which cracks your lips, makes you gasp, irritates your skin, and lays you open to heat prostration. In the tropics the equal length of day and night throughout the year acts as a powerful factor in tempering the more violent variations of over-all climate, so that even in areas of great natural turbulence the weather tends, on the whole, to be equable; while both the seasonal and daily ranges of temperature are very modest compared to those of the so-called temperate and polar regions.

A certain mellowing, or perhaps one might better say amelioration, of the climate to which northerners are accustomed is noticeable in the southeast of this country, in Florida and other Gulf states, and in southern California, especially in winter. The difference is sometimes quite noticeable as far north, for instance, as the mouth of the Susquehanna River, where there is almost invariably a "change in climate." But this is as nothing to that which takes place when one enters the true tropics.

The earth is girdled by a wide equatorial or tropical belt, outside which, to north and south, lie the two "temperate" belts; while it is capped, top and bottom, by two circular polar areas. Between the tropics and the temperate belts lie the imaginary lines called the Tropic of Cancer and the Tropic of Capricorn. These lines represent the points farthest north and south above which the sun is at some time in the year directly vertical. The Arctic and Antarctic Circles represent the lines farthest from the poles at which the sun disappears completely for at least one day per year. These conditions are due to the tilt of the earth at 23 degrees to the plane of its travel around the sun. These divisions, although not marked by neat lines on the earth's surface—except by thoughtful governments such as the Mexican—are, moreover, real change-over points for many features of the earth's surface; and, notably, its vegetation. Even when the major belts have been pushed far to the north or south by other factors, marked changes invariably occur as you cross any of these empirical lines.

In Mexico these changes are quite startling, because on the narrow coastal belts everything seems suddenly to be different. To the north side the land is still typically "northern"; to the south it is almost aggressively tropical.

THE TROPICALES

When it comes to vegetation, even of a most abstruse nature, the Mexicans almost invariably have, as I have already hinted, "a word for it." All over this province you will hear about the *tropicales.* Finding himself already in a country choked with palms, parrots, and bananas, the average traveler becomes considerably confused about this when he is told, often with a knowing wag of the head, that he should visit the areas so named. The fact is that the Mexicans have no such misconceptions about the tropics as we have.

Not a few visitors to the Florida Everglades come away with the impression that they have visited the tropics, and even textbooks sometimes still refer to the Gulf coasts as being "subtropical." Tourists getting sufficiently far south of the border to be out of the Desert Belt are sometimes convinced that they have entered the "jungle," as it is popularly called, and that they are in the periphery of a land of mighty forests. They do not usually know that they will not reach the true tropics till they pass south of the tenth parallel, or that both the equatorial and the subtropical regions are just as varied as the temperate, and divided into as many major belts and subdivisions. The Mexicans know otherwise, and they have for centuries appreciated the importance and influence of the mountains on these and other types of vegetation. They make a clear distinction between the two truly tropical types of forest and all others, and they collectively call the former the *tropicales.*

The best way to visit these is by means of a number of little roads that now push into the Sierra Madre Oriental from the eastern coastal plain. By one of these—that goes due west into the mountains a little south of the Tropic of Cancer—you go straight up and over five ranges to a small town named Ciudad del Mais and, some ten miles beyond this, you come to the divide or watershed leading down onto the central plateau. By following this route you may, in a distance of only forty miles as the crow flies, inspect the whole northern part of the eastern Sierra complex.

The first range is clothed on its east face with a very peculiar growth of assorted deciduous trees and some palms. Its west side is much more arid and has many cactuses. The valley beyond (the one containing a place called Nuevo Morales) is however fully tropical, with many large trees, considerable groves of tall palms, and a special type of white-headed cactus. The next range is clothed on both faces with lush *tropicale,* with many palms in the gulleys and a mixture of deciduous and evergreen trees loaded with bromeliads, other epiphytic plants, and vines. Large-leafed herbs gather in the moister corners where there is deep shade. This growth leads down onto a second valley (that of El Naranjo), which is a well-watered flood plain dotted with tall palms and clumps of deciduous trees of small stature but mostly of true tropical forms.

The feet of the next range, the third one from the coast, are clothed in an almost solid stand of tall Cabbage and other palms intermingled with the beautiful coppery-barked Madrone tree. But, as you go up the east face, you first enter and then continue upward for two thousand feet through a mixed deciduous and evergreen *tropicale,* positively choked underneath its canopy with a riot of broad-leafed small trees and shrubs and giant herbs with vast fleshy leaves. This, however, is the end of the

tropicale, for suddenly, at a little over 2500 feet, everything tropical vanishes and you find yourself among massed oaks of tall stature, all loaded to the tips of their limbs with small orchids and related epiphytes. These continue over the crest of the range and down its west face, to march out onto the next valley. This is an upland one, clothed in short open grass, on which the oaks separate and stand about to create a perfect parkland. We are in fact, here, back into the Parklands. The soil of this valley is of a brilliant red; it contains limonite or red ocher which, when handled, will dye even the palms of your hands for considerable periods.

Beyond this valley there is another lower range of mountains, and as you ascend them you run "back" through the Prairies into the montane Scrub Zone once more, complete with huisaché and some stunted mesquite, lowly cactus, sage, and many of our other old friends. The next valley, the fourth (containing the town of Ciudad del Mais), is arid to the point of desolation and becomes even more nearly a desert as you approach the crest of the fifth and last range. And there, at the summit of a low pass, you may look out to the west over range upon range of mountains and hills, at first slowly descending in altitude but then mounting again into the endless ridges of the central plateau. You are now at the highest point of the Sierra Madre Oriental, and you are back in the "desert." It is puzzling; but I only hope that by this time it will no longer be incomprehensible, and that by combining the principle of vegetational belting by latitude and of its zoning by altitude you may have realized that, as you have been driving up from the hot, dry coastal plains of the Gulf, you have returned, botanically speaking, to where you started.

EL SALTO DE NARANJO

In the valley of this name there is a river which joins the Santa Maria on the coastal plain at Valles and then flows on to the Gulf at Tampico. It rises a short distance to the north in the third range and descends into the valley by a fall named El Salto.

Right: The Sierra del Sur. The upper slopes are clothed in a short montane scrub; this becomes montane tundra and then barren grounds and snowfields above.

Below: The Beaded Lizard (Heloderma horridum), *the only relative of the Gila Monster—and also poisonous—is an inhabitant of the lower slopes of the western Sierras.*

I have visited uncountable waterfalls, and I can safely say that this El Salto is among the most beautiful in the world. Although neither its volume nor height—about five hundred feet—is great, it more than makes up for any lack of grandeur by its incredible coloring, its other novel features, and its great beauty.

The falls have eaten back some 250 yards into the mountain face, down the top of which the river descends by a series of rapids and subfalls over great domes of rock. It then plunges over one even greater dome in two major and several minor spillways, the former descending directly into a large pool, the lesser ones meandering into and out of the rock face via a series of huge caves that go up and under the great dome. The most striking feature of this part of the fall is that the whole of it, and even under the lesser falls, is entirely clothed in a velvety mass of dwarf aquatic and semiaquatic plants ranging in color from the deepest bottle green to the vividest jades, emeralds, and apple greens. Still more thrilling is the pool beneath.

This is an enormous rimstone pool almost two hundred yards across, contained by a thin, meandering wall of calcareous material deposited by the water. Beyond and below this, a series of other similar pools of every configuration step some five hundred yards down the gentle incline like a series of fountains described by some ancient teller of fairy tales, till a base level is reached and the resulting river meanders off amid billowing tropical forest. But this is not all, for every bit of the ten-foot-tall, three-foot-thick rims of these pools, even under the pouring waters, is also clothed in a continuous mat of brilliant green plants. And just to bring the whole to perfection, the waters themselves are slightly milky and of an intense blue color that rivals the sky and in dull weather gives an ethereal and somewhat uncanny appearance to the whole place.

This river is throughout its course a road of enchantment, vistas of the utmost beauty coming into view around every bend as it winds between high cliffs that are festooned with tropical growth and topped by great feathery trees loaded with strange epiphytic plants, while eagles soar in the air above and parrots flash in the sunlight below. Lower down, out on the plain, it is bordered by a gallery of tall trees, including many Mexican Cypress—which, unlike their northern counterpart, support wide-spreading branches and thick, billowing foliage. There is a place some miles down the valley where the milky blue waters gurgle endlessly through some boulder-strewn rapids into a large pool surrounded by trees in which thousands of birds make their homes, among them orioles caparisoned in vivid orange and black. In the pool are large numbers of huge water tortoises (a species of Map Turtle) and equally huge softshell turtles. Both seem extremely friendly, for, although the latter can give a terrible bite, they simple come and nudge you if you float still in the water.

THE SNAKE PASS

Crossing these same Sierras only 130 miles farther south, you meet an entirely different state of affairs. Starting along the magnificently engineered highway from Tamazunchale—called by everybody, even the Mexicans themselves, "Thomas-and-Charlie"—that nestles in a tropical valley at a height of only 675 feet, you go straight up, and continue to do so until you reach a village named La Culebra (the Snake), which is perched on a knife-edged ridge only a few hundred feet wide. This, however, is still not the top, since the road crawls on upward to a col at an altitude of over 8500 feet before it descends to Jacala on the edge of the central plateau at 4500 feet altitude. Here the

Sierras form a compound mass rather than a series of ranges, so that when you top the first ascent you go down a little and then start climbing again; and you repeat this, rising in the aggregate ever higher until you reach the pass. The descent on the other side is the same—brief down-goings interrupted by briefer up-goings, all ending in a descent of about four thousand feet.

The vegetation along this route is first an evergreen and then, almost but not quite to the summit, a deciduous montane tropical forest ending at about seven thousand feet in a belt of almost pure dwarf beech. Above this the trees open out, then rapidly become sparser and stunted and grass appears; and then, above La Culebra on the eastern face, trees die away altogether. We have passed through all the montane zones including the orchardbush and savannahs and find ourselves amid montane scrublands. Over the summit on the west face we go through these zones in reverse, then enter parkland with short grass below the scattered trees. But here the trees are piñons and other pines, junipers, and scrub oaks. As we descend, the upper peaks and ridges are clothed in solid stands of these, the bigger pines at the top, the junipers at the bottom, and then we gradually come back into the cactus- and scrub-covered aridity of the central plateau. But a lot of this is hard to see today because of the works of man.

On the eastern faces of the up-going slopes you will be amazed to see cultivated fields going to the very tops of the steepest peaks. Some of these fields are almost perpendicular, so that one wonders not only how the cultivators can get up to these dizzy heights, but also why the soil is not immediately washed into the valleys below. The answer to the latter is a complex business related to rainfall, type of rock, and other factors into which we will not go. The point of particular interest to us is that, with the exception of some deep and steep gullies on the northwest faces of these mountains, every bit of the growth that clothes them has been stripped away time and time again throughout the ages, so that there is not the slightest hope of reconstructing with any certainty what their cover was before the arrival of man. And we must not forget that toolmaking and bone-carving men were resident upon the central plateau of Mexico certainly by 20,000 B.C., when elephants still roamed that land, and probably tens of thousands of years before that.

These mountains are not unique in their cultivation. To the contrary, though there are still today vast areas on every continent that are not inhabited by man, a great part of the entire land surface of the earth, from the centers of what are now real deserts to the polar tundras, has not only been roamed over by hunting man for hundreds of thousands of years, but has been profoundly altered by agricultural man. Even hunting and berry-picking have their effects on the natural economy, and both herding and agriculture can alter its entire aspect. Mexico, with the possible exception of some inner areas of the western Sierras, is a land that has supported a large human population for countless centuries and during considerable climatic changes. While man cannot change the weather, he can change the surface "climate" of the land by clearing away its natural vegetative cover, thus causing erosion, rapid run-off, and finally deserts which heat up in the sun and cause columns of hot air to rise. This hot air may push up the lower cloud cover as it passes over. There have been deserts throughout geological history, but man appears to have played a not inconsiderable part in extending or

The Jaguar, the great spotted cat of the American tropics, is common in the Mexican Sierras, especially in the west, and strays over the United States border.

even forming many of those existing today—an exercise in which, in the Old World, the otherwise worthy goat, with his predilection for eating every scrap of vegetation, has been man's staunchest ally.

We noted at the beginning of this chapter that the Western Sierras mirror the Eastern except for the little wedge of territory down at the southeast corner of the latter, where a montane zone of the evergreen tropical forest pushes north out of Central America. A glance at the map will explain this statement. First, the Southern Scrub swings far south into the plateau "lining" the west face of the East Sierras, then curving west and north to "line" the east face of the West Sierras, where it squeezes through Arizona to the west chaparrals of Sonora. Behind and above these scrublands, the upland oak forest forms a wide belt that almost rings the plateau and reaches up into Sonora.

see canyons that put those of the Colorado to shame, or visit villages of original Americans who still spurn so much as a store-bought blanket.

Here is a land where great jaguars pad around your camp at night, armies of coatis forage through villages, unclassified birds scream at you from orchid-festooned trees in gorges filled with the mists of giant waterfalls, and—in the grass-carpeted uplands under the spreading oaks—family parties of wolves step over your sleeping bag to rake over the dead embers of your fire in search of charred bones.

Of course I cannot describe this vast land adequately, for it is still mostly unexplored, and I have personally only entered it at three points, while there appears to be nothing recorded about it at other points. On one journey to it, I was guided by a tyrannical-looking gentleman—I use the term deliberately—of the

Coatimundis are a form of Raccoon and go trekking about and foraging in large companies. They are found as far north as mountainous districts in Oklahoma.

A large Southern Soft-shelled Turtle, a strange aquatic creature that is found in the rivers of the eastern Sierras of Mexico.

The Sierra Madre Occidental is a vast, virtually unknown land of immense subparallel mountain ranges that march, one after the other, from the Pacific to the central plateau. They stretch from the United States border to the valley of the Rio Grande de Santiago. In area this province exceeds that of Texas, yet there is still today but one road up its western edge along the Pacific coast and one up its eastern fringe along the western edge of the plateau, passing from Leon via Aguascalientes, Durango, and Chihuahua to El Paso. Only one route crosses this vast mass— the one from Durango to Mazatlan—and this is little traveled. The very size of this country is not realized by foreigners, and even most Mexicans stare at you blankly if you say there is a virtually unexplored valley over four hundred miles long in this part of their country. What is more, none of the millions of travelers who for half a century have passed up and down the Pacific coast by rail or by car knows that within sometimes no more than ten miles inland you may lie under a vast forest tree with two hundred bright green military macaws perched in it,

Yaqui people, whom I happened to meet among the foothills while collecting small animals among the dried scrub bordering a wide waterless river bed. He spoke some Spanish and happened to have a spare horse, and after an outdoor meal he invited me to travel with him and visit his village. As my total equipment was contained in two small bags, I climbed aboard the horse and we headed into the mountains. At sundown we reached a small hut at the foot of the towering Sierras and bedded down for the night. Then for three days we rode upward, downward, and upward again, first through tangled scrub, then up a narrow gorge choked with *tropicale* and positively screaming with parrots, into a vast oak forest where the trees grew in ranks one above the other—their spreading heads just meeting—beneath which grew knee-high, rich, green grass. It was there that the wolves tidied up our fire. On the fourth day we reached a village at the very bottom of an immense valley with towering cliffs in front and behind and mountain shoulders alternating like a child's drawing as far as the eye could see to left and right.

Here it was very hot, and both of us had removed most of our clothes, bundled them up, and put them away in bags attached to our saddles; we were riding with bare feet. My new friend had a sort of traditional "Chinese" moustache that had long, drooping ends. He also had a huge, bladelike nose, and he was of a pleasant coppery color and of magnificent physique. I will never forget the shock I got when I first saw him wearing only an improvised loincloth, for he had all kinds of intricate designs on his chest and back. When we rode into the village I thought that I must be dreaming. The whole place looked like a prepared set for a movie about pre-Columbian life in America —in full color—but this was genuine and perfectly natural; yet it was not two hundred miles from the United States border.

There were manufactured objects in use in this village, but the people seemed to prefer their own artifacts, clothes, and ornaments. The knives, few guns, tin cans, clocks, and other rare items were used along with their native counterparts without special discrimination. Above all, the people themselves lived their own lives in their own way. They were interested in what I had to say about the rest of the world, as interpreted by my host, who was one of only a handful who spoke Spanish; but there, for the first time in many years of wandering, I did not encounter any particular interest in the affairs of others, other than normal curiosity, and nobody seemed to have any preconceived notions of hostility or of friction. The word "gringo" was known, and it was clearly understood that I happened not to be of that genre; but no opprobrium was attached to that term as it is so widely in most of the rest of the Americas. Gringos lived to the north and did other things, and that was all there was to it. Living there, in fact, were people of the olden times. They were perfectly integrated with their local environment and, as far as I could ascertain in my all too brief stay of three weeks, with the basic precepts of nature.

THE LAND OF VULCAN

Just south of the twentieth parallel of latitude, the country is composed of what is virtually one great volcano. The land surface is almost entirely volcanic debris and outpourings, and almost all the peaks are either volcanos or bits of previous volcanos. The principal peaks are, from west to east: Colima, 14,235 feet; the brand-new Paricutín just west of the town of Uruapan; Toluca, 15,016 feet; the famous Popocatepetl, 17,893 feet; his sister Ixtaccihuatl, 17,343 feet; and the mighty Citlaltepetl, otherwise known as Mt. Orizaba, 18,320 feet. This range of active volcanicity is separated by four hundred miles from the Central American volcanic group to the south and by almost a thousand miles from the New Mexican group to the north.

Paricutín, which appeared in the form of a jet of earth in a farmer's cornfield in 1943, without warning and on a piece of perfectly level country, and which then grew to a height of 1400 feet, has become inactive; the only one of these peaks that is acting up at present is Colima. He growls and rumbles persistently, and a dull glow may be seen reflected in the clouds above his head at night. He also from time to time rocks the surrounding countryside, cracking houses and sending the frightened citizenry flying into the streets. The last time he blew his stack in earnest was in 1940, when he spewed forth some impressive lava flows that blackened the upper parts of his gently sloping sides. The other great volcanic peaks are at present inactive and are now snow-capped all year round; but there are forever mutterings down below, and the land is often rocked gently or bounced up and down violently by earthquakes, while fumaroles and *solfataras* pump away regularly or spout periodically all over the place, most notably in the Orizaba region. Then there are a number of suspect peaks that are obviously no more than temporarily dormant.

Volcanos are probably the most awe-inspiring things in nature. Their sheer power so far surpasses anything else, including the greatest hurricanes, tsunamis, and even earthquakes, that all things quake before them when they are in an obstreperous mood. They are alive, and they have individual characters. They may sleep, or they may just lie and groan for long periods. Then they may shake themselves awake by easy stages and again either lapse back into sleep, or they may suddenly blow up without warning. The performances put on by such giants as Mt. Katmai in Alaska in 1912, Krakatoa in the East Indies in 1883, Mont Pelée on the island of Martinique in the West Indies in 1902, and Vesuvius in Italy, have at various times literally rocked the earth. But there is one thing about volcanos that is significant and almost ultimately terrifying. Except those utterly "fossilized" since earliest geologic times, all of them, sleeping or awake, are related, and in a manner of speaking actively in league. What affects one seems to affect all, and it is now thought that from time to time the infliction may be so great that they all act in concert. If even half a dozen Katmais or Krakatoas blew their stacks at the same time, we would be in for some very unpleasant experiences, because each of these alone shot dust into the upper atmosphere that took years to settle and that noticeably upset the weather of the whole earth. Half a dozen would make us quite uncomfortable; a dozen would herald a world-wide disaster.

It is still not decided whether volcanos are direct outlets from the layer beneath the crust of the earth—which some believe to be in a state of fluidity like taffy and which is called the asthenosphere or the magmatic layer—or whether they are merely the outlets of great "carbuncles" of lava contained in the crust itself. Nevertheless, and in either case, the slightest shift in the earth's crust—as in an earthquake caused by the buckling of some strata, by its splitting apart, or by its slipping—may squeeze this quasi fluid below and cause a volcano to erupt. The surface of the earth is covered with a series of vast cracks along which almost all the volcanos are strung; so that, if one of these cracks suddenly opens up or makes a move to close a little, a whole string of them might go off at once.

A journey westward from Mexico City, via Morelia and Guadalajara, to Tepic in the state of Nayarit on the west coast will demonstrate to anybody that, not too long ago geologically speaking, a whole host of volcanos did so go off in this area. The mountains are split and wracked on every hand, and there are vast seas of black, gnarled, and "frozen" lava everywhere, not only cascading down mountain sides but spilling out over level plains, and even pushing some way up inclines. In other words, there was a time not so long ago when verily "the earth shook" right at the bottom of our continent.

I can but end our journey and my story by observing that we are still literally sitting on a volcano, and that nature is not, as I hope I have demonstrated, subject to the whims of man or in any way immutable. This continent seems to have been wrought in fiery blasts, by shattering quakes, and under the crushing forces of mountains of moving ice. These mighty works are not finished, for nature never builds for keeps; everything is in a constant state of flux, and all that we have seen today will assuredly be changed tomorrow. There is still nothing we can do about it, so let us get to know a little better this fabulous continent we live on.

An Explanation and Glossary of Special Terms

WHEREVER you travel on the land surface of this earth, sooner or later and usually in a very short space, you will encounter what we call a change of scenery. This is so even in the midst of what appear on maps to be featureless deserts, prairies, or even vast plains covered with forest. The most notable aspect of this is the constant change in and variety of the land surface as a whole, but this is not its only aspect. Often nothing about the topography of the land changes but still the scene does, and drastically, so that even the least observant may notice it. Such innovations (which may come either suddenly or gradually, either widely spaced or in rapid succession) are due to changes in the vegetation; and they may be quite stunning.

Vegetation is the link that binds what Dr. Oosting—as quoted in my Foreword—calls the environment with the organisms, both plants and animals, and even ourselves. It is also a key that can unlock many of the mysteries of nature that we encounter as we travel about the land surface of our earth.

VEGETATIONAL BELTS AND ZONES

Within limited compass these are brought about by such circumstances as the availability of soil moisture, but they also occur as a result of much more basic realities that are not so apparent. Further, they need not, and very often do not, entail alterations of the botanical character of the vegetation—i.e., in the kinds of plants—but in what is called the *facies* of the vegetation itself. As an example, one may be crossing a flat plain covered with shortish grass and dotted with an orchard of only one kind of acacia tree of a rather grand stature, when suddenly one finds oneself walking through the same grass but waist high and between the same trees but of a smaller size. None of the plants has changed, but the manner in which they grow and their relationships have done so—even to the size, shape, and abundance of their leaves. We have here entered what is called another facies, a geologist's term that means "make, form, figure, or shape" and denotes to those specialists that a stratum of rock has changed its appearance in space but not in time. This is to say that as it is followed from one area to another—horizontally—it undergoes a change from, say, a fine clay to a coarse sand.

The study of vegetation as opposed to mere plant distribution is a special department of phytogeography which actually has little to do with the distribution of individual species of plants, or even of plant groups, genera, families, and so forth. While the presence of certain plants may in some cases be important to the growth of other plants, such as parasites and vines, it is invariably paramount in the distribution of animals, including man. However, variations in botanical constitution are insignificant compared to those in the facies of the vegetation and its distribution. Thus, in our orchard, the species of grass and of acacia are of almost no importance, but the way in which both grow—their density, size, and so forth—is. Even further, you can substitute almost any grass-shaped herb for the grass, and a palm or almost any other tree—even a cactus—for the acacia tree, without affecting the animal life. But step from an orchard into a forest or onto a savannah and, in a matter of paces, the entire fauna may change absolutely.

Such changes in vegetation are everywhere to be seen, and at first they appear to be arbitrary and often chaotic; but if one travels far enough, especially north or south or up a mountain, it is apparent that there is a definite succession in their appearance. It is also manifest that some are repeated and that others are not; and that similar facies occur at different latitudes, or latitudes in different areas. Even a glance at a world map on which vegetational types are displayed will demonstrate that the major facies—forests, orchards, savannahs, scrublands, deserts, prairies, parks, tundras, et cetera—form continuous *belts* around the globe, regardless of the seas and oceans that intervene between the land masses. However, these major belts do not go round the planet in neat straight bands but waver to north and south (in different phases in the northern and southern hemispheres) and expand and contract in width as they do so. Further, just as they appear to "run under" or skip over the oceans, so they also seemingly disappear into mountain ranges on one side and come out unscathed, as it were, on the other.

Closer examination discloses the fact that these belts are repeated in miniature in an upward succession on all highlands and mountains, in exactly the same succession as they are found at sea level going from the equator to either of the poles. Moreover, we find that a very tall mountain standing on the equator will have all belts found between its base and either of the poles duplicated as zones on its slopes, starting at the bottom in tall, wet, equatorial forest, composed of three or four tiers of evergreen plants, and ending at the top in an icefield. By the same token, a mountain standing in, say, one of the hot deserts will display only those belts that lie between the latitude where it stands and the nearer pole. Then

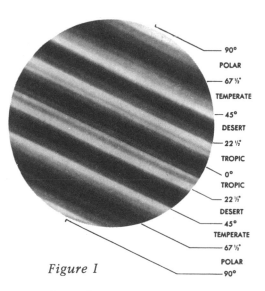

Figure I

*Our planet as
it would appear if
there were no oceans
or mountains and all the
vegetational belts girdled it
without interference.*

90°
POLAR
67½°
TEMPERATE
45°
DESERT
22½°
TROPIC
0°
TROPIC
22½°
DESERT
45°
TEMPERATE
67½°
POLAR
90°

TUNDRA

NORTHERN FOREST

NORTHERN GRASSLANDS

NORTHERN DESERT
NORTHERN SAVANNAH
TROPICAL FOREST
SOUTHERN SAVANNAH
SOUTHERN DESERT
SOUTHERN GRASSLANDS

SOUTHERN FOREST

Figure II

Our planet, showing the major vegetational belts girdling it but oscillating and varying in width due to the influence of the ocean currents.

there is a further point: it will be found that these zones start and stop at different heights above sea level at different latitudes, and that they start at lower and lower levels as one approaches the poles, so that mountains near the poles are covered with snow and ice from their bases to their apices. In point of fact, each degree of latitude proves to be equivalent to six hundred feet of altitude, so that a climber can calculate in advance just when he will pass from one vegetational type to another—provided, of course, the latitude is known.

OCEAN CURRENTS

These facts clearly indicate that there is some underlying order here. We would naturally like to know upon what "laws" or principles this is based, so let us start by imagining that our planet is without seas and oceans but that it has just the same moisture and climate that it now enjoys. (This of course is impossible, even theoretically.) If also it should be perfectly flat all over but still tilted at 23 degrees to the plane upon which it revolves around the sun, what would be its phytogeographical appearance? For purposes of simplicity and explanation, let us say that it appears as in Figure I, with all major belts encircling it latitudinally.

However, our planet is not all land and perfectly flat, while the vegetational belts manifestly sway about to north or south, and widen or contract as we follow them around. Is there any connection between these two facts, and if so is there any one cause? It turns out there is a very definite connection and, surprisingly, only one basic cause. This is the distribution and behavior of the major ocean currents. This force is paramount and is apparently the cause not only of the nature, direction, and extent of the swings but also of other factors that control the width of the belts at any one point. In fact, "climate" is basically controlled by the ocean currents and is only secondarily affected by the atmospheric circulation. Altitude moreover has almost nothing to do with the swings made by the major vegetational belts. The actual state of affairs may be seen in Figure II, wherein the ocean currents are seen circulating in their opposed manners as in the north and south hemispheres, the cold ones pushing all the belts toward the equator, the hot, toward the poles.

Given the distribution of land and the circulation of ocean currents, certain parts of each of the continents will be dry, others wet, because atmospheric moisture comes from the oceans and hot oceans evaporate faster, while the winds blowing from them carry more water than do those blowing off cold oceans. The details of this need not be dwelt upon here; they are mechanical; they conform to physical law; and their results all over the earth are exact. What are these results on North America?

This is shown on the general map on page 8. All the belts are pushed south far down the Pacific coast, then far north just inland. From there they follow a great curve to the southeast to the inner or western face of the Appalachians, then around them, and finally north again up the east coast and out into the Atlantic. The pattern is exaggerated but basically simple. Moreover, even the greatest mountain ranges have no effect upon these swings: they are just dumped down, as it were, athwart them, and partake of their own arrangements of "belts"—called more properly *zones* when applied to altitude.

DEFINING NORTH AMERICA

There comes, then, the question of the definition of North America as a continent. Our theme is phytogeographical and based primarily on the distribution of the various types of vegetation, but it is also to some extent concerned with the actual plants and animals that live in each of these. The distribution of these latter is now pretty well known to botanists and zoologists, but that of even the major belts themselves, let alone the innumerable subdivisions of these, and more especially of the zones on the uplands and mountains, is widely ignored.

There are no less than five ways in which North America has been defined. In all cases its northern, western, and eastern boundaries are clear, precise, and coincident: the dispute concerns the southern. None of these suggestions is wholly satisfactory from all points of view. There is, however, another choice which avoids most of the objections to all the others, and this is the one that we have adopted in this book. By this, the southern boundary of North America is placed arbitrarily along the twentieth parallel north. This line cuts across south-central Mexico, near Mexico City, and follows the great range of volcanic peaks that stretch across that country and divide it clearly into two parts. To the north of it, there are no lowland or true tropical growths, though there are outliers of montane tropical and subtropical forests; to the south of it, there are no true deserts. In fact, it lies athwart the Southern Scrub Belt of the northern hemisphere.

In North America, as thus defined, we have eleven major belts—namely, reading from the North Pole: the Arctic Icefields, the Barren Lands, the Tundra, the Boreal Coniferous Forests, the North Temperate Woodlands closed-canopy forests, the Parklands, the Prairies, the Northern Scrublands, the Hot Deserts, the Southern Scrublands, and the subtropical Savannahs and Orchardbush. The vast boreal forests may be further subdivided into a northern Spruce-Aspen, a central Pine-Spruce, and a southern Transition of Softwood-Hardwood mixed-forest subbelts. The continent straddles seventy degrees of latitude and is thus some five thousand miles long. It forms a triangle of the same width at its widest, and it has an area of 9,355,000 square miles, which is just 16 per cent of the total land surface of the earth and makes it the third-largest continent or land mass. The flags of five nations fly over it—those of Denmark (Greenland), Canada, the United States, Mexico, and France (the islands of Saint-Pierre and Miquelon in the Gulf of St. Lawrence). Its highest point is Mount McKinley in Alaska, which tops 20,320 feet. The greater part of it is clothed in coniferous forests, those of its northern part forming the second-largest continuous forest in the world.

Our approach to this continent is, as it were, as from the North Pole, across the Arctic snow and icefields to the Barren Lands to the east side, and south into the Spruce-Aspen belt of the boreal forests. From there we turn west, following this same forest across the top of the continent to Alaska; then south to the next belt, and east once more. Arriving at the east coast, we again drop southward into the next belt and once again travel west to the Pacific coast; and then repeat the process going east, then west and east again, until we have reached the Northern Scrub Belt at the southern tip of Florida. From there we go west for the last time, following that belt in its great northward bow to the Canadian border and then south to southern California, from where we pass east into the Hot Deserts. These narrow into the funnel of upland Mexico which is cupped by the mighty Sierras, which are themselves ringed by the Southern Scrublands, the subtropical Savannahs, and the Orchardbush.

Since the belts are of such great length, I have divided them up into what we call *natural provinces*. There are twenty-one of these in North America, most of which are already well known in their own right under the names used in this book. These provinces form our chapter heads. Each is one of Nature's major *oikoi* or "houses," and each is clothed in a unique flora and supports a particular fauna. The boundaries between these provinces are not arbitrary and are mostly prescribed by very definite and often well-known physiographic features. From the point of view of flora and fauna they should be looked upon primarily as transition belts, but in many cases they represent lines at which distribution of individual species or even groups of plants or animals makes the most abrupt changes.

NOTE ON THE DELIMITATION OF DESERTS

There is only one area on the North American continent where the boundary between two major vegetational belts is in question. This is the junction of the Hot Desert (with red soils) and the North Scrub Belt (with gray soils) in the Great Basin (see Chapter 17). The soil types change abruptly along an arc bowing northward across the southern end of this province. However, there is every reason to assume that the southwestern half of the Colorado Plateau is true desert. Also, Death Valley definitely lies in that belt. Thus, by protracting a northwardly curving line from the east of the former to the western edge of the latter across the Great Basin, we find that the true Hot Desert Belt encompasses almost half of this province. I tend to accept this as the dividing line between the two belts, despite the findings of soil analysis and classification, principally because it conforms with the curves made by all other major belts throughout the western third of this continent.

Glossary

Adiabatic winds. Winds caused by extremely cold and heavy air following the contours of icecaps.

Areole. A structure composed of special cells on the surface of a cactus.

Asthenosphere. A layer of rocks below the surface crust of the earth; it is made "soft" by heat and pressure.

Avifauna. The bird population of any region.

Biotopography. Special features of the land surface caused by the actions of animals.

Bolson. A surface structure forming a flat-bottomed bowl without outlet.

Butte. An isolated tall hill or small mountain with precipitous sides.

Cirque. A natural arena or amphitheater; such a structure caused by an icefield on a mountain.

Climax growth. An area of vegetation that is stabilized in form and in botanical make-up.

Closed canopy. Any plant growth which forms a continuous cover at any elevation.

Col. A depression or dip in a mountain chain or ridge.

Commensals. Two or more kinds of plants or animals that live together and are dependent upon each other.

Coquina. A material composed mostly of the shells of mollusks held together by limy deposits.

Deciduous. Capable of shedding or of being shed, as leaves.

Deedees (or Didis). Small tornado-like whirligigs of dust.

Drumlin. A dome-shaped low hill or hillock of gravel and sand deposited by an icecap.

Dyke. A wall of lava or other igneous material forced up through other rock strata; sometimes left standing free when the latter are eroded.

Ecology. Literally, the study *(logos)* of houses *(oikoi);* thus, the groupings of living things and their relations with their environment.

Erratic. In geology, a piece of rock not indigenous to the place where it lies.

Esker. A long, low, straight or meandering deposit of gravel, etc., left by a retreating icecap.

Facies. In geology, the form (composition) of a stratum of any kind in one particular area. In botany, the growth form and plant composition of an area.

Falces. A pair of curved, pointed appendages under the head of a spider or certain other arthropods.

Fall-off line (or Fall-out line). A term applied to the edge of an escarpment or other continuous sudden drop in elevation over which many rivers fall.

Feral. Wild; applied to an animal, or plant, or even man, which has "run away from" domestication.

Firn. Snow compacted to a point where its crystals have been rearranged in the process of forming ice.

Fumarole. A crevice in the earth from which gases or vapors issue.

Gallery forest. A forest that borders a river or lake but does not extend far back therefrom.

Geoclimatological. Pertaining to the over-all climate of the whole earth.

Glabrous. Free from hair or down; smooth-skinned.

Gravitic creep. Slow movement of objects downhill due to the pull of gravity.

Interstadial. The pause during which a major ice advance temporarily retreats and the climate ameliorates.

Isostasy. A condition in which the weight upon and the compressibility of a stratum are in balance.

Magma. Molten or plastic layers beneath the earth's crust.

Massif. A mass of mountains or a mountain range.

Montane. Typical of, first described from, or descended from mountains.

Moraine. Debris carried and deposited by a glacier.

Muskeg. A growth of bushes, sedges, grasses, mosses, and lichens on bogs or swamps in areas of permafrost.

Ning-ning. Guianese term for the shimmering of air over a highly heated surface.

Nunatak. The tip of an isolated mountain appearing above an icecap.

Open canopy. Any plant growth which does not form a continuous cover and permits sunlight to reach the ground.

Palaeocrystic. Pertaining to very ancient ice which has a recognizable structure, especially when in frozen earth or in newer ice.

Parkland. Land covered with isolated trees standing in grass.

Permafrost. A condition of permanent frost or sub-zero temperature; also, ground that is permanently frozen.

Phytogeography. The geography of plants.

Podology. The study of soils.

Rain forest. A forest that has more than one tier and occurs in an area of very high rainfall.

Regelation. Refreezing.

Saprophyte. A plant that grows upon but is not parasitic on another plant.

Scoria. A form of volcanic exude; also, clay baked by underground fires in coal beds.

Scree. A mass of loose stones or rocks on a mountain slope.

Solfatara. A spring expelling sulphurous mud, liquid, or gas.

Stomata. Small pores on the undersides of leaves, through which plants breathe (exude moisture).

Subdued relief. Uplands that have been rounded by erosion so that no naked rock is visible.

Succulents. Fleshy-stemmed and/or fleshy-leafed plants that can tolerate high salinity.

Taiga. The spruce forests of northern Eurasia and North America.

Tectite. A glassy meteorite.

Tundra. A type of vegetative growth, mostly of lichens, mosses, and dwarf willows, found in Arctic regions.

Xerophyte. A plant adapted to surviving extreme lack of moisture.

Note on the Capitalization of Names of Animals and Plants:

Following an internationally approved rule, the names of species, genera and larger groupings are capitalized. When referring to an individual species, capitals are used: thus the "Red Fox" but, when referred to in general terms, the "foxes." For the dog family, "Canines"; for dogs in general, "dogs."

Index

Photographic Credits

Maps executed
by Caru Studios

THIS BOOK WAS ENGRAVED AND PRINTED BY CONZETT AND HUBER OF ZURICH

THE DESIGN AND TOPOGRAPHY ARE BY ULRICH RUCHTI